COPYING
METHODS
MANUAL

LTP Publications · No. 11

COPYING METHODS MANUAL

WILLIAM R. HAWKEN

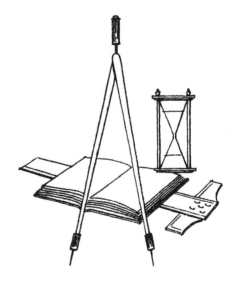

Library Technology Program
American Library Association
Chicago

PREFACE

The need for a comprehensive discussion of the characteristics of research materials and the problems encountered in making copies of them has been evident for many years. Important publications in the past have treated parts of this topic —among them, Robert Binkley's *Manual on Methods of Reproducing Research Materials,* Herman Fussler's *Photographic Reproduction for Libraries,* and the *Manual on Document Reproduction and Selection* issued by the International Federation for Documentation. Yet the most recent of these was issued more than a decade ago, and all three are out of print. Expanding knowledge in the technology of copying, the development of new processes, and the vastly increasing demand for copies of library materials have necessitated the publication of a new manual.

William R. Hawken's earlier studies for the Library Technology Program—*Photocopying from Bound Volumes* and its supplements, *Enlarged Prints from Library Microforms,* and a number of equipment evaluation studies published in *Library Technology Reports*—might be regarded as preliminary works toward the *Manual.* Although they were never specifically intended to serve as manuals, they do function as such because, in each, attention has been given to how copying equipment can best be used efficiently and economically in libraries.

Mr. Hawken commissioned Allen Veaner, Chief Librarian, Acquisitions Department, Stanford University Libraries, to prepare the annotated bibliography. Charles F. Gosnell, Librarian, New York University, was asked to write the appendix statement on copyright.

To Melville Ruggles, Vice President, Council on Library Resources Inc., must go the credit for the idea of the *Manual,* and for valuable counsel throughout its preparation. Donald Holmes, Chief, Photoduplication Service, Library of Congress; Hubbard Ballou, Head, Photographic Services, Butler Library, Columbia University; and Vernon Tate, Librarian, U.S. Naval Academy, worked with the author in the development of the original plan for the *Manual.* These men plus Neal Harlow, Dean, Graduate School of Library Service, Rutgers University, and two representatives designated by the executive committee of the Copying Methods Section of ALA's Resources and Technical Services Division, Allen Veaner and Charles LaHood, Chief, Serials Division, Library of Congress, served on an advisory committee named by LTP. David R. Hoffman, Head of Technical Information Service for LTP, served as chairman of the committee. Members of the committee brought to the *Manual* their experience in librarianship, library education, and photoduplication, and a background of active participation both in library associations and in the National Microfilm Association. To them go the thanks and appreciation of the Library Technology Program for their contribution.

A grant from the Council on Library Resources, Inc., in December, 1963, has made possible the preparation of this *Manual.*

Library Technology Program
Chicago
August, 1966

v

CONTENTS

TABLES

FIGURES

INTRODUCTION

The field of document reproduction

The current need for a manual of copying methods dealing with the processes, methods, techniques, and types of equipment which can be used for reproducing documents of a great many different kinds arises from two factors:

(1) The great importance of document reproduction processes in the acquisition, preservation, dissemination, and communication of information vital to the conduct of research work in all fields of human endeavor and on an international scale.

(2) The complexity of the field of document reproduction today which has resulted from the enormous technical advances made in the past fifteen years.

The need for the coining of the new class word —*reprography* (an unfortunate graft of a Latin fragment on a Greek root)—is in itself indicative of the great changes that have come about. Processes and methods which formerly were discrete and distinctive have now become intricately interrelated. New processes and combinations of processes with different and astonishing capabilities continue to appear. This revolution in the document copying field has been powerfully augmented by intensive competition on the part of manufacturers for a share of the vast and lucrative office-records copying field. The results, however, have led to highly important applications in the reproduction of research materials as well.

For more than a century, document reproduction was accomplished by means of a very few systems of *photo*-graphy—i.e., systems based on the fact that certain substances were sensitive to the action of light. In earlier days, the substances employed for the formation of photographic images were limited not only to the action of light within the visible spectrum but to only a part of that spectrum—the region of blue light. Only gradually, as the technology of photography improved, was it possible to record images across the entire visible spectrum from blue through green to yellow and orange and finally to red, and into the invisible spectrum beyond the response of the human eye—ultraviolet at one end and infrared at the other.

One of the most important advances in the technology of document reproduction was the discovery that the conversion of the radiant energy of infrared rays into heat energy could be used as the basis of a document reproduction process. This was the accomplishment of Dr. Carl S. Miller, the inventor of the "Thermo-Fax" thermographic process. Since this process first appeared, a great deal of research has been done in developing and improving the utility of heat energy as an image-forming agent.

Today there are several processes which employ radiant energy in the form of heat as the means for reproducing documents, and research in this area continues apace. Thus it is that "photoreproduction" and "photocopying" which were once generic terms are no longer inclusive enough. Today we have to include "thermoreproduction" and "thermocopying" as well.

Beyond this, heat not only plays an important role for the formation of an image in such processes as the Thermo-Fax process, the Eichner process, the Ektafax process, and the Imagic process (and for the fixation of images in xerography and Electrofax), but also has become increasingly important in its role as the only requisite for the development of a latent image formed photographically—i.e., by the action of light—in such processes as Dual Spectrum, Dry Silver, thermal diazo, and Kalvar. This has proved to be of great importance since it makes possible completely dry reproduction processes. Dry means fast, since the wetting of the sensitized materials which occurs in conventional reproduction processes involves, of course, the subsequent driving off of moisture—a process which, for a variety of reasons, can seldom be unduly hastened.

Fifteen years ago, eye-legible copies were produced, for the most part, by means of a few well-known processes. These included classical silver halide photography and certain variations such as photostating and autopositive printing. Non-silver processes which were in widespread use included blue-printing and diazo printing. The preparation of masters for edition printing by mimeography, spirit duplication, or offset involved still other processes and methods, some manual and others photographic. Each of the processes required equipment which was large and costly and often entailed high installation costs. The processes also were in the class of crafts which required training, experience, and the development of skills on the part of the operators of the equipment. The cost of copies was consequently relatively high.

Today, the overwhelming bulk of the vast amount of copying being done is done with machines which require virtually no skills on the part of the operator and which deliver inexpensive copies ready for immediate use in a matter of seconds. Many of these machines fit comfortably on a desk top and can be purchased for a relatively small capital outlay. Furthermore, with many of the machines now available, it is possible to produce not only "use" copies but masters for spirit duplication, offset printing, and diazo printing; transparencies for use with overhead projectors; color-coded copies; or copies on a variety of paper stocks from tissue to card weight.

To the list of processes formerly in use there now must be added gelatin-dye-transfer (Verifax, Readyprint, Ektalith), diffusion-transfer-reversal, Polaroid, stabilization processing, Thermo-Fax, the Eichner process, Ektafax, Dual Spectrum, Dry Silver, Kalvar, xerography, Electrofax, an electrolytic process, and others as well. Still other processes such as the Imagic process and thermoplastic and photochromic recording are in an active stage of development.

In microcopying, some of the new processes have been highly influential in extending the utility of microcopies and making possible applications which hitherto were too time-consuming and too expensive. The development of an electrolytic process made possible the first successful push-button reader-printer. Subsequently, reader-printers employing the stabilization process, xerography, Electrofax and the Dry Silver process were introduced. The invention of the Xerox Copyflo

machine made possible the production of eye-legible copies from microtransparencies in roll form at unprecedentedly low per-print costs and thus opened up a whole new area of applications and systems uses for microcopies. Large quantities of research materials in the form of Copyflo copies are now being produced daily. Improvements in the diazo process and the invention of the Kalvar process took the duplication of microtransparencies out of the photographic darkroom and brought it to a level of push-button simplicity.

Despite all that has been accomplished thus far to make the reproduction of documents faster, simpler and cheaper, new developments in processes, equipment, and methods and in systems and applications continue to appear at an impressive rate. Publications in the field are often out of date before they are issued. The field of document reproduction has thus become not only a fairly complex one with a myriad of possible choices of processes, methods, and equipment, but promises to become increasingly so as time goes on. With this picture in mind, the purposes which this *Manual* attempts to serve may be summarized as follows:

(1) To provide a detailed description of the principal factors in reproduction processes which affect the characteristics of copies.

(2) To provide an analysis of the characteristics of a wide variety of types of documents which fall under the broad heading of "research materials" and which can have profound effects on their reproducibility.

(3) To provide a description of the numerous extant document reproduction processes and their materials and to indicate their suitability for the reproduction of various classes of research materials.

(4) To provide specific, practical advice on techniques for reproducing different types of research materials by the various methods and processes available.

(5) To provide supplementary information in the form of appendices on topics related to or having an important bearing on the reproduction of research materials.

At the rate the document reproduction field is growing and changing a revised edition of this *Manual* will be needed in the not-too-distant future. It is planned that in addition to changes in the field itself any omissions or errors in the present text will also be corrected. To this end, comments, corrections, and suggestions from users of the *Manual* will be welcomed.

Types of reproduction

Reproductions of documents fall into two main classes—eye-legible copies and microcopies. Both of these classes can be sub-divided in a great many ways according to a wide variety of criteria as is shown in Parts 3 and 4, "Processes" and "Methods and Techniques" which follow. For introductory purposes however, only those broad sub-classifications will be dealt with which are needed to set the stage for a discussion of the problems involved in reproducing research materials.

Eye-legible copies are copies which are either the same size as the original documents from which they were made or of a different size—either larger or, more commonly, smaller—but in any case easily legible with the unaided eye. Microcopies, on the other hand, are copies which have been so greatly reduced in size that some optical aid in the form of a magnifier or projecting device is required to read them.

Eye-legible copies. Eye-legible copies may first be sub-divided according to the *method* of their production. They may be made either by *contact* methods in which a sheet of a suitable sensitized material is held in firm and even contact against the surface of the document being copied, or by *optical* methods in which a "picture is taken" of the document through a lens. In copying by contact methods, the copies are always the same size as the original document. In copying by optical methods, the size of the copy can be controlled, and may be either larger or smaller than the original, depending on the purpose for which the copy is intended. Microcopying is a particular form of optical copying in which the copy produced is very greatly reduced in size. Since microcopies can be enlarged, a third method for the production of eye-legible copies is by *projection printing* in which the micro-image is enlarged on a sheet of photo-sensitive paper. Each of these three methods—contact copying, optical copying, and pro-

jection printing—plays an important role in the reproduction of research materials.

In the production of eye-legible copies by optical methods, the use of a prism over a camera lens permits the making of right-reading copies directly onto a sheet of sensitized paper in a single step. Such copies generally are reversed in values with the text appearing as a white image on a black background. These *negatives* can be recopied to obtain a *positive*. The best-known exemplar of this type of eye-legible copy is the photostat.

If a transparent light-sensitive film is used in a camera without a prism, the resulting negative can be used to make positive, eye-legible copies on paper either by contact printing, if the image is large enough, or by projection printing. This method is thus a two-step method in which the film serves as an intermediate for the production of the final copy.

This same general schema of a one-step and a two-step method of optical copying is found in the electrostatic processes which are now widely used for the reproduction of documents. In the Electro-fax process, an image is formed directly onto a sensitized receiving sheet, whereas in the xerographic process, a selenium-coated plate or drum is employed as an intermediate on which an image is formed and then transferred to the final receiving sheet. The nature of the processes is such, however, that with either process the resultant copy is positive rather than negative.

Microcopies. Microcopies also fall into two main classes—microtransparencies and micro-opaques—depending on the type of base material on which the images are formed. Microtransparencies can be further sub-divided by format according to whether they are in the form of rolls in which successive images appear in a strictly linear arrangement or in the form of sheets known as microfiches having a number of rows of images. Micro-opaques may also be divided into two classes according to whether the method of production used was photographic or photolithographic. Microtransparency images are enlarged for reading or projection printing by means of transmitted light whereas micro-opaques require the use of reflected light.

1. FACTORS AFFECTING THE CHARACTERISTICS OF COPIES

Original documents, whether handwritten, typewritten, or printed, are produced principally through the application of pressure—a mechanical phenomenon which causes graphite, inks, or other substances to adhere to some support, the most common of which is paper. Reproductions of documents, on the other hand, are produced by means of a wide variety of complex physical and chemical phenomena including optics, photosensitivity, thermal sensitivity, photoconductivity, electrolysis, photochromism, electrostatics, and others. Because of these fundamental differences in the methods by which images are produced, reproductions inevitably exhibit characteristics which will be different in one or perhaps several important respects from original documents. Varying degrees of difference may be present in:

(1) Size
(2) Physical characteristics
(3) Image clarity
(4) Permanence

The causative factors for these differences will be the method used and the characteristics of each process employed. A detailed description of the characteristics of each process is given in the third part of the *Manual*, "Processes."

Size

In optical copying by means of cameras, provision is usually made for some degree, or perhaps even a great degree of control over the size of the copy. In photostat-type cameras it is usually possible to make copies which range from 50 percent of original size to twice the original size measured linearly, or from one-fourth the area to four times the area of the original. Copying cameras employing film are generally limited in the extent to which they can enlarge an image but offer a much greater degree of reduction than photostat-type

cameras. With microfilm cameras, the linear reduction capability is commonly in a range of from 1:5 to as high as 1:30 which gives an area reduction of from 1/64th to 1/900th the size of the original. Projection printing from film negatives also offers considerable control over the size of the finished copies, ranging from somewhat smaller than the size of the negative from which the print is made (reduction printing) to very much larger (enlarging).

Physical characteristics

The nature of the various processes suitable for document reproductions necessitates the use of a support (usually paper, in the final copy) on which the sensitized material is coated or the image affixed, and which may differ greatly in its physical characteristics from those of the original. It may be thicker or thinner; it may be white or have a tint; it may be limited to having an image on one side only or may be two-sided; it may be opaque or translucent; it may have a coated surface which may crack when folded and which may be unreceptive to ink or pencil. Each of these factors, taken singly or in combination, can affect the utility or the suitability of the material for particular copying applications. In some instances, the physical characteristics of the copy may be such as to make it superior to the original from which it was made, while in others the copy will be decidedly inferior.

Image clarity

When optical copying methods are employed, image clarity will depend first of all on the quality of the lens used to form the image and on the accuracy of focus. With contact methods, firm, over-all contact is the first requirement. Beyond these fundamental requisites are several others relating to the performance characteristics of reproduction processes in general and come under the headings of:

   (a) Exposure
   (b) Contrast
   (c) Exposure latitude
   (d) Resolving power
   (e) Color sensitivity

While each of these factors can be described and discussed separately, the effect of each on image clarity is related to that of the others. Exposure will affect resolving power, color sensitivity will affect exposure latitude, and so on.

Exposure. Since radiant energy in some form is used to create the image on a copy, exposure plays a prominent role in image quality. The principal forms of energy employed in document reproduction processes for image formation are light and heat. Light-sensitive materials may be exposed by optical methods or by contact methods, depending on their sensitivity, or speed. Light-sensitive materials are usually grouped, according to their speed, into four classes:

   (1) Contact speed—room light
   (2) Contact speed—darkroom
   (3) Projection speed
   (4) Camera speed

CONTACT SPEED—ROOM LIGHT. Such materials are, as the term implies, slow enough to be handled under conditions of ordinary room light for reasonable periods of time without adverse effects from ambient light.

CONTACT SPEED—DARKROOM. These materials are too sensitive to be handled under room light but are too slow for projection printing.

PROJECTION SPEED. These materials are considerably faster and can be used for making enlargements at relatively short exposure intervals.

CAMERA SPEED. These materials are the most sensitive and can be used, under proper light conditions, for recording events at exposures shorter than 1/1,000,000 of a second.

Speed of heat-sensitive materials: Heat-sensitive materials are very rapid in their response to heat but, since heat rays cannot be used to form an image through a lens, heat-sensitive materials can only be exposed by contact methods.

Tone-value responses to exposure: The different types of materials employed with different processes respond, on exposure to light or heat, in

different ways, depending on whether the particular process is:

   (1) Negative-working
   (2) Negative-positive
   (3) Additive direct-positive
   (4) Subtractive direct-positive

Conventional silver halide processes and certain variant forms used for document reproduction are *negative-working processes*—i.e., the finished product is reversed in its tonal values. If a positive copy is needed, a second copying or printing operation must be performed. Other processes such as diffusion-transfer-reversal (DTR) and gelatin-dye-transfer, which are variants of the silver halide process, are *negative-positive* processes—i.e., both a negative and a positive copy are produced.

Still other processes, such as the Thermo-Fax process and diazo, are *direct-positive* processes, i.e., processes which do not require the production of a negative intermediate. Direct-positive processes also differ in accordance with the way in which the image is formed. In the Thermo-Fax process, for example, the image is formed directly by heat radiated from the text itself. Hence the longer the exposure, the greater the amount of heat radiated from the text and the darker the resultant image. Processes which work in this fashion can be described as *additive* direct-positive processes. In other direct-positive processes, such as dual spectrum and diazo, the nature of the materials is such that, if they are developed without any exposure to light whatsoever, the material will develop out as a solid, dark tone. The action of light reflected from white background areas destroys the ability of the material to darken when developed, but, in the text areas where light is not being reflected, the ability to darken on development remains, thus yielding a positive image. Processes which behave in this fashion can be described as *subtractive* direct-positive processes.

With negative-working processes, underexposure yields a white image with some broadening of fine lines against a grayish background, while overexposure yields a partially veiled image with narrowing or loss of fine lines against a heavy black background (Figures 2 and 3).

With negative-positive processes, underexposure yields a heavy image with broadening of fine lines

abcdefg

abcdefg

abcdefg

abcdefg

abcdefg

abcdefg

abcdefg

abcdefg

abcdefg

abcdefg

abcdefg

abcdefg

abcdefg

abcdefg

abcdefg

Fig. 1. Type samples used for succeeding illustrations.

against a background usually mottled and uneven in tone, while overexposure yields a faint image with narrowing and breaking of fine lines against a clear background (Figure 4).

With additive direct-positive processes, underexposure yields a faint image with narrowing and breaking of fine lines against a clear background;

overexposure yields a heavy image with broadening of fine lines against a background which may be clear or slightly spotty (Figure 5).

With subtractive direct-positive processes, underexposure yields a heavy image with some broadening of fine lines against a grayish or mottled background, while overexposure yields a faint image with narrowing and breaking of fine lines (Figure 6).

Contrast. The term "contrast" refers to the relationship between the tonal gradation of the subject being copied and the tonal gradation of the copy. If a copy is made of a gray scale and exhibits approximately the same gradation of tones as the original, contrast is said to be *normal* (Figure 7). If the copy exhibits a lesser degree of separation of the various shades of gray, contrast is said to be *low* (Figure 8). If, on the other hand, the differences between shades of gray are greatly exaggerated so that grays below a middle shade reproduce as black and lighter grays as white, contrast is said to be *high* (Figure 9).

The contrast of light-sensitive materials is generally expressed by means of a graph called a *sensitometric curve* or H&D curve, after the names of the two English scientists who introduced it—Hurter and Driffield. The horizontal coordinate in this graph is the degree of exposure, while the vertical coordinate is the density of the image resulting from exposure and development. With low-contrast materials, or low-contrast development, progressive increases in exposure result in relatively small increases in density, thus causing the gradient of the curve to be rather shallow. With high-contrast materials, or high-contrast development, small increases in exposure cause substantial increases in density, thus causing the gradient of the curve to be quite steep (Figures 10 and 11).

The contrast of the sensitized materials employed in most document reproduction processes ranges from above normal to fairly high. In many cases, the heightening of contrast can be a distinct advantage. Pencil lines which are relatively faint, typewritten material done on a machine with a worn ribbon, or printed texts which are grayish and lacking in contrast can often be considerably improved by copying them on high-contrast materials (Figure 12).

Fig. 2. Negative-working process. Left: underexposed negative. Right: positive from underexposed negative.

Fig. 3. Negative-working process. Left: overexposed negative. Right: positive from overexposed negative.

 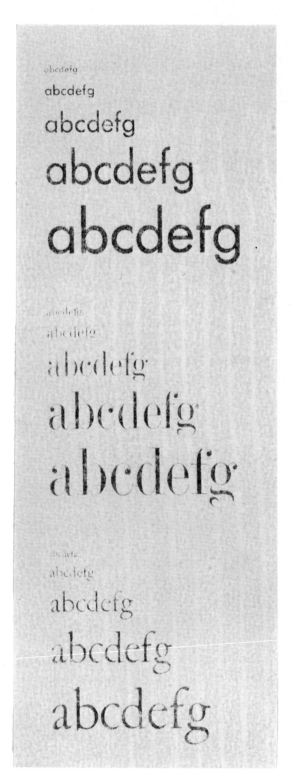

Fig. 4. Negative-positive process. Left: underexposure. Right: overexposure.

Fig. 5. Additive direct-positive process. Left: underexposure. Right: overexposure.

Fig. 6. Subtractive direct-positive process. Left: underexposure. Right: over-exposure.

Fig. 7. Above: original. Below: normal-contrast copy.

Fig. 8. Above: original. Below: low-contrast copy.

Fig. 9. Above: original. Below: high-contrast copy.

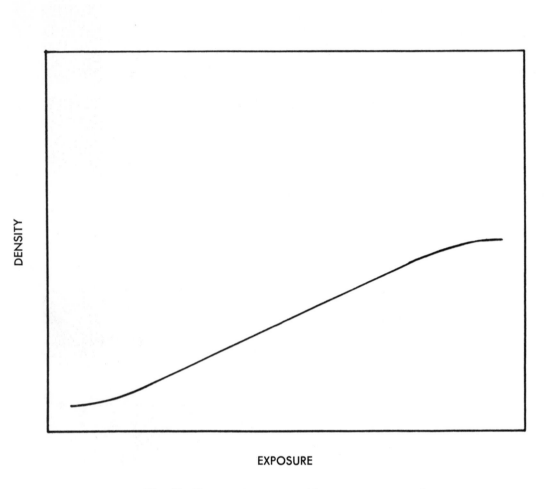

Fig. 10. Characteristic curve of low-contrast material.

High contrast can also be a serious disadvantage, however, in copying certain types of originals. Photographic illustrations of normal contrast, when copied on high-contrast materials, exhibit extensive loss of detail in both highlight and shadow areas (Figure 13). In copying texts, any unevenness which causes variations in the grayness or blackness of the lines making up the characters of the text may become so exaggerated by heightened contrast that considerable loss in legibility may occur. Unevenness in the tonality of text may be the result of uneven inking, poor-quality press work, or the use of worn type. In handwritten or typewritten documents, uneven

pressure or "touch" create a similar condition. As is shown in Figure 14, a text which is fairly uniform in tone copies well on high-contrast materials, whereas a text in which the tonality of the lines is not uniform copies poorly. The extent of the loss will depend on the relationship between the tone range of the original and the tone-range capability of the sensitized material. The higher the contrast of the sensitized material, the more limited is its ability to reproduce tonal differences.

Even when evenness of impression is satisfactory, another factor can be present which can make copying with high-contrast materials difficult or even impossible. This is the presence of

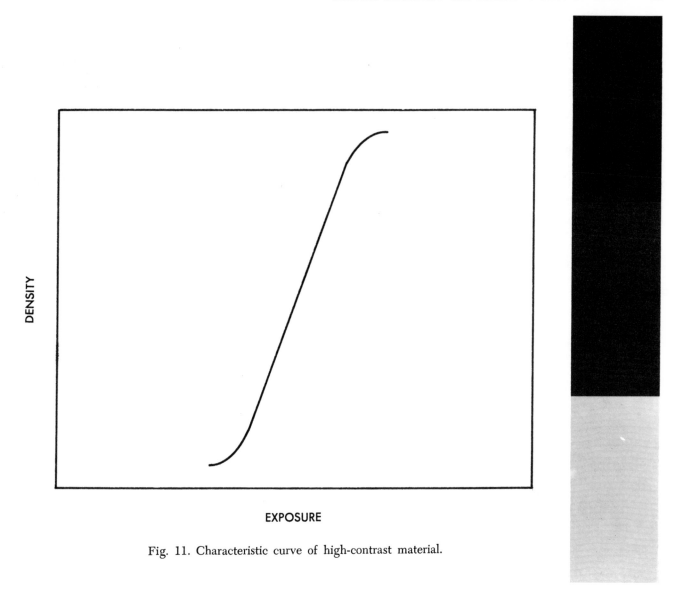

DENSITY

EXPOSURE

Fig. 11. Characteristic curve of high-contrast material.

both bold and fine lines in the text. Fine lines do not have the same ability to absorb light or heat as bold ones do. These differences appear in exaggerated form when high-contrast materials are used. At normal exposures, fine lines tend to break or to disappear completely. If exposure is increased to strengthen the fine lines, broader lines tend to thicken and to close up small spaces within letters (Figure 15). High contrast thus limits exposure latitude.

The relative contrast of sensitized materials may be *inherent* or *controllable*. Materials in which contrast is inherent yield copies which, within fairly narrow limits, have a fixed tonal range in relationship to the original being copied. For example, the electrolytic process yields copies which are inherently low in contrast, whereas "litho" or "process" films yield copies that are high in contrast.

Materials in which contrast is controllable are of two types, and each employs a different method of control. The contrast of the first type, of which many silver halide films are examples, can be controlled over a wide range by varying the composition of the developer used, the temperature of the developer solution, and/or the length of time the film is in the solution. Very subtle control over contrast is possible by such methods.

The second method of control entails the use of "graded" silver halide materials and is used extensively in making prints from silver halide films. Both contact and projection speed papers are manufactured in four or five and sometimes six contrast grades ranging from very low contrast (soft) to very high (hard). By-choosing the appropriate grade of paper, copies can be made which will have equal contrast, less contrast, or more contrast than the subject being copied or printed. Stabilization process materials are also available in various contrast grades.

A different method of achieving the same kind of control over contrast requires the use of filters. The spectral sensitivity of the silver halide materials used is such that light rays of different colors (wave lengths) alter the contrast of the material from low through high. This system offers greater subtlety of control, because the number of filters to choose from is greater than the number of contrast grades available.

One further aspect concerning contrast should be stressed. High contrast does not necessarily mean extremes of black and white. While copies

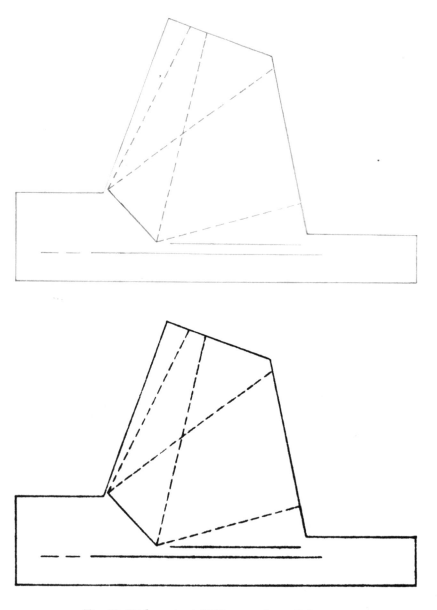

Fig. 12. High-contrast DTR copy of pencil drawing.

Fig. 13. High-contrast copy (DTR) of continuous-tone original showing loss of detail in both highlight and shadow areas.

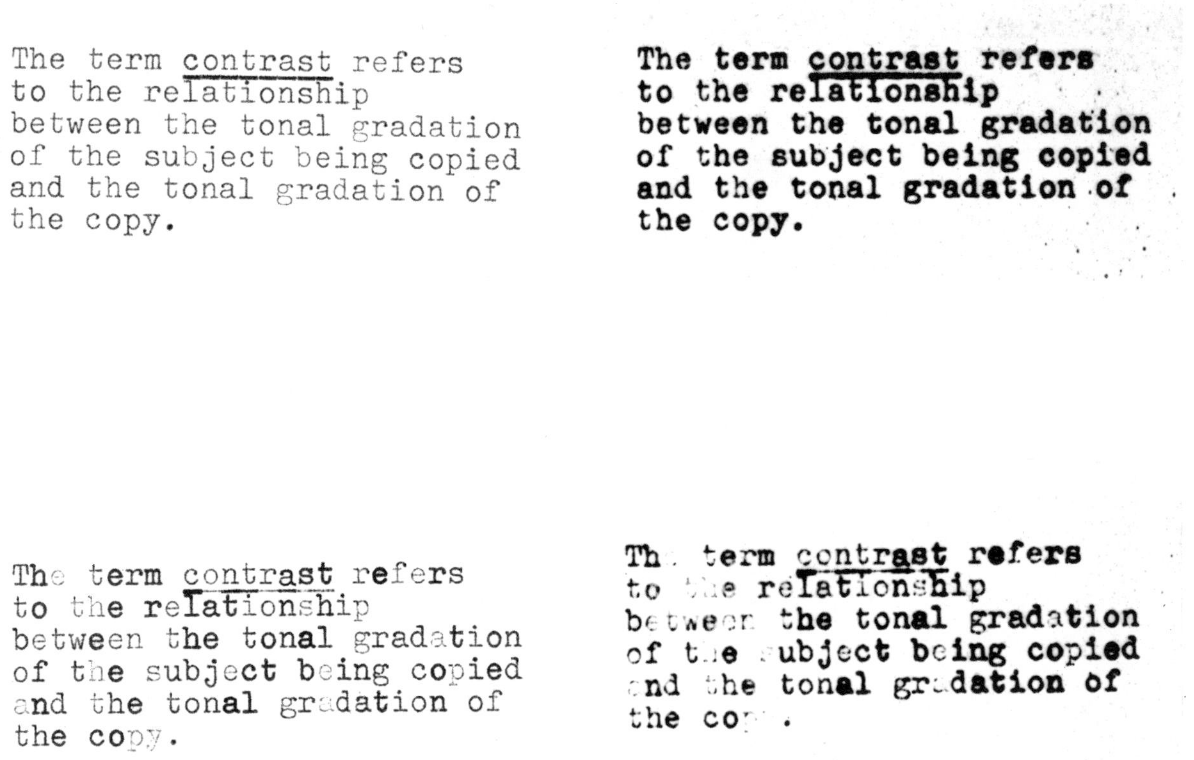

```
The term contrast refers
to the relationship
between the tonal gradation
of the subject being copied
and the tonal gradation of
the copy.
```

```
The term contrast refers
to the relationship
between the tonal gradation
of the subject being copied
and the tonal gradation of
the copy.
```

```
The term contrast refers
to the relationship
between the tonal gradation
of the subject being copied
and the tonal gradation of
the copy.
```

```
Th  term contrast refers
to  he relationship
between the tonal gradation
of t e subject being copied
 nd the tonal gradation of
the co  .
```

Fig. 14. Variations in quality of copy caused by uneven tonality. Upper left: text with even tonality. Lower left: text with uneven tonality. Right: high-contrast copies.

made by some processes yield an intense black, which, visually, is in strong contrast with a white background, other processes may yield copies in which the darkest possible tone will be a shade of gray. Both, however, may be classed as high-contrast processes, because the range of tones in each case between the darkest and the lightest is very short. The darkest shade possible is usually referred to as maximum density and is often abbreviated "D-Max." While maximum density is a factor in *visual* contrast, it is not to be misconstrued as an index of *relative contrast* (Figure 16).

Exposure latitude. Variations in exposure can have a substantial effect on the quality and hence the legibility of copies. Exposure is the product of two factors—intensity and duration. Some copying devices provide control over exposure by means of a rheostat, which varies the intensity of the light while the duration is held constant. Others employ a timing device with which the duration of the exposure interval can be varied, while the light output is held constant. Still others

employ a belt or roller-drive system with a variable speed control which passes the material being copied past a constant output light (or heat) source. Control over the rate of travel is used to shorten or lengthen the exposure interval. Another variant on the belt or roller-drive system is the use of a slit which can be narrowed or widened to increase or decrease the amount of light falling on the material as it passes the light source.

Theoretically there is only one "correct" exposure, i.e., an exposure of precisely the intensity and duration that will yield a copy of optimum quality. In practice, however, there is usually an allowable margin of error within which exposures somewhat shorter or longer than optimum will still yield satisfactory copies. This margin of error is referred to as *exposure latitude*. Exposure latitude is by no means a constant. It will vary principally with:

(1) The contrast of the sensitized material used;

abcdefg
abcdefg
abcdefg
abcdefg
abcdefg

abcdefg
abcdefg
abcdefg
abcdefg
abcdefg

abcdefg
abcdefg
abcdefg
abcdefg
abcdefg

abcdefg
abcdefg
abcdefg
abcdefg
abcdefg

abcdefg
abcdefg
abcdefg

abcdefg
abcdefg
abcdefg

Fig. 15. High-contrast copy of original having marked variations in stroke width.

Reflectance:
.70

Reflectance:
.22

Reflectance:
.40

DTR
Copy

Gray
Scale

Verifax
Copy

Fig. 16. Relative contrast vs. visual contrast. The *relative* contrast of both the Verifax and DTR copies is high, despite the fact that the *visual* contrast (D-Max) of the Verifax copy is much lower.

(2) The relative contrast of the document being reproduced;

(3) The clarity and evenness of impression of the original;

(4) The fineness of the details being reproduced; and

(5) The resolving power of the sensitized material used.

These factors affect exposure latitude both separately and in combination.

As is shown schematically in Figure 10, the increase in image strength or density is gradual when low-contrast materials are used. Small incre-

present in the original, exposure latitude will be very limited. If, however, the resolving power is well in excess of the finest details present, the exposure latitude will be proportionally greater.

Resolving power. Resolving power (i.e., *resolution*) is a term which refers to the ability of different types of reproduction materials to resolve, i.e., to separate, fine lines and spaces. The terms are also used to describe the optical performance of lenses. Resolving power is customarily expressed in lines per millimeter (1/mm.). A typical test chart used to measure resolving power is shown in Figure 18. Blocks of vertical and hori-

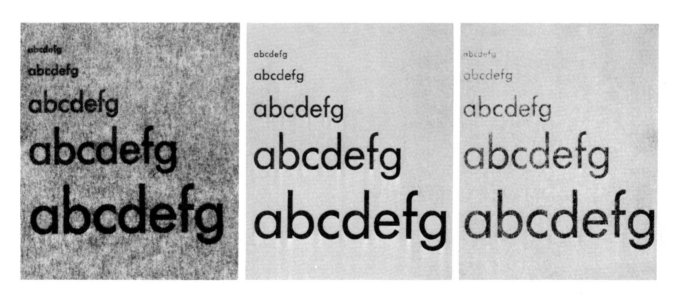

Fig. 17. The effect of character size and stroke width on exposure latitude. Left: underexposure. Center: normal exposure. Right: overexposure.

ments or decrements in the exposure interval have little effect on the appearance of the image. When high-contrast materials are used, the reverse is true: small changes in the exposure interval have profound effects on the density of the image (Figure 11).

Low- to moderate-contrast materials provide greater latitude in the reproduction of fine details than do high-contrast materials, but the finer the details, the narrower the limits become. Exposure latitude is especially limited if very fine details are being reproduced on high-contrast materials (Figure 17).

If the resolving power of the sensitized material is just capable of reproducing the finest details

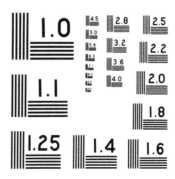

Fig. 18. National Bureau of Standards Microcopy Resolution Test Chart.

zontal lines and spaces in this chart are arranged in a series beginning with one line and one space per millimeter and ending with ten lines and ten spaces per millimeter. The resolution of full-size copies can be readily determined by reference to the figure above the smallest block that is adequately resolved on the copy. The resolution of micro-images can be determined by multiplying the figure above the smallest block that is adequately resolved by the reduction ratio used in filming. For example, if the 5.0 block is the smallest block resolved on a microfilm made at a reduction ratio of 1:20, resolution on the film would be 100 lines per millimeter.

The resolving power of the different types of materials used in various reproduction processes

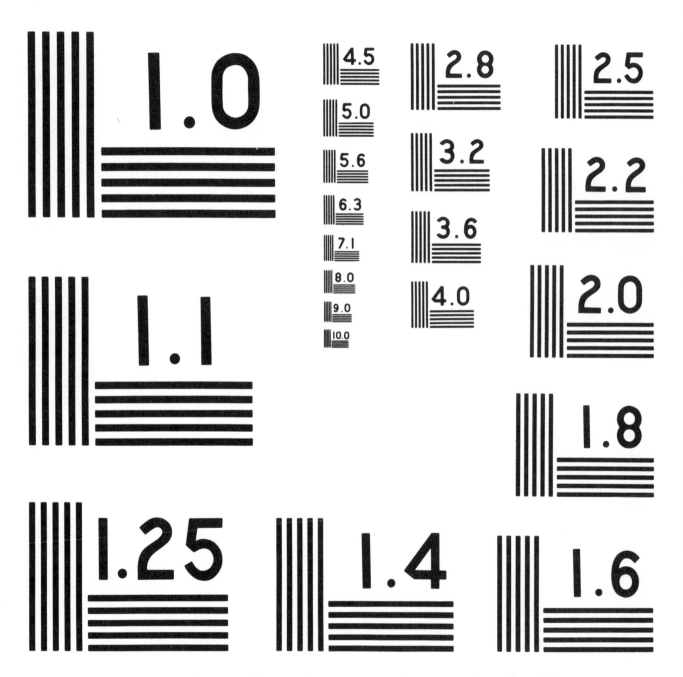

Fig. 19. National Bureau of Standards Microcopy Resolution Test Chart enlarged four times to show line patterns.

varies widely. Materials used in contact and contact-reflex copying may have a maximum resolution of 4 lines per millimeter (100 lines per inch) or even less. Coatings on silver halide microfilm stocks, on the other hand, are capable of resolving well in excess of 100 lines per millimeter (2,500 lines per inch). Photochromic materials are reported to be capable of resolution as high as 1,100 lines per millimeter (almost 28,000 lines per inch).

Resolving power is especially susceptible to influence from other factors in reproduction processes such as exposure, degree of development (in processes in which development is controllable), and contrast. In optical copying, the achievement of the maximum resolution of which a given sensitized material is capable requires high-quality lenses, accuracy of focus, evenness of illumination over the film plane, and freedom from any movement or vibration. In contact copying, contact must be as firm and as uniform as possible. Once the necessary physical conditions have been met, precise control must be exerted over the exposure and development of the sensitized material.

In discussing *exposure,* it was pointed out that under- or overexposure can have a marked effect on line width. If, in any given original, the spaces between lines are small, any broadening of line width caused by errors in exposure tends to cause the spaces between lines to fill, thus impairing resolution. Resolution will also be impaired if the effect of exposure causes narrowing of fine lines (Figure 20). If contrast is excessive, both effects may occur simultaneously (Figure 21). As these figures show, any factor affecting resolving power will affect it in inverse proportion to the size of the lines and spaces in the original being copied.

Image clarity will also be affected by what is known as "generation printing." The first copy of a document, whether it be made by contact or optical methods, is referred to as a first-generation copy. If a second copy is made from the first copy, it becomes a second-generation copy. In many applications, both first- and second-generation copies are used as *masters* for the production of quantities of additional copies of the third generation. As each successive generation is made, a finite loss of image quality occurs which, in some cases, may be negligible through quite a number of generations; in others, the loss may limit the number of generations to very few.

The principal factors affecting generations in printing are image sharpness and contrast. In contact printing, light-scattering effects, small deviations from optimum exposure times, and other factors can cause a slight loss of image sharpness in a second-generation copy. The copy then becomes the master from which a third-generation copy is made, and the same factors cause still greater degradation of the image. An example of an actual case in which image degradation was measured through three generations is given in Myers' report on Photo-Chromic Micro-Images.[1] Resolution of the photochromic master was measured at approximately 1,000 lines per millimeter. The second-generation contact print on a high-resolution photographic emulsion had a resolution of approximately 800 lines per millimeter. Third-generation dissemination copies made from this second-generation intermediate had resolution in a range of 650 to 750 lines per millimeter. Further experimental work indicated that, for each succeeding generation, an additional resolution loss of 6 percent would occur.

A more serious problem in generation printing arises if successive generations are made on materials which are high in contrast (Figure 22). High contrast, as has been shown, tends to cause thin lines to break and small spaces within letters to fill, and both of these effects are strongly affected by variations from optimum exposure settings. Under such conditions, even a second-generation copy may not be legible. This factor becomes of considerable practical importance in view of the fact that the use of photocopying by a great many processes, most of which are high-contrast processes, has become so widespread. If a high-contrast photocopy is the only available copy and must be reproduced by the same or by another high-contrast copying process, the resulting copy may be unusable (Figure 23).

---

[1] Wilbur C. Myers, *PCMI Technology and Potential Applications,* National Cash Register Company, Hawthorne, California, May, 1964.

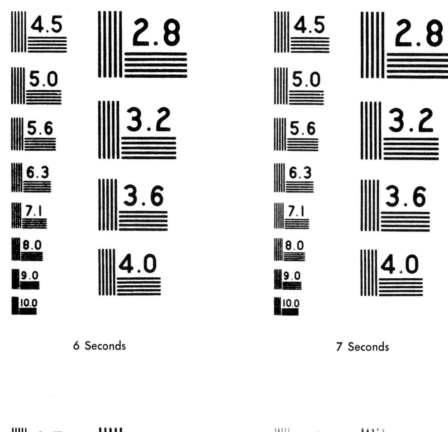

Fig. 20. DTR copy of four-times enlargement of NBS Microcopy Resolution Test Chart showing the effect of exposure on resolution of fine lines.

There are situations, however, in which the high contrast produced by copying through successive generations can be helpful. If an original is very low in contrast, recopying it through two or more generations can result in a copy which is substantially better than the original, or first-generation, copy. An example of this would be a negative microfilm which has been seriously underexposed and/or underdeveloped. By printing it on high-contrast positive materials, contrast can be increased in this second generation to provide an intermediate positive which, when printed

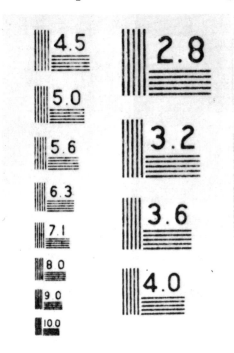

Fig. 21. Thermographic copy on very high-contrast materials, showing both breaking and filling in of line patterns. (NBS Microcopy Resolution Test Chart enlarged four times.)

again on high-contrast materials, will yield a third-generation negative from which good-quality, fourth-generation film positives or hard copy can be produced. This technique can be quite effective in salvaging an otherwise useless microfilm, provided that image clarity is good enough to withstand printing through four generations.

In the past, generation printing of micro-images seldom passed the second generation. Distribution copies from roll film are usually second-generation positives, as also are micro-opaques—Microcards and Microlex. The use of higher generations, however, is now becoming increasingly widespread, particularly in the production of microfiches. Two methods are used for producing microfiches. In the *strip-up method,* short lengths of roll film are arranged in rows on a transparent support. Either a diazo or a silver halide film contact print is then made which becomes the master copy for making third-generation distribution copies. In the *step-and-repeat method,* a succession of images are recorded in a series of rows on a sheet of film in a camera. This, when processed, is a negative which can be used for the printing of second-generation positive or negative distribution copies, depending on what materials are used. Since the camera negative produced by the step-and-repeat method is relatively costly to produce, and must be protected from damage which might occur from repeated handling, a duplicate is often made from it which is used as the master for third-generation distribution copies. From third-generation distribution copies, fourth-generation hard copy may be made. Or, because of the ease and simplicity with which microfiches can be duplicated by means of diazo or Kalvar, fourth-generation microfiches may be made from which fifth-generation hard copy can be produced. Since some resolution loss with consequent degradation of the image occurs with each successive generation, the first-generation copy must be of exceptionally high resolution, and the quality of each succeeding generation must be controlled quite carefully.

What constitutes a satisfactory level of resolution, whether for single copies or copies destined to be printed through several generations, is by no means a constant.

Although resolution can be tested by using calibrated test charts and the results then expressed quantitatively in lines per millimeter or lines per inch, the figures may have little meaning except to a technician. They cannot accurately be translated into another set of terms which could be used to determine whether or not a particular process or material is capable of clearly reproducing a given original. The variables in both line and space widths in printed texts are very great indeed, but there is no system of measurement in

v3r1n0e4a6w7c9s8m2o5
w7a5v8c9s1e6r4m8o0n2
n8a4o5c1r2e7i3m6w0v9
w3v6s9r2o5n8m7e1c4a0
v0r4n1a7e8w5s2o9m8c3
o2m8s9c7w6a4e0n1r3v5
a4o9c0r0e7s1m5v8n2w3

s3w0r6v4n5o1c2m7a9e8
n4o5m3r0a8w6c6v9e1s2
w2n8v5m1s7e6r0c9o4a3
e9a7m2c1o5n4v6r0w3s8
s1e9v7c6w8a0r3m5o4n2
m8c5v7a6w1e9s2r0n3o4
n2m9e5c0a3s6r7o1v8w4

v0r1n3e7a6w4s5o2m8c9
w1a8v4c0s3e6r2m9o5n7
n0o8m4r6e1s9c8v5a7w2
v6w0m3s7e2r1c5o4a8n9
o3n0r2s9e1w6a7v5c8m4
w8v1o7r6s3a0c5e9m2n4
c8m2o4s5w6a7e3n1r0v9

Fig. 22. Progressive legibility loss in generation printing on high-contrast materials. Left: first generation. Center: third generation. Right: fifth generation.

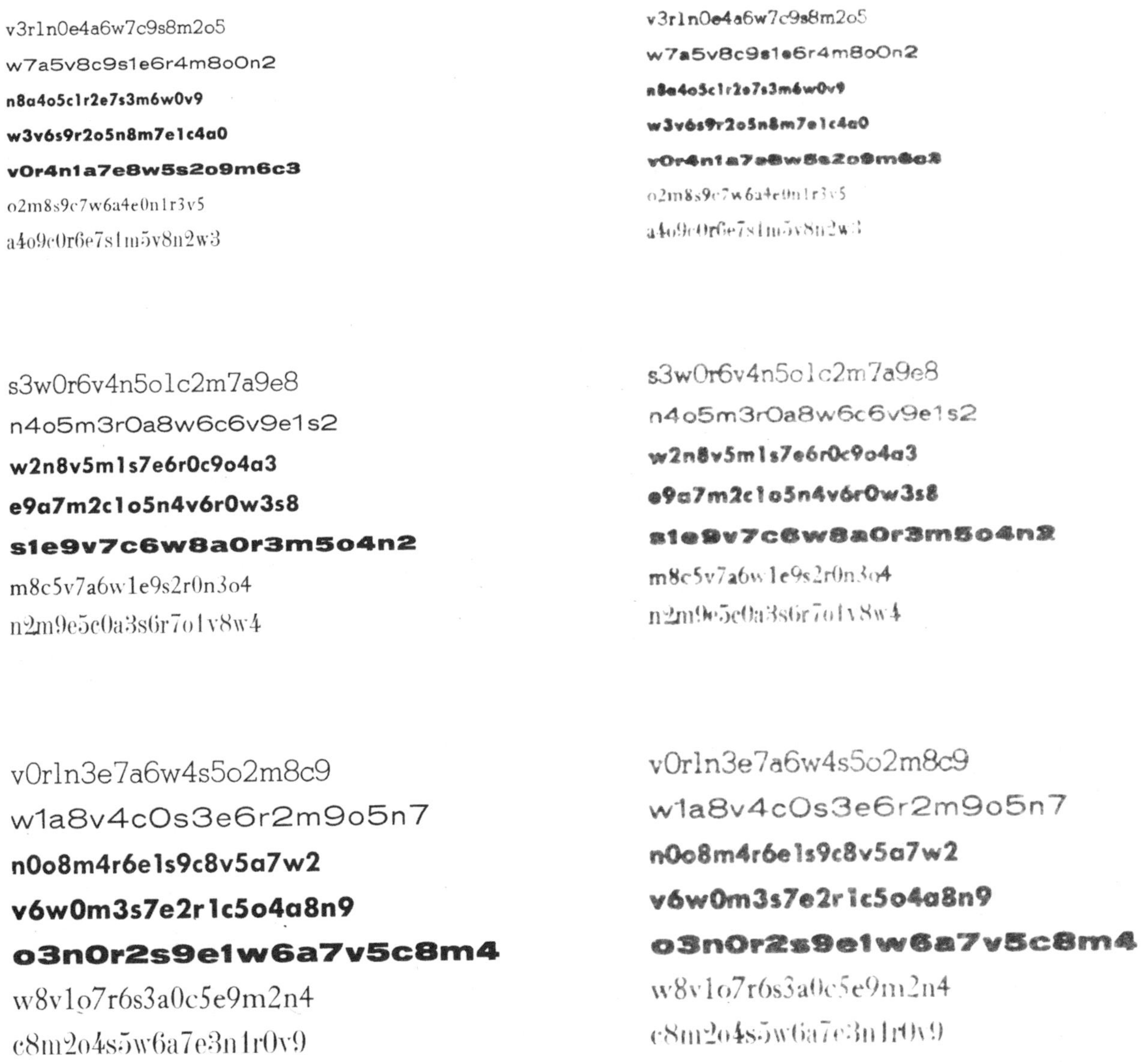

v3r1n0e4a6w7c9s8m2o5

w7a5v8c9s1e6r4m8oOn2

n8a4o5c1r2e7s3m6w0v9

w3v6s9r2o5n8m7e1c4a0

v0r4n1a7e8w5s2o9m6c3

o2m8s9c7w6a4e0n1r3v5

a4o9c0r6e7s1m5v8n2w3

v3r1n0e4a6w7c9s8m2o5

w7a5v8c9s1e6r4m8oOn2

n8a4o5c1r2e7s3m6w0v9

w3v6s9r2o5n8m7e1c4a0

v0r4n1a7e8w5s2o9m6c3

o2m8s9c7w6a4e0n1r3v5

a4o9c0r6e7s1m5v8n2w3

s3w0r6v4n5o1c2m7a9e8

n4o5m3r0a8w6c6v9e1s2

w2n8v5m1s7e6r0c9o4a3

e9a7m2c1o5n4v6r0w3s8

s1e9v7c6w8a0r3m5o4n2

m8c5v7a6w1e9s2r0n3o4

n2m9e5c0a3s6r7o1v8w4

s3w0r6v4n5o1c2m7a9e8

n4o5m3r0a8w6c6v9e1s2

w2n8v5m1s7e6r0c9o4a3

e9a7m2c1o5n4v6r0w3s8

s1e9v7c6w8a0r3m5o4n2

m8c5v7a6w1e9s2r0n3o4

n2m9e5c0a3s6r7o1v8w4

v0r1n3e7a6w4s5o2m8c9

w1a8v4c0s3e6r2m9o5n7

n0o8m4r6e1s9c8v5a7w2

v6w0m3s7e2r1c5o4a8n9

o3n0r2s9e1w6a7v5c8m4

w8v1o7r6s3a0c5e9m2n4

c8m2o4s5w6a7e3n1r0v9

v0r1n3e7a6w4s5o2m8c9

w1a8v4c0s3e6r2m9o5n7

n0o8m4r6e1s9c8v5a7w2

v6w0m3s7e2r1c5o4a8n9

o3n0r2s9e1w6a7v5c8m4

w8v1o7r6s3a0c5e9m2n4

c8m2o4s5w6a7e3n1r0v9

Fig. 23. High-contrast photocopy recopied by another high-contrast process which also has inferior resolving power.

which such variables can be numerically expressed. The importance of these variables and the influence of type design in general on the problem of reproducibility are discussed in detail in the second part of the *Manual*, "The Physical Characteristics of Research Materials."

Color sensitivity. Document reproduction materials vary considerably in their color sensitivity, depending upon the nature of the process and the manufacturing techniques employed. Simple silver halide emulsions for black-and-white copying may be sensitive to blue light only and are usually referred to as *color blind*. Other emulsions, referred to as *orthochromatic*, have, through the addition of sensitizing dyes, a response to both blue and green light. *Panchromatic* coatings are those that respond to all portions of the visible spectrum, but not necessarily in the same balance perceived by the human eye. A panchromatic coating which is oversensitive to red will record a strong red as a dark gray tone on a negative and a weak gray tone on a positive.

Still other coatings are available in which spectral response is carried beyond the visible spectrum into either the infrared or ultraviolet regions.

Documents, for the most part, are black on white or gray on white. Handwritten documents and some typewritten or duplicated documents, depending on the ink used, may be colored, but are usually monochromatic. Reproduction processes yielding black and white copies are thus suitable for most documents. Where color is used, such as in maps or in color-coded graphs and diagrams, it is important that the reproduction process used be capable not only of reproducing colored lines or areas as shades of gray but also of differentiating colors by reproducing them as different shades of gray. The latter is not always possible since the response to color, i.e., the color sensitivity of the materials used, will be such that, in some instances, two quite different colors will reproduce as identical shades of gray.

In document reproduction, two problems occur in which color sensitivity is an important factor. The first of these is the reproduction with ample clarity and contrast of colored lines on a white background. The second is the reproduction of text on a colored background. A process which might be used quite successfully for the first may be a failure with the second. For reproducing colored lines, the ideal situation would be one in which the response of the sensitized material during exposure would be the same as it is for black lines. Hence, lines of any color would reproduce strongly and clearly just as if they had been black. This, however, would make the copying of texts on colored backgrounds impossible, since both the background and the text would reproduce as solid black with no differentiation between the two. A balance must therefore be struck which will make it possible to record colors as shades of gray, thus yielding gray reproductions of colored lines against a white background, and a gray reproduction of a colored background against which a black text can easily be read. Some processes come closer to achieving this balance than others. The problem is illustrated in Figures 24, 25, and 26, in which a graph in red and black is reproduced by two different processes. One is a negative-positive process in which the negative is low in red sensitivity, thus recording red as a solid black on the positive. The other,

a subtractive direct-positive process, has a higher degree of red sensitivity and records red as a shade of gray. While the latter copy does not have the clarity of the original, it is nonetheless legible, whereas the loss of information in the former makes the copy quite useless.

Another aspect of color sensitivity occurs in thermographic processes. More properly, it can be called a problem in thermal sensitivity which happens to occur in connection with color. Text which is printed with ink not containing a carbon or metallic component cannot be reproduced thermographically, since such texts do not absorb heat. Because most colored inks, being dye-based, fall into this class, they do not reproduce at all. A copy of the same graph (Figure 27), reproduced thermographically, thus reproduces all of the information quite legibly, but only in this particular case, because red lettering appears against a black background. If red lettering appeared against a white background or white lettering against a red background, in neither case would the text reproduce.

To some extent, the color sensitivity of certain types of reproduction materials can be altered to suit particular purposes or to meet specific needs. In optical copying, filters can be placed in the optical path. In contact copying, it is sometimes possible to introduce a filter in the form of colored, translucent sheeting to strengthen an image which records too weakly when copied normally. Filters, therefore, can be used to reduce the color sensitivity of a particular material in areas of the spectrum where sensitivity may be too high, but they cannot be used to increase color sensitivity.

Permanence

"Permanence" is ordinarily defined in two ways:

(1) Lasting or intended to last indefinitely without change.

(2) Lasting a relatively long time.

When one speaks of "archival permanence," he is, of course, using the word in the first sense, but, in connection with document reproduction processes and their products, the word is used more and more in the second sense. Archival permanence is simply not a requirement for most of the copies now being produced, nor is it necessary that

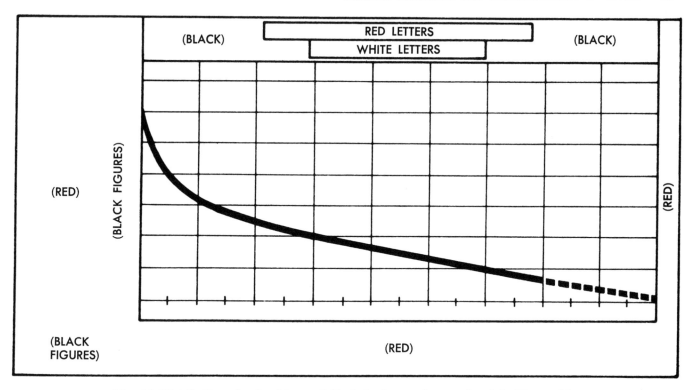

Fig. 24. Distribution of red, white, and black in the graph reproduced in Figures 25, 26, and 27. (This graph is taken from: Byrne Conley, "Voltage Change vs. K°," *Industrial Photography*, January, 1965, p. 23, and is reproduced by courtesy of United Business Publications, Inc., publishers of *Industrial Photography*.)

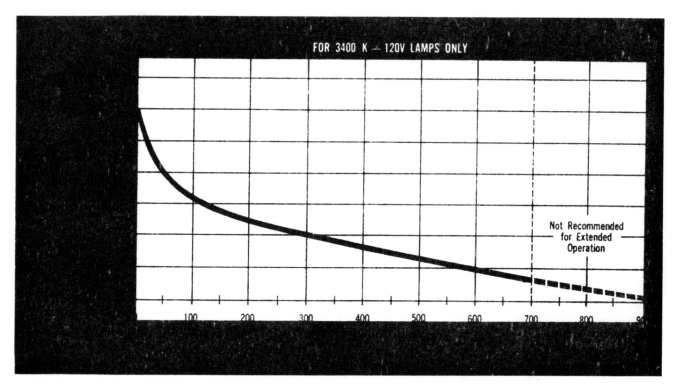

Fig. 25. Copy of the graph (Figure 24) by a process low in red sensitivity.

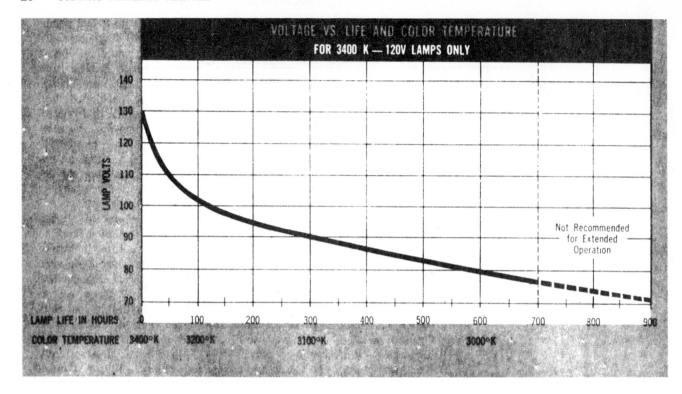

Fig. 26. Copy of the graph (Figure 24) by a process moderately high in red sensitivity.

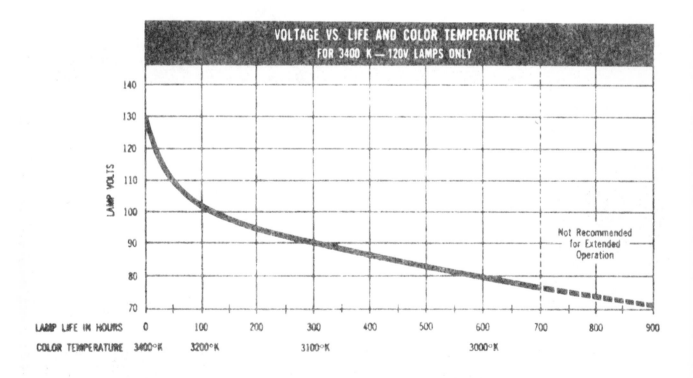

Fig. 27. Copy of the graph (Figure 24) made by a thermographic process that is incapable of recording the red-inked portions.

copies last "without change." Indeed, most copies produced today are classed as "convenience" copies. So long as the text remains readable, it may be of no importance if the text changes color or fades somewhat over a period of time, or if the background darkens. Whether or not a copy is "permanent" must therefore be defined in terms of the user's needs, not against an arbitrary yardstick of time.

In the reproduction of research materials, there are instances in which the copies must have archival permanence. For example, it may be desirable to reproduce a disintegrating manuscript at full size. This copy will then take the place of the original in providing scholars of future generations with the content of the manuscript, and such a copy should be permanent according to the first definition. The same holds true for a microfilm of an extensive newspaper file. The original itself is not permanent, but the copy, which may cost a great deal to produce, must be, if the record is to be preserved for posterity. However, in innumerable other instances, the requirements for permanence are by no means so stringent. Most reproduction processes in use today provide copies which, under reasonable conditions of storage, will last at least a number of years. During this time, changes in the appearance of some may occur, but the text will remain legible. Others are truly permanent and can be expected to last indefinitely without change. It is only in instances in which the requirement of life expectancy is known to be indefinite that the choice of process used must be made only from those which do, in fact, provide archival permanence.

2. THE PHYSICAL CHARACTERISTICS OF RESEARCH MATERIALS

The number of different types of graphic records of human thought and activity that can be included under the heading of "research materials" is very broad indeed, since it covers the entire history of recorded knowledge from stone and clay tablets to computer output. But, in terms of numbers and frequency of use on the part of the research community who must acquire, preserve, disseminate, or use research materials, most of them can be collected into eleven main classes and divided according to the method of production—those printed and those in which the image is formed by methods other than printing.

Printed research materials

(1) Books and serials
(2) Newspaper files
(3) Maps
(4) Printed continuous-tone illustrations
(5) Printed card files

Non-printed research materials

(1) Manuscripts
(2) Typescripts
(3) Original continuous-tone illustrations
(4) Hand-written and typewritten card files
(5) Microforms
(6) Copies of originals

While many share the properties of being printed, written, or typewritten on sheets of paper, this common denominator is overwhelmingly submerged by a seemingly endless array of differences which have profound effects on the reproducibility of the materials by any known process or method.

The tremendous volume of records produced by business, industry, and government tends, by and large, to conform to certain general standards of document size and type size. Such a degree of conformity greatly simplifies the problem of repro-

ducing such documents. The principal classes of research materials, however, with the exception of printed card files, exhibit the widest possible range of non-conformity. In books and serials alone, almost every imaginable size, paper stock, color, or physical condition, plus a host of other factors affecting reproducibility, can be found. Microform collections held by research libraries are copies of research materials which not only retain some of the variables of the originals from which they were made but also vary in type, size, format, size reduction, density, contrast, and sharpness.

Other kinds of copies of originals exhibit still other characteristics. Already an extensive body of out-of-print material is available in the form of xerographic reproductions. Diazo copies, negative photostats, or copies made by numerous other processes are frequently used in typescript reports of research work. The "copying of copies" entails problems which are often quite different and more difficult than the copying of originals. In manuscript collections, the variables and combinations of variables are almost innumerable.

Each of the many characteristics present in research materials, whether occurring separately or in combination with others, creates technical and/or physical problems in reproduction. It is of importance, therefore, to examine in detail the nature of these characteristics and the ways in which they affect the making of reproductions.

Each of the principal classes of research materials exhibits certain physical characteristics which, separately or in many combinations, become the determinants of the methods and techniques which must be employed in reproducing them. These characteristics may be divided into two main classes: those requiring the solution of technical problems and those requiring the solution of physical problems. In addition, there are some instances in which a single characteristic will pose problems in both areas. In the two main classes, the problems may range from the simple to the formidable and, in some cases, to the impossible.

The starting point in determining how best to reproduce any document will be an examination of the text itself—whether printed, typewritten, handwritten, or produced by other means. The primary question then becomes: What are the *technical* problems entailed in reproducing a particular text? When this question has been decided, the next consideration will be the solution of any *physical* problems presented by the particular document in question. (Techniques which have been devised to cope with the various problems encountered in copying research documents are presented in the fourth part of the *Manual,* "Methods and Techniques.")

TECHNICAL PROBLEMS: PRINTED ORIGINALS

A variety of technical problems arise in copying printed originals, such as books, serials, and newspaper files. Since the vast majority of research materials are printed documents—books, serials, newspapers, maps, and, in certain instances, card files—it is necessary at the outset to explore quite thoroughly the characteristics of printed images, starting with the nature of the type itself and going from there to a consideration of certain characteristics of the printing process which affect the appearance and hence the reproducibility of printed materials. At the outset, it is important to bear in mind that the word "type" is frequently used in two different senses. On the one hand, it is used to refer to the forms, dimensions, and other features of letters, numerals, and other symbols as they appear on a printed page. "Type" is also used, however, to refer to the pieces of metal used in printing, each of which has the raised design of a letter, numeral, or symbol on its surface.

Type design and size

Type design and size are important characteristics. They are intimately related, but no system of measurement exists which would be helpful in determining their reproducibility. The only system of measurement used in connection with

type is the *point system* used in typography. While the point system is a valid system for expressing size relationships which are important in the fields of typography and printing, it fails to provide any measurement of those characteristics of type which have the greatest effect on reproducibility. These characteristics are *line width* (the width of the strokes that make up the characters) and *space width* (the width of spaces both within and between characters). Both of these characteristics can vary over a considerable range, not simply between fonts (a font is a complete assortment of type in one size and style) of different designs and sizes but even within a single font of a single size.

A point, for all practical purposes, is equal to $\frac{1}{72}$ of an inch, but not precisely, since 72 points actually measure 0.9962 inch. Type size, along with other measurements, is expressed in points—e.g., 6-point type, 12-point type, etc. "Type size" expressed in points does not refer to the dimensions of characters as they appear on the printed page, but to the "body height" of the surface of the piece of metal on which the raised design of a letter, numeral, or other symbol appears (Figure 28). Since the body height of these pieces of metal must provide room for letters which have ascenders and descenders, a rule of thumb for determining fairly closely the size of a given type face in points would be the measurement of the distance between the bottom of the lowest descender and the highest ascender of two lower-case letters, such as "p" and "d."

As is shown in Figure 29, four guidelines are used to mark the relative heights of the various parts of letters. The distance between the *base line* and the *mean* (or *waist line*) which defines "x" *height* is not a fixed dimension but one which varies considerably with different styles of type faces. (This is called the "x" height, since the letter "x" which touches the lines at four points is the preferred letter for measurement.) Some type fonts are designed with quite a large "x" height and short ascenders and descenders, while others are designed with a small "x" height and long ascenders and descenders. As is shown in Figure 30, these design variations can make large differences in the "x" height of the letters of two different fonts having the same point size. It is even possible to have letters in a 36-point size in one design which are actually *smaller* in "x" height than the same letters in a 24-point size of a different design (Figure 31).

Another factor about type design which appears to be widely misunderstood and which has a decided effect on the reproducibility of small type faces concerns the relative proportions of the strokes and the spaces within letters between fonts of the same design but of different type size. Six-point type is often thought to be an exact replica of 24-point type on a smaller scale. This

comes close to being the case in certain designs in which the strokes that make up the letters are fairly broad and uniform in width, but does not hold true for designs in which there is a great variation in stroke width from very broad to very fine. This is illustrated in Figure 32, in which Futura Medium and Torino faces in 8-, 12-, 24-, 36-, and 48-point sizes are compared. The stroke width of Futura Medium remains almost proportional to "x" height in the different sizes, but this is not the case with Torino, in which the cross stroke of the "e" in the 48-point size is a very fine

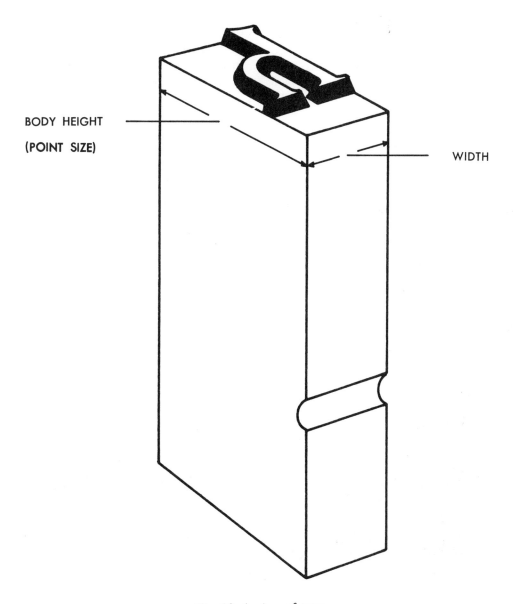

BODY HEIGHT

(POINT SIZE)

WIDTH

Fig. 28. A piece of type.

CAP, OR ASCENDER LINE

MEAN, OR WAIST LINE

"X" HEIGHT

BODY HEIGHT (POINT SIZE)

BASE LINE
DESCENDER LINE

Fig. 29. Measurements of type design.

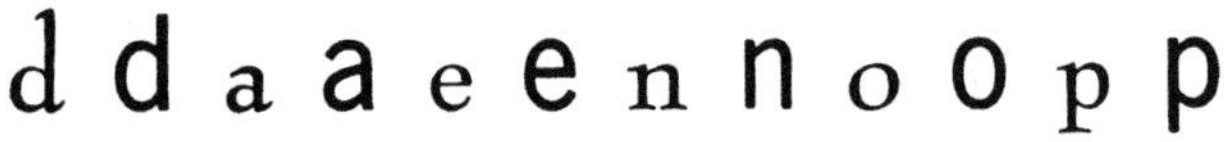

line which, if reduced in width in proportion to "x" height, would be indiscernible in the smaller fonts. Stroke width, in faces such as this, is thus greater in proportion to "x" height in inverse ratio to size, causing the design of small faces to differ from their larger counterparts. This is shown in Figure 33, in which 6-point Garamond type has been photographically enlarged to heights equivalent to 12, 24, 36, and 48 points. Not only is stroke width proportionally larger, as is shown in the cross stroke of the "e," for example, but space within letters is proportionally smaller, as is shown in the "g." Small type faces in designs which exhibit considerable variation in stroke width are thus somewhat more even in stroke width than their larger counterparts, which makes them somewhat easier to reproduce than otherwise would be the case.

The presence of small spaces within letters can, however, pose just as difficult a problem from the standpoint of reproducibility as the presence of fine strokes. In variations on type designs

d d a a e e n n o o p p

Fig. 30. Differences in "x" height between two fonts of the same point size. The smaller letters are 24-point Bernhard Modern Roman. The larger letters are 24-point News Gothic.

abcdefg abcdefg

Fig. 31. Although the type size of the News Gothic face (left) is only 24 points, the "x" height of this face is actually greater than the "x" height of the 36-point Bernhard Modern Roman face (right).

abcdefg
abcdefg
abcdefg
abcdefg
abcdefg

abcdefg
abcdefg
abcdefg
abcdefg
abcdefg

Fig. 32. Left: Futura Medium in 8-, 12-, 24-, 36-, and 48-point sizes.
Right: Torino in 8-, 12-, 24-, 36-, and 48-point sizes.

known variously as *demibold, bold, extra bold, ultra bold,* stroke width is proportionally thicker, which causes the spaces within letters to become smaller (Figure 34). In *condensed* and *extra condensed* varieties, stroke width remains constant, but the space within letters becomes smaller in proportion to the degree of condensation (Figure 35). Still another factor affecting space size occurs in connection with the way type is set. If it is set without additional spacing between letters, the spaces *between* letters may be very small, and the smaller the size of the font, the smaller such spaces will be (Figure 36).

70 percent greater than that of the smallest face, but variations in stroke width and space within letters are far greater. In the Ultra Bodoni "a" alone (which is an extreme example of variation in stroke width), the broad strokes are fifteen times wider than the fine strokes. "X"-height measurements of the twenty-six letter "a"s are given in Figure 40.

To illustrate the great importance that design variations have in relation to a number of characteristics of reproduction processes, a random arrangement of letters and numerals was set in 8-,

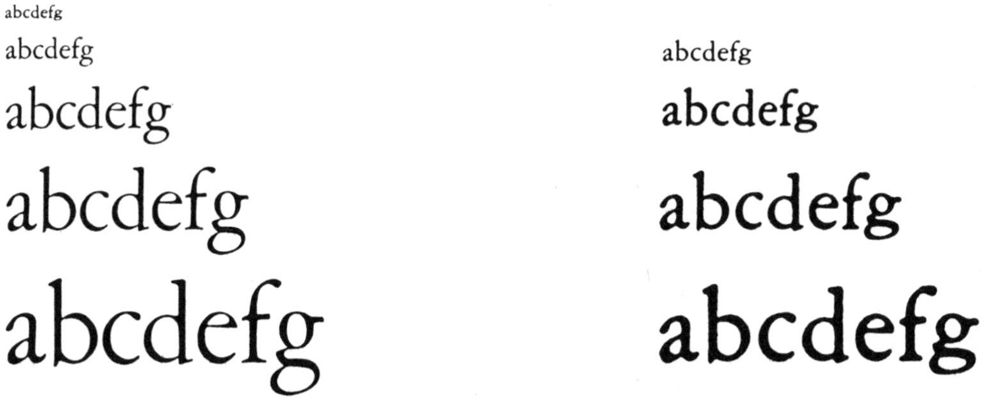

abcdefg

abcdefg

abcdefg

abcdefg

abcdefg

abcdefg

abcdefg

abcdefg

Fig. 33. Left: Typeset Garamond in 6-, 12-, 24-, 36-, and 48-point sizes. Right: Six-point Garamond photographically enlarged to heights equivalent to 12-, 24-, 36-, and 48-point sizes.

Another situation in which the space within and between letters becomes a factor in reproducibility is in copying tightly bound volumes in which the text at the inner margin curves away from the plane of focus, thus causing the letters to be condensed, as shown in Figures 37 and 38.

The extent to which "x" height, stroke width, and space within letters can vary between different type designs and variations on these designs, all of which are the same point height, is shown in Figure 39, in which twenty-six different 36-point lower-case letter "a"s are reproduced. There are, of course, hundreds of different type designs, but the twenty-six faces shown will suffice to show that the differences are of a considerable order of magnitude. The "x" height of the largest face is

abcdefg

abcdefg

abcdefg

abcdefg

Fig. 34. From top (24-point): Futura Medium, Futura Demibold, Futura Bold, and Futura Ultra Bold.

abcdefg

abcdefg

abcdefg

Fig. 35. From top: News Gothic, News Gothic Condensed, and News Gothic Extra Condensed.

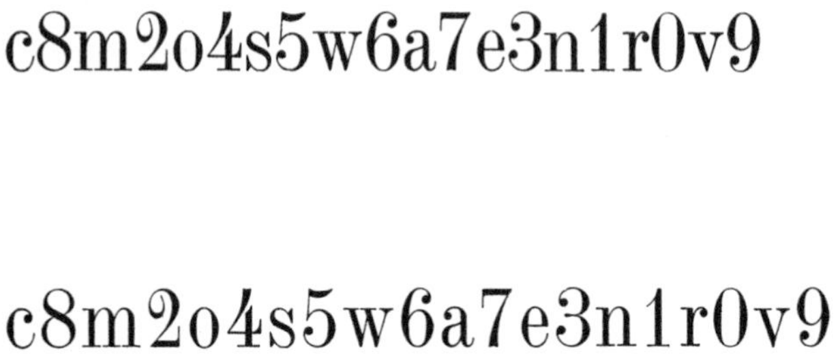

c8m2o4s5w6a7e3n1r0v9

c8m2o4s5w6a7e3n1r0v9

Fig. 36. Above: type set without letter spacing. Below: type set with one-point letter spacing.

e e e e ee

Fig. 37. Condensation of letter forms on a curving surface.

10-, and 12-point fonts of the following faces (Figure 41):

(1) Stymie Light
(2) Venus Light Extended
(3) Futura Demibold
(4) Futura Bold
(5) Venus Extra Bold Extended
(6) Caslon 540
(7) Torino

These faces were chosen because they have approximately the same "x" height and offer a wide range of stroke and space sizes. This test object was then reproduced under a variety of different conditions.

Two things will be evident from the foregoing illustrations: Not only does type design have a marked effect on reproducibility, but type height expressed in points has no validity whatsoever as a measure or index of reproducibility.

Type faces exhibiting either very fine stroke widths or very small spaces within the letters require a high degree of optical, mechanical, and sensitometric control in the reproduction process. Since exposure latitude is limited, exposures must be quite accurate if a fully legible reproduction is to be obtained; contrast must be controlled and

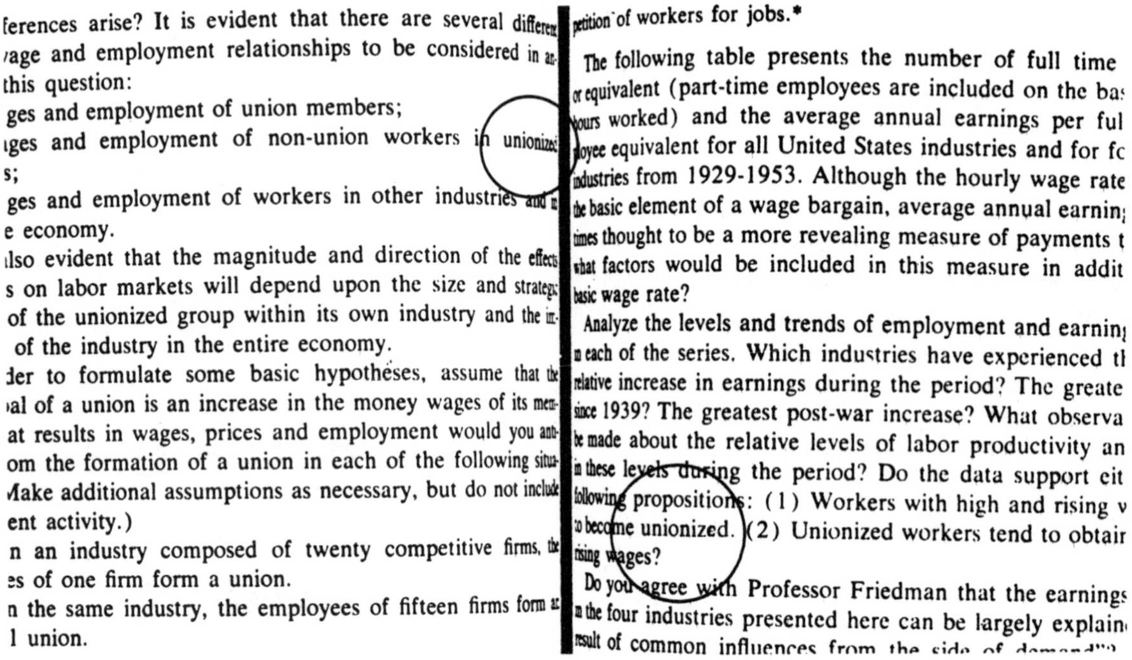

ferences arise? It is evident that there are several differen
rage and employment relationships to be considered in as
this question:
ges and employment of union members;
iges and employment of non-union workers in unionize
s;
ges and employment of workers in other industries and g
e economy.
ilso evident that the magnitude and direction of the effects
s on labor markets will depend upon the size and strategy
of the unionized group within its own industry and the in
of the industry in the entire economy.
ler to formulate some basic hypotheses, assume that the
al of a union is an increase in the money wages of its mem
at results in wages, prices and employment would you anti
om the formation of a union in each of the following situa
Make additional assumptions as necessary, but do not includ
ent activity.)
n an industry composed of twenty competitive firms, the
es of one firm form a union.
n the same industry, the employees of fifteen firms form a
l union.

petition of workers for jobs.*

The following table presents the number of full time
or equivalent (part-time employees are included on the bas
hours worked) and the average annual earnings per ful
loyee equivalent for all United States industries and for fc
industries from 1929-1953. Although the hourly wage rate
the basic element of a wage bargain, average annual earning
times thought to be a more revealing measure of payments t
what factors would be included in this measure in addit
basic wage rate?
Analyze the levels and trends of employment and earning
n each of the series. Which industries have experienced th
relative increase in earnings during the period? The greate
since 1939? The greatest post-war increase? What observa
be made about the relative levels of labor productivity an
in these levels during the period? Do the data support eit
following propositions: (1) Workers with high and rising v
to become unionized. (2) Unionized workers tend to obtain
rising wages?
Do you agree with Professor Friedman that the earnings
n the four industries presented here can be largely explain
result of common influences from the side of demand"?

Fig. 38. Condensation of line and space width in the word "unionized."

aáaaaaaaaaaaaaaaaaaaaaaáaaaaa

1   5   10   15   20   25

Fig. 39. Variations in "x" height, width, stroke width, and size of spaces within letters of twenty-six lower case "a"s in 36-point type. The uneven alignment of the letters is caused by variations in design. The base line for lower-case letters is higher in fonts having long descenders.

1. Bernhard Modern Roman
2. Alternate Gothic No. 1
3. Optima
4. Bodoni
5. Franklin Gothic
6. Century Schoolbook
7. Garamond
8. Corvinus
9. News Gothic Condensed
10. Venus Extra-Bold Extended
11. Baskerville
12. Futura Bold
13. Torino
14. News Gothic Bold
15. Century Bold Condensed
16. Stymie Light
17. Futura Demibold
18. Helvetica
19. Ultra Bodoni
20. Caslon 540
21. Craw Modern
22. Futura Medium
23. Century Expanded
24. Onyx
25. Lucian Bold
26. Craw Clarendon Book

excessive contrast avoided; in optical copying, the lens employed must be capable of a high degree of resolution and must be accurately focused; in contact copying, contact must be firm and uniform. And, finally, the degree of precision and control required becomes increasingly critical in inverse proportion to the size of the particular font being reproduced.

It must also be remembered that the type faces used were chosen to illustrate the fundamental problems encountered in reproducing type faces of different designs and sizes but do not represent the limit of the problem, since four of the type faces—Stymie Light, Futura Demibold, Futura Bold, and Caslon 540, which were set in 8-, 10-, and 12-point sizes—are available in a 6-point size as well. But, even beyond the size of the smallest type face that can be set, there lies a still more difficult problem affecting both legibility and reproducibility. This problem, which is frequently encountered in the literature of the sciences, is the result of the common practice of photographically reducing maps, graphs, drawings, and the like to a size which will fit the page size or column width of the publication in which they appear. This procedure often results in letters and numerals which are of a size smaller than the smallest known printing type. Such characters are often at the very borderline of legibility and can be extremely difficult to reproduce (Figure 54).

Still another consideration in an over-all view of the problems of reproducing printed materials is the fact that the fundamental line-width and space-width problem is not limited to the Roman alphabets used as examples but is common to other alphabets and symbol systems as well, as is shown in Figures 55 and 56.

If the design exhibits adequate and uniform stroke width and ample space within the letters (irrespective of what the alphabet or symbol system may be), the conditions under which a legible reproduction can be made are far broader and less critical. Reproducibility, and also ease of reproducibility—which, in many instances, will also include factors of economy—is thus seen to turn on a balance between stroke width and space size. Undoubtedly, a type face could be designed in the interests of optimum reproducibility, and certain existing designs may already approach this quite closely, but whether such a face would meet the broader requirements of optimum legibility—which entails other factors, including psychological and esthetic ones—is another question.

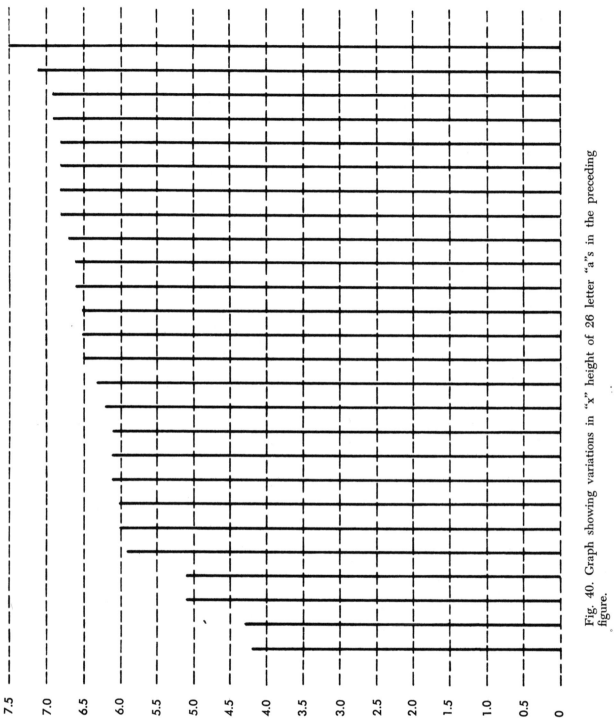

Fig. 40. Graph showing variations in "x" height of 26 letter "a"s in the preceding figure.

"X" HEIGHT, IN MILLIMETERS

8 Point

1. v3rln0e4a6w7c9s8m2o5
2. w7a5v8c9s1e6r4m8o0n2
3. **n8a4o5c1r2e7s3m6w0v9**
4. **w3v6s9r2o5n8m7e1c4a0**
5. **v0r4n1a7e8w5s2o9m6c3**
6. o2m8s9c7w6a4e0n1r3v5
7. a4o9c0r6e7s1m5v8n2w3

10 Point

1. s3w0r6v4n5o1c2m7a9e8
2. n4o5m3r0a8w6c6v9e1s2
3. **w2n8v5m1s7e6r0c9o4a3**
4. **e9a7m2c1o5n4v6r0w3s8**
5. **s1e9v7c6w8a0r3m5o4n2**
6. m8c5v7a6w1e9s2r0n3o4
7. n2m9e5c0a3s6r7o1v8w4

12 Point

1. v0rln3e7a6w4s5o2m8c9
2. w1a8v4c0s3e6r2m9o5n7
3. **n0o8m4r6e1s9c8v5a7w2**
4. **v6w0m3s7e2r1c5o4a8n9**
5. **o3n0r2s9e1w6a7v5c8m4**
6. w8v1o7r6s3a0c5e9m2n4
7. c8m2o4s5w6a7e3n1r0v9

1. Stymie Light
2. Venus Light Extended
3. Futura Demibold
4. Futura Bold
5. Venus Extra Bold Extended
6. Caslon 540
7. Torino

Fig. 41. Three sets of type showing variations in size for succeeding illustrations.

v3r1n0e4a6w7c9s8m2o5
w7a5v8c9s1e6r4m8oo0n2
n8a4o5c1r2e7s3m6w0v9
w3v6s9r2o5n8m7e1c4a0
v0r4n1a7e8w5s2o9m6c3
o2m8s9c7w6a4e0n1r3v5
a4o9c0r6e7s1m5v8n2w3

s3w0r6v4n5o1c2m7a9e8
n4o5m3r0a8w6c6v9e1s2
w2n8v5m1s7e6r0c9o4a3
e9a7m2c1o5n4v6r0w3s8
s1e9v7c6w8a0r3m5o4n2
m8c5v7a6w1e9s2r0n3o4
n2m9e5c0a3s6r7o1v8w4

v0r1n3e7a6w4s5o2m8c9
w1a8v4c0s3e6r2m9o5n7
n0o8m4r6e1s9c8v5a7w2
v6w0m3s7e2r1c5o4a8n9
o3n0r2s9e1w6a7v5c8m4
w8v1o7r6s3a0c5e9m2n4
c8m2o4s5w6a7e3n1r0v9

Fig. 42. The effect of underexposure and overexposure at normal contrast (contact copy from film negative). Left: underexposed. Center: correctly exposed. Right: overexposed.

Fig. 43. The effect of progressive overexposure at high contrast (contact print from film positive).

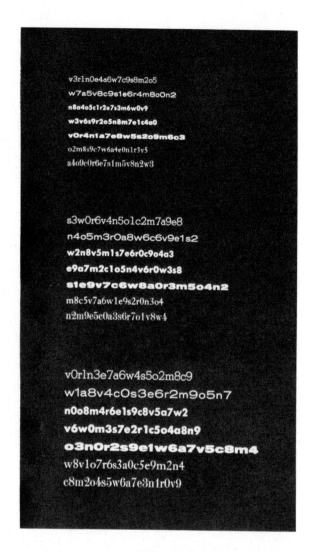

Fig. 44. The effect of reduction in size. Left: 75 percent of original size. Right: 50 percent of original size.

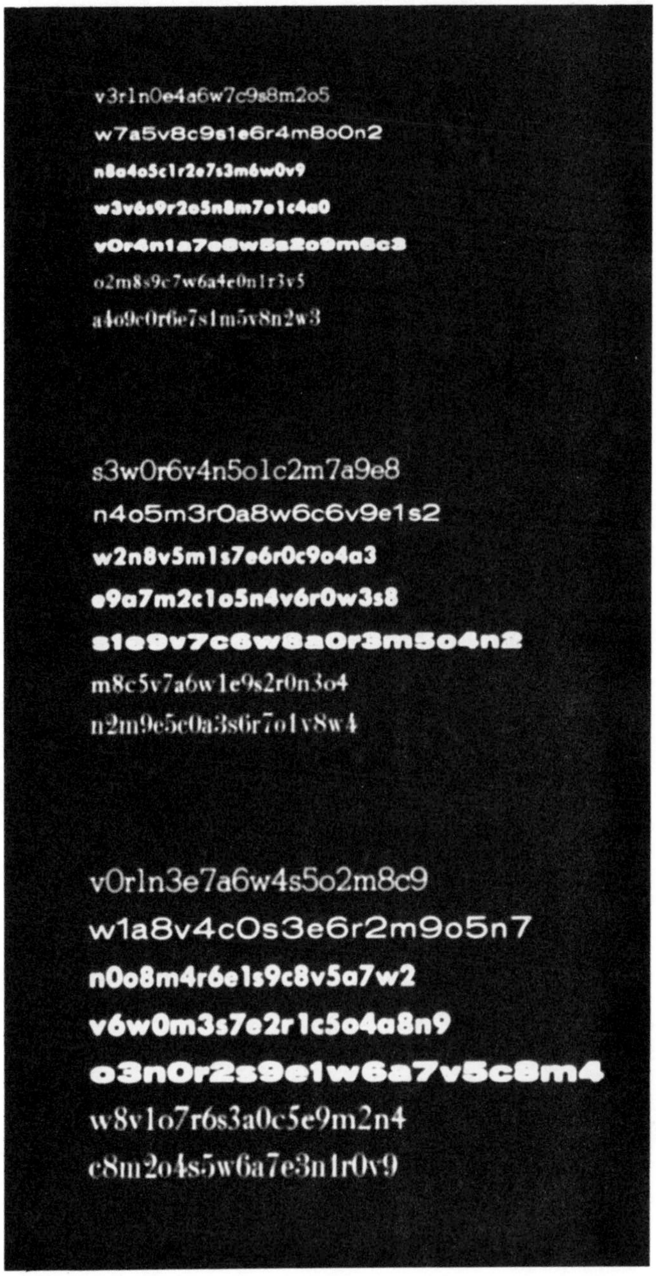

Fig. 45. The effect of improper focus.

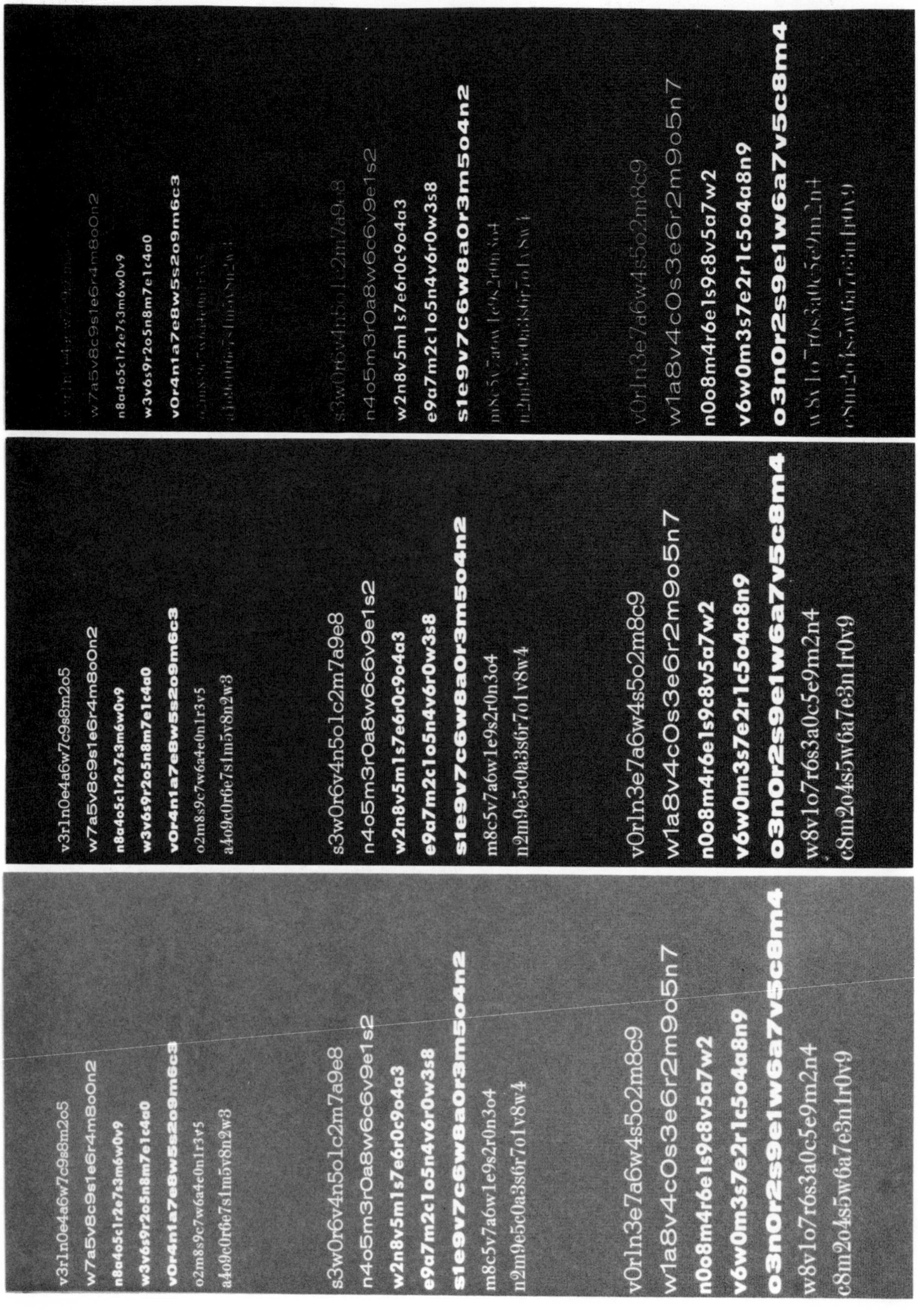

Fig. 46. The effect of exposure in negative photostats. Left: underexposed. Center: correctly exposed. Right: overexposed.

v0r1n3e7a6w4s5o2m8c9
w1a8v4cOs3e6r2m9o5n7
n0o8m4r6e1s9c8v5a7w2
v6w0m3s7e2r1c5o4a8n9
o3nOr2s9e1w6a7v5c8m4
w8v1o7r6s3a0c5e9m2n4
c8m2o4s5w6a7e3n1r0v9

s3w0r6v4n5o1c2m7a9e8
n4o5m3rOa8w6c6v9e1s2
w2n8v5m1s7e6r0c9o4a3
e9a7m2c1o5n4v6r0w3s8
s1e9v7c6w8aOr3m5o4n2
m8c5v7a6w1e9s2r0n3o4
n2m9e5c0a3s6r7o1v8w4

v3r1n0e4a6w7c9s8m2o5
w7a5v8c9s1e6r4m8oOn2
n8a4o5c1r2e7s3m6w0v9
w3v6s9r2o5n8m7e1c4a0
v0r4n1a7e8w5s2o9m6c3
o2m8s9c7w6a4e0m1r3v5
a4o9e0r6e7s1m5v8n2w8

Fig. 47. The effect of exposure in positive photostats made from negative photostats shown in Figure 46. Left: from underexposed negative. Center: from correctly exposed negative. Right: from overexposed negative.

v3r1n0e4a6w7c9s8m2o5
w7a5v8c9s1e6r4m8o0n2
n8a4o5c1r2e7s3m6w0v9
w3v6s9r2o5n8m7e1c4a0
v0r4n1a7e8w5s2o9m6c3
o2m8s9c7w6a4e0n1r3v5
a4o9r0r6e7s1m5v8n2w3

s3w0r6v4n5o1c2m7a9e8
n4o5m3r0a8w6c6c9e1s2
w2n8v5m1s7e6r0c9o4a3
e9a7m2c1o5n4v6r0w3s8
s1e9v7c6w8a0r3m5o4n2
m8c5v7a6w1e9s2r0n3o4
n2m9e5c0a3s6r7o1v8w4

v0r1n3e7a6w4s5o2m8c9
w1a8v4cOs3e6r2m9o5n7
n0o8m4r6e1s9c8v5a7w2
v6w0m3s7e2r1c5o4a8n9
o3n0r2s9e1w6a7v5c8m4
w8v1o7r6s3a0c5e9m2n4
c8m2o4s5w6a7e3n1r0v9

Fig. 48. The effect of overexposure, high-contrast material (diffusion-transfer-reversal).

v3r1n0e4a6w7c9s8m2o5
w7a5v8c9s1e6r4m8oOn2
n8a4o5c1r2e7s3m6w0v9
w3v6s9r2o5n8m7e1c4a0
v0r4n1a7e8w5s2o9m8c3
o2m8s9c7w6a4e0n1r3v5
a4o9c0r6e7s1m5v8n2w3

s3w0r6v4n5o1c2m7a9e8
n4o5m3rOa8w6c6v9e1s2
w2n8v5m1s7e6r0c9o4a3
e9a7m2c1o5n4v6r0w3s8
s1e9v7c6w8aOr3m5o4n2
m8c5v7a6w1e9s2r0n3o4
n2m9e5c0a3s6r7o1v8w4

v0r1n3e7a6w4s5o2m8c9
w1a8v4cOs3e6r2m9o5n7
n0o8m4r6e1s9c8v5a7w2
v6w0m3s7e2r1c5o4a8n9
o3nOr2s9e1w6a7v5c8m4
w8v1o7r6s3a0c5e9m2n4
c8m2o4s5w6a7e3n1r0v9

Fig. 49. The effect of underexposure, high-contrast material (diffusion-transfer-reversal).

Fig. 50. The effect of exposure, high-contrast thermographic material. Left: under-exposure. Center: optimum exposure. Right: overexposure.

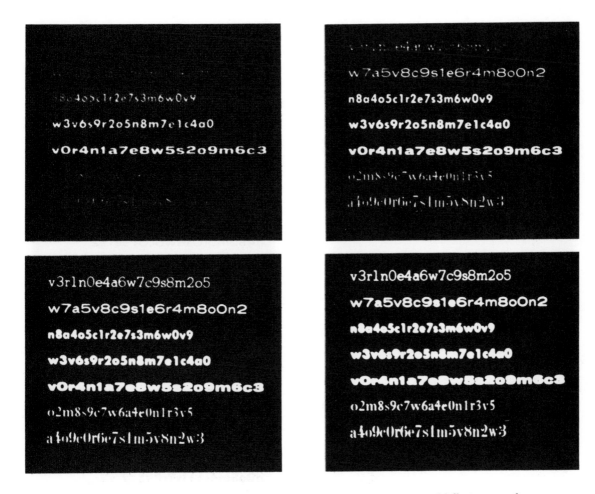

Fig. 51. The effect of under- and overexposure at extreme contrast (diffusion-transfer-reversal hard copy from microfilm negative).

v3r1n0e4a6w7c9s8m2o5

w7a5v8c9s1e6r4m8o0n2

n8e4o5c1r2o7s3m6w0v9

w3v6s9r2o5n8m7o1c4e0

v0r4n1a7e8w8a2o8m6c3

o2m8s9c7w6a4e0n1r3v5

a4o9e0r6e7s1m5v8n2w3

s3w0r6v4n5o1c2m7a9e8

n4o5m3r0a8w6c6v9e1s2

w2n8v5m1s7e6r0c9o4a3

e9a7m2c1o5n4v6r0w3s8

s1e9v7c6w8a0r3m5o4n2

m8c5v7a6w1e9s2r0n5o4

n2m9e5c0a3s6r7o1v8w4

v0r1n3e7a6w4s5o2m8c9

w1a8v4cOs3e6r2m9o5n7

n0o8m4r6e1s9c8v5a7w2

v6w0m3s7e2r1c5o4a8n9

o3n0r2s9e1w6a7v5c8m4

w8v1o7r6s3a0c5e9m2n4

c8m2o4s5w6a7e3n1r0v9

Fig. 52. The effect of improper focus: enlarged print from a microfilm negative made with the camera out of focus.

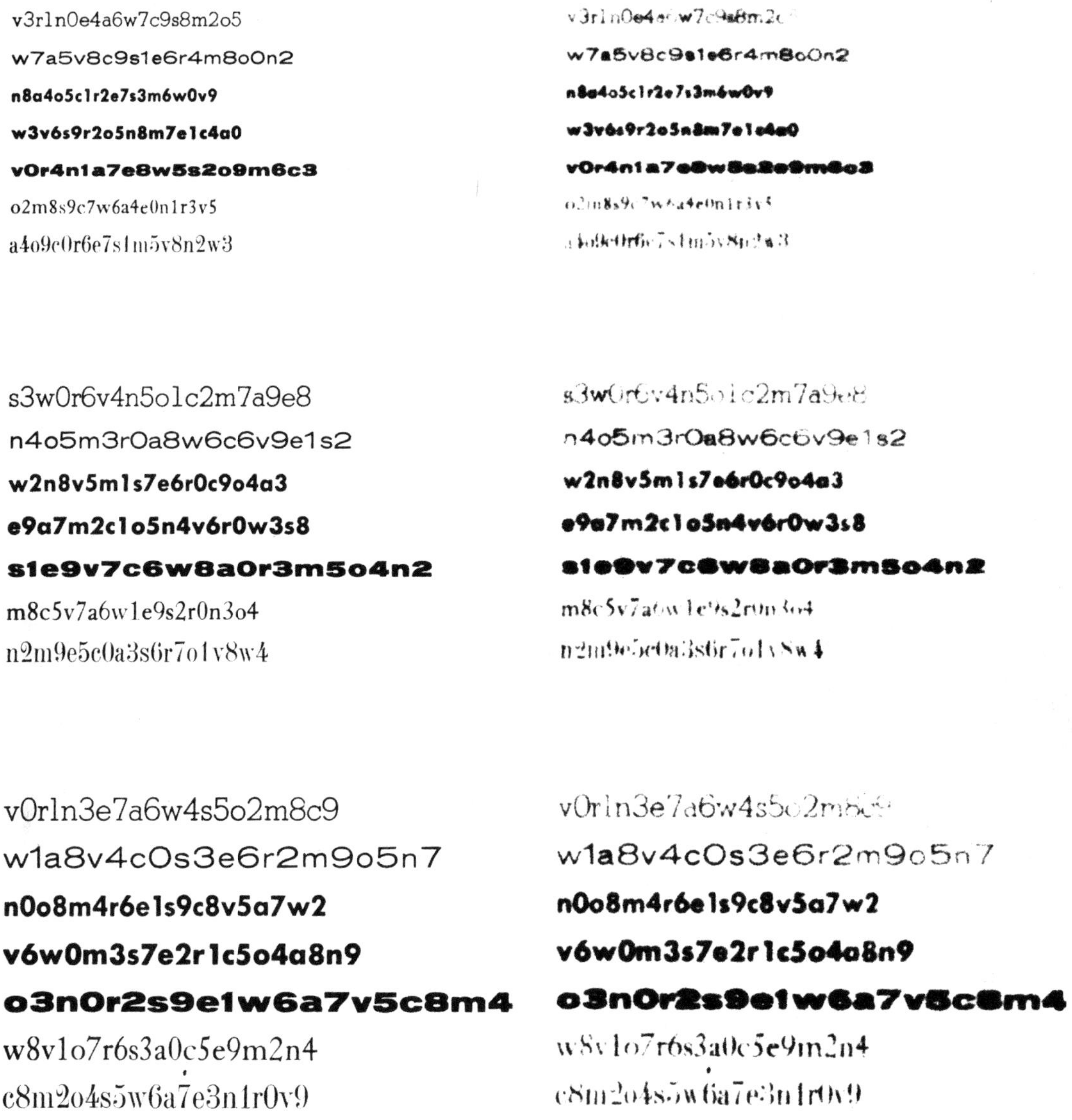

v3r1n0e4a6w7c9s8m2o5
w7a5v8c9s1e6r4m8o0n2
n8a4o5c1r2e7s3m6w0v9
w3v6s9r2o5n8m7e1c4a0
v0r4n1a7e8w5s2o9m6c3
o2m8s9c7w6a4e0n1r3v5
a4o9c0r6e7s1m5v8n2w3

v3r1n0e4a9w7c9s8m2c9
w7a5v8c9s1e6r4m8o0n2
n8a4o5c1r2e7s3m6w0v9
w3v6s9r2o5n8m7e1c4a0
v0r4n1a7e8w8s2o9m8c3
o2m8s9c7w6a4e0n1r3v5
a4o9c0r6e7s1m5v8n2w3

s3w0r6v4n5o1c2m7a9e8
n4o5m3r0a8w6c6v9e1s2
w2n8v5m1s7e6r0c9o4a3
e9a7m2c1o5n4v6r0w3s8
s1e9v7c6w8a0r3m5o4n2
m8c5v7a6w1e9s2r0n3o4
n2m9e5c0a3s6r7o1v8w4

s3w0r6v4n5o1c2m7a9e8
n4o5m3r0a8w6c6v9e1s2
w2n8v5m1s7e6r0c9o4a3
e9a7m2c1o5n4v6r0w3s8
s1e9v7c6w8a0r3m5o4n2
m8c5v7a6w1e9s2r0n3o4
n2m9e5c0a3s6r7o1v8w4

v0r1n3e7a6w4s5o2m8c9
w1a8v4c0s3e6r2m9o5n7
n0o8m4r6e1s9c8v5a7w2
v6w0m3s7e2r1c5o4a8n9
o3n0r2s9e1w6a7v5c8m4
w8v1o7r6s3a0c5e9m2n4
c8m2o4s5w6a7e3n1r0v9

v0r1n3e7a6w4s5o2m8c9
w1a8v4c0s3e6r2m9o5n7
n0o8m4r6e1s9c8v5a7w2
v6w0m3s7e2r1c5o4a8n9
o3n0r2s9e1w6a7v5c8m4
w8v1o7r6s3a0c5e9m2n4
c8m2o4s5w6a7e3n1r0v9

Fig. 53. The effect of contact. The print on the left was made with firm, uniform contact. The print on the right was made with poor contact.

TABLE 7—*Continued*
OFFSET DUPLICATION
Costs and Staff Time

METH-OD	EQUIPMENT	MASTERS (Per 100 Titles) (5)	MATE-RIALS (Per 100 Titles) (6)	MATE-RIALS (Per 1,000 Cards) (10)	CARDS (1,000) (11)	STAFF HOURS PER 100 TITLES (16) Cards Per Title					
						4	8	12	16	32	64
1	All offset equipment	$1.60[a]	......	$1.00	$6.00	7.6	9.1	10.6	12.2	18.3	30.6
2	All offset equipment	3.20[f]	......	1.00	6.00	9.5	10.0	10.6	11.1	13.2	17.5
3	Thermo-Fax & offset	6.35[b]	......	1.00	6.00	3.9	5.4	6.9	8.5	14.6	26.9
4	Xerox No. 1 System & offset	1.60[f]	$2.00	1.00	6.00	4.6	6.1	7.6	9.2	15.2	27.5
	Xerox 914 & off-set	1.55[f]	....[d]	1.00	6.00	4.1	5.5	7.1	8.7	14.7	27.0
	Ektalith & offset	2.42[f]	5.00	1.00	6.00	4.0	5.5	7.1	8.6	14.7	27.0
	Photo-Direct & offset	4.58[f]	.46	1.00	6.00	3.4	4.9	6.4	8.0	14.1	26.3
	Platemaster & offset	3.18[f]	.32	1.00	6.00	3.3	4.8	6.3	7.9	14.0	26.3
5	Xerox No. 1 System & offset	1.51[f]	1.33	1.00	6.00	4.4	5.9	7.5	9.0	15.1	27.4
	Photo-Direct & offset	4.21[f]	.42	1.00	6.00	3.3	4.8	6.4	7.9	14.0	26.3
	Platemaster & offset	2.66[f]	.27	1.00	6.00	3.3	4.8	6.3	7.9	14.0	26.2
6	Xerox No. 1 System & offset	3.20[f]	2.00	1.00	6.00	7.0	7.5	8.0	8.6	10.7	15.0
	Xerox 914 & off-set	3.15[f]	....[d]	1.00	6.00	6.5	7.0	7.5	8.1	10.2	14.5
	Ektalith & offset	4.02[f]	5.00	1.00	6.00	6.5	7.0	7.5	8.1	10.2	14.5
	Photo-Direct & offset	6.18[f]	.46	1.00	6.00	5.9	6.4	6.9	7.5	9.6	13.9
	Platemaster & offset	4.78[f]	.32	1.00	6.00	5.8	6.3	6.9	7.4	9.5	13.8
7	Xerox No. 4 & offset	3.11[f]	1.33	1.00	6.00	5.8	6.3	6.9	7.4	10.6	14.8
	Photo-Direct & offset	5.81[f]	.42	1.00	6.00	5.8	6.3	6.9	7.4	9.5	13.8
	Platemaster & offset	4.26[d]	.27	1.00	6.00	5.8	6.3	6.8	7.4	9.5	13.8

(For description of methods and notes to Table 7, see page 64.)

TABLE 7—*Continued*
OFFSET DUPLICATION
Costs and Staff Time

METH-OD	EQUIPMENT	MASTERS (Per 100 Titles) (5)	MATE-RIALS (Per 100 Titles) (6)	MATE-RIALS (Per 1,000 Cards) (10)	CARDS (1,000) (11)	STAFF HOURS PER 100 TITLES (16) Cards Per Title					
						4	8	12	16	32	64
8	Xerox No. 1 System & offset	$1.13[b]	$2.00	$1.00	$5.33	4.1	5.6	7.1	8.6	14.5	26.5
	Xerox 914 & off-set	1.55[c]	....[d]	1.00	5.33	3.6	5.1	6.6	8.1	14.0	26.0
	Ektalith & offset	2.42[e]	5.00	1.00	5.33	3.6	5.1	6.6	8.0	14.0	26.0
	Photo-Direct & offset	4.58[f]	.46	1.00	5.33	2.9	4.4	5.9	7.4	13.4	25.3
	Platemaster & offset	3.18[f]	.32	1.00	5.33	2.8	4.3	5.8	7.3	13.3	25.3
9	Xerox No. 1 System & offset	1.51[c]	1.33	1.00	4.40	3.6	5.1	6.6	8.1	14.1	26.0
	Xerox 914 & off-set	1.02[c]	....[i]	1.00	4.40	3.5	5.0	6.5	8.0	14.0	25.9
	Ektalith & off-set	1.61[f]	3.33	1.00	4.40	3.2	4.7	6.2	7.7	13.7	25.6
	Photo-Direct & offset	4.21[f]	.42	1.00	4.40	2.8	4.3	5.8	7.3	13.2	25.1
	Platemaster & offset	2.66[f]	.27	1.00	4.40	2.7	4.2	5.7	7.2	13.2	25.1
10	Xerox No. 4 System & offset	1.13[c]	1.00	1.00	3.33	3.6	5.1	6.6	8.1	14.0	25.9
	Photo-Direct & offset	3.15[f]	.32	1.00	3.33	2.7	4.2	5.6	7.2	13.1	25.0
	Platemaster & offset	2.59[f]	.26	1.00	3.33	2.7	4.1	5.6	7.1	13.1	25.0
11	Xerox No. 1 System & offset	4.53[e]	4.00	1.00	4.40	6.2	6.7	7.2	7.7	9.7	13.6
	Xerox 914 & off-set	3.06[e]	....[j]	1.00	4.40	5.0	5.5	6.0	6.5	8.4	12.4
	Ektalith & off-set	4.83[e]	10.00	1.00	4.40	5.1	5.6	6.0	6.5	8.5	12.4
12	Xerox No. 4 System & offset	3.39[e]	3.00	1.00	3.33	6.0	6.5	7.0	7.5	9.5	13.4
13	All offset equipment	1.13[e]	......	1.00	3.33	7.1	8.6	10.1	11.6	17.6	29.5

(For description of methods and notes to Table 7, see page 64.)

Fig. 54. A table photographically reduced in size to fit the page width. Note the size of the lower-case letters used to denote footnotes.

Василий Петрович. Но на какой работе? Вот, граждане покупатели могут подтвердить. Что есть корзина цветов? Подарок! Человек сам никогда не купит себе корзину цветов. Может, только тенор какой-нибудь! И я этот подарок людям приношу. Они мне от всего сердца -- не обижайте! А я их обижу? Ни за что! Сегодня я три раза пытался отказаться. Ни разу не удалось. Уж очень они здоро-

周掌櫃的,你有熟識的銀行没有,給我介
紹一下。
我們的舖子在銀城銀行有賬,你要是看
着相當我可以同你去,你是要存錢呢還
是開個活賬呢。
我手裏有五六千塊錢,打算存起來生些

इसलिए उसने उसी रात में भागने का निश्चय कर लिया। शाम को नहाने के बहाने कुएँ के पास वाली दिवाल की ओर जाकर पत्थर का ठीक से निश्चय कर लिया। रात के अन्धेरे में दिख सके इसलिए एक कपड़ा भी वहां रख आया। अब तो आधीरात के समय की प्रतीक्षा थी। जब सिपाही ऊँघे या इधर-उधर हो और वह भाग निकले। उसने निश्चय कर लिया था कि यदि सिपाही के हथियार छीनकर या उसे जान से मारकर भी भागना पड़ा तो वह उसमें भी किसी तरह का आगा-पीछा नहीं करेगा।

πίνω, drink	πίομαι	ἔπιον	πέπωκα	πέπομαι	ἐπόθην
πράττω,⁴ do, fare	πράξω	ἔπραξα	πέπραχα	πέπραγμαι	ἐπράχθην
στρέφω, twist	στρέψω	ἔστρεψα	ἔστροφα	ἔστραμμαι	ἐστράφην
σῴζω, save	σώσω	ἔσωσα	σέσωκα	σέσωσμαι	ἐσώθην
τέμνω, cut	τεμῶ	ἔτεμον	τέτμηκα	τέτμημαι	ἐτμήθην
τρέπω, turn	τρέψω	ἔτρεψα	τέτροφα	τέτραμμαι	ἐτράπην
τρέφω, nourish	θρέψω	ἔθρεψα	τέτροφα	τέθραμμαι	ἐτράφην
φαίνω show	φανῶ	ἔφηνα		πέφασμαι	ἐφάνθην

ברנש אלא מסיק על כן החליפה בנרן והבליעו נ' התוספת בני הכינוי כמנהגם. ואם תאמר כי נון ישמרנו נ' התוספת והדגש בעבור ה' ישמרנהום כבר הקדרתנו כי אין דרך דנש להביא אות שלאחריו אלא אות שקדם. ותהיה נרן לעצמו.

בכ וחתא קסין ואברכהו גם ברוך יהיה קטמצה חו"ז. גם ב לכנו היחיר. נב לעצמו. ים ב חסר. יב ואפילו הכי הכי. וב סוסי כמו מה שמא ועיין לעיל. וב סוסי וסמלת אנד. ימה שמה למה אין ראיה לפי שהגנינה כתם מלעיל מש"כ במלת בתים. ם מ ב סוסי שחסרה.

يقدره من بعد المسلمات ولم يجر للمسلمات ذكر * والقول السابع أنه حرم عليه أن يبدل بعض نسائه بيهودية أو نصرانية أبعد من ذلك لأن نص القرآن (ولا أن تبدل بهن من أزواج) وليس في القرآن ولا أن تبادل * وحكى ابن زيد عن العرب أنها كانت تبادل بأزواجها يقول أحدهم خذ زوجتي وأعطني زوجتك وهذا غير معروف عند الناقلين لأفعال العرب * والقول الثامن أن النبي ﷺ كان له حلال أن يتزوج من شاء من النساء ثم نسخ ذلك قول محمد بن كعب القرظي

Fig. 55. Variations in stroke width and space size in non-Roman printed material.

$$\int_{t_1}^{t_2} m_i \mathbf{V}_i \cdot \frac{d}{dt} \delta \mathbf{R}_i \, dt = \int_{t_1}^{t_2} m \mathbf{V}_i \cdot \delta \mathbf{V}_i \, dt$$

$$= \tfrac{1}{2} \int_{t_1}^{t_2} m_i \, \delta(\mathbf{V}_i \cdot \mathbf{V}_i) \, dt = \tfrac{1}{2} \delta \int_{t_1}^{t_2} m_i v_i^2 \, dt. \qquad (51.5)$$

Summing over all particles we finally get:

$$\int_{t_1}^{t_2} \overline{\delta w^e} \, dt = \delta \int_{t_1}^{t_2} \tfrac{1}{2} \, \Sigma \, m_i v_i^2 \, dt - \delta \int_{t_1}^{t_2} V \, dt$$

$$- \, [\Sigma m_i \mathbf{V}_i \cdot \delta \mathbf{R}_i]_{t_1}^{t_2}. \qquad (51.6)$$

Fig. 56. Variations in stroke width and space size in mathematics symbols and music.

Reproducibility is, of course, related to legibility, and here again, what would constitute satisfactory legibility *in a reproduction* turns on many factors and admits of many degrees. Criteria for legibility will vary with the nature and characteristics of the data reproduced and, for want of a better term, the "characteristics" of the user and the purpose which the reproduction is intended to serve.

Printing quality

It will be evident from the foregoing examples that quality of the impression in printing will also play a role in the reproducibility of any given subject. If the particular font used is small and is of a design which exhibits marked contrasts in line and space widths, the impression must, of course, be of very good quality. A poor impression would cause either fine lines to be faint or broken or small spaces to become filled, thus adding to the difficulty of making a satisfactory reproduction.

Evenness of impression. If the inking is light but the impression nonetheless sharp and clear, the use of materials which will yield a copy somewhat higher in contrast than the original will be helpful. But if the impression is at all uneven, the problem becomes considerably more difficult. Originals in which the impression is uneven become, in effect, continuous-tone originals. This is because, instead of the impression being a relatively even shade of black or gray against a white background, different tonalities occur according to whether the impression is strong or weak. High-contrast materials, therefore, cannot be used since high contrast tends to accentuate any unevenness in the original (Figures 57, 58, 59, and 60).

Embossing. If, in the process of printing, the pressure applied to transfer the ink to the paper is excessive, *embossing* may occur, causing the recto image to be slightly below the paper surface and, under certain conditions, creating a blind image on the verso of the sheet which is higher than the verso surface. If this process is repeated in the imprinting of the verso image, both of the images are partially recessed and partially raised. Such pages present no problems in optical copying but make copying by contact methods quite difficult or even impossible, because the recessed portions of the image cannot be brought into contact with the surface of the sensitized material.

The effect of worn type. Pages which have been printed with worn type will exhibit not only poorer definition of individual characters but also unevenness in tonality. The latter is the result of the fact that all of the pieces of type that make up a font are not used with the same degree of frequency. Those used most often eventually become slightly shorter in height than those which are seldom used. This difference in height prevents the worn characters from making as strong an impression as that made by the taller, less badly worn characters, thus causing the tonality to be uneven and the problem of reproducing such pages more difficult.

Offset. This is a condition which occurs when printed sheets are stacked before the ink is dry, causing a partial impression of the text of one page to become superimposed on that of another. Offset can vary from a very faint superimposed image, which may have little effect on legibility, to a fairly strong image which not only interferes with the legibility of the original but also makes reproduction of such originals quite difficult (Figure 61).

Show-through. This occurs when text is printed on two sides of a sheet of paper of insufficient opacity. The text on the verso of such a sheet thus appears intermixed with the text on the recto, and vice versa. Like offset, this condition varies in degree, depending on the relative opacity of the paper stock. The greater the degree of show-through, the more difficult the problem of making a satisfactory reproduction becomes. Show-through also occurs in bound, single-sided materials (e.g., typescripts) if the paper lacks opacity.

Color

Colored plates. Since the photosensitive recording materials ordinarily used for document reproduction do not reproduce colors in the same tonal relationship in which they appear to the human eye, and since different processes reproduce colored lines and areas with markedly different results, the making of satisfactory black-and-white copies from colored plates is limited to

upper forwarding roller by means of a one-way freewheel- 50
ing clutch 148. When the copy sheet is being advanced
into the crotch of the rollers 74 and 75, the follower 145
is at a dwell point on the cam 143 so that the rollers are
stationary. On the subsequent rise of the cam 143, the
roller 74 is driven counterclockwise and the copy sheet 55
is forwarded between the rollers to the crotch of the cylinder 32 and the impression roller 81. On the fall of the
cam 143, the one-way clutch 148 prevents the gear 147
from driving the roller 74 clockwise.

To facilitate the positioning of the stack on the feed 60
table 70, a vertically movable stop plate 150 is connected
to the arms 111 which support the feed roller 72. When
the feed is turned off by raising the feed roller 72, the
plate 150 is moved upwardly to serve as a stop against
which the leading end of the stack may be positioned. 65
Lowering the feed roller 72 drops the plate below the top
of the stack so that the plate does not affect the normal
feeding of the copy sheets.

The operation of the feed mechanism is controlled by
a hand lever 152 (Figs. 14 and 15) which may be swung 70
up and down to turn the feed on and off. An over center
spring 153 is effective to hold the lever 152 in either position. The lever 152 is connected to a downwardly extending link 154 by means of a lost motion connection
comprising a pin 156, mounted on the lever, and a slot 75

Fig. 57. Original printed with an even impression.

will result in the coöperative action of the
two relays, the closing of the local circuit,
and the giving of the signal at the substation
45 corresponding to and represented by the said
key and at no other, so that we may say that
the operation of any particular key will ring
the bell of one particular and corresponding
substation.
50   It is desirable that when any station is using
the main circuit for conversation other sta-
tions shall not interfere by calling the central station, connecting their telephones, or
by other forms of interruption. To this end
55 we place at each station, in circuit with the
station - relays, a polarized electromagnet
whose armature is responsive in one direction
to a particular central-station key-and-current combination and in the other direction
60 to another key-and-current combination. We
find it convenient for this purpose to employ
two neighboring keys and like but opposed
current combinations.
     The special polarized magnets of all stations
65 are constructed and are arranged alike, and
their armature-levers are arranged to carry a
visual busy-signal and to serve as a locking

Fig. 59. Original printed with an uneven impression.

upper forwarding roller by means of a one-way freewheel- 50
ing clutch 148. When the copy sheet is being advanced
into the crotch of the rollers 74 and 75, the follower 145
is at a dwell point on the cam 143 so that the rollers are
stationary. On the subsequent rise of the cam 143, the
roller 74 is driven counterclockwise and the copy sheet 55
is forwarded between the rollers to the crotch of the cylinder 32 and the impression roller 81. On the fall of the
cam 143, the one-way clutch 148 prevents the gear 147
from driving the roller 74 clockwise.

To facilitate the positioning of the stack on the feed 60
table 70, a vertically movable stop plate 150 is connected
to the arms 111 which support the feed roller 72. When
the feed is turned off by raising the feed roller 72, the
plate 150 is moved upwardly to serve as a stop against
which the leading end of the stack may be positioned. 65
Lowering the feed roller 72 drops the plate below the top
of the stack so that the plate does not affect the normal
feeding of the copy sheets.

The operation of the feed mechanism is controlled by
a hand lever 152 (Figs. 14 and 15) which may be swung 70
up and down to turn the feed on and off. An over center
spring 153 is effective to hold the lever 152 in either position. The lever 152 is connected to a downwardly extending link 154 by means of a lost motion connection
comprising a pin 156, mounted on the lever, and a slot 75

Fig. 58. High-contrast copy of original shown in Figure 57.

will result in the coöperative action of the
two relays, the closing of the local circuit,
and the giving of the signal at the substation
45 corresponding to and represented by the said
key and at no other, so that we may say that
the operation of any particular key will ring
the bell of one particular and corresponding
substation.
50   It is desirable that when any station is using
the main circuit for conversation other sta-
tions shall not interfere by calling the central station, connecting their telephones, or
by other forms of interruption. To this end
55 we place at each station, in circuit with the
station - relays, a polarized electromagnet
whose armature is responsive in one direction
to a particular central-station key-and-current combination and in the other direction
60 to another key-and-current combination. We
find it convenient for this purpose to employ
two neighboring keys and like but opposed
current combinations.
     The special polarized magnets of all stations
65 are constructed and are arranged alike, and
their armature-levers are arranged to carry a
visual busy-signal and to serve as a locking

Fig. 60. High-contrast copy of original shown in Figure 59.

optical copying on specially chosen silver halide materials, and often with the aid of correction filters. Copies in color can, of course, be made by using color films, but all forms of color copying are considerably more expensive than those for equivalent black-and-white materials.

Texts on colored paper stock. A common instance in which a text appears on a colored paper stock is in the covers of serial publications. Often the table of contents of the issue is printed on the cover or the inside cover. The successful copying of such materials will depend largely on the color sensitivity of the process or materials available.

JASPERS, Karl. *Nietzsche: an Introduction to the Understanding of His Philosophical*

Fig. 61. Extreme example of offset.

Foxed, stained, or discolored paper. Foxed or damp-stained paper exhibits spots or areas which are usually yellow-brown or brown in color (Figures 62 and 63). The most common cause of paper discoloration is excessive exposure to bright light. High-quality, rag-content papers are little affected by exposure to light but poor-grade, wood-pulp papers turn brown. Frequently, only a portion of a page is discolored, but this can pose a more difficult problem in copying than if the entire page were uniformly discolored (Figures 64 and 65). A common problem in copying such originals arises from the fact that the reflectance of foxed, stained, and discolored areas is very low, which causes

them to record with a background tone much darker in appearance than the original.

Still another kind of staining is caused by the use of certain types of adhesive materials (mucilage, glue) which react with substances in paper, particularly sulfite paper, to form a dark-brown stain. Such stains are often encountered in album-type collections of newspaper clippings or correspondence.

Another form of discoloration encountered in manuscripts is the fading or discoloration which occurs when impermanent inks are used. The change in color is usually toward brown or yellow and, in extreme cases, may result in a serious loss of contrast. The problem of reproducing such faded texts will vary with the degree of fading and the color of the paper on which the text is written.

PHYSICAL PROBLEMS: PRINTED ORIGINALS

Some of the physical problems in copying printed originals occur in connection with *dimensions* of books, in the characteristics of paper, and the nature of bindings.

Dimensions

Size. One of the most important variables to be found in books and serial publications is that of size. While most books and serials are in the octavo-quarto range, a great many books of both smaller and larger sizes are to be found on the shelves of most libraries (Figure 66), and extremes of size (Figure 67) are not uncommon. Small volumes seldom present special problems in copying merely because of their size. However, large books often do present difficulties because most of the equipment available for reproducing research materials is designed for the copying of only moderately large originals.

Shape. While, in general, pages in vertical rectangular formats predominate, there are many exceptions. Square books are not uncommon and often a horizontal rectangular format may be employed either because of the nature of the material or the dictates of esthetics (Figure 68). Odd shapes are sometimes a problem in copying, since most book copying equipment has been designed primarily for conventional formats.

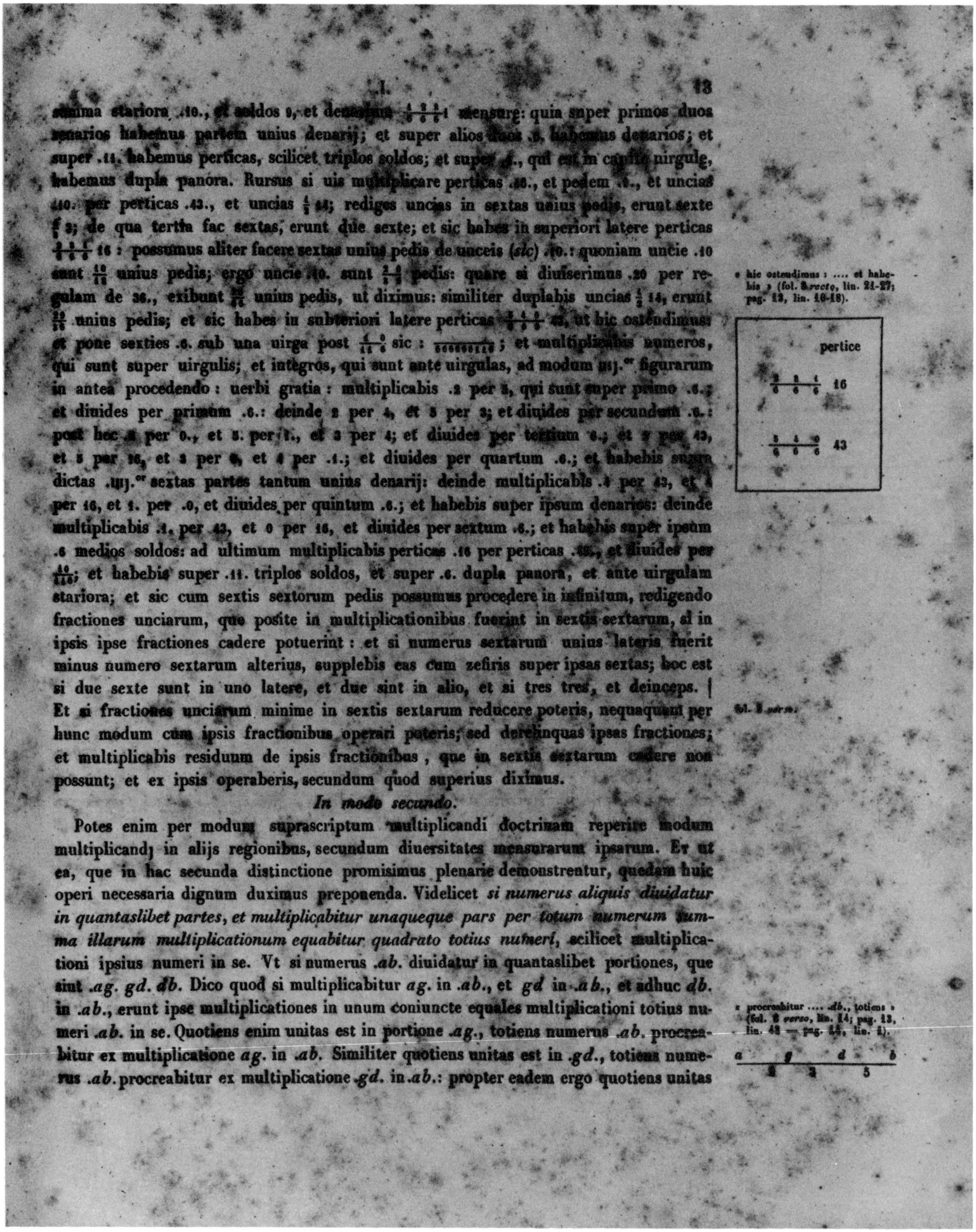

1.   13

summa stariora .10., et soldos 9, et denarios $\frac{1}{2}\frac{1}{4}\frac{1}{4}$ mensure: quia super primos duos denarios habemus partem unius denarij; et super alios duos .1. habemus denarios; et super .11. habemus perticas, scilicet triplos soldos; et super .d., qui est in capite uirgule, habemus dupla panora. Rursus si uis multiplicare perticas .88., et pedem .1., et uncias .10. per perticas .43., et uncias $\frac{1}{2}$ 14; rediges uncias in sextas unius pedis, erunt sexte f 8; de qua tertia fac sextas, erunt due sexte; et sic habes in superiori latere perticas $\frac{1}{4}\frac{1}{4}\frac{1}{4}$ 16 : possumus aliter facere sextas unius pedis de unceis (sic) .10.: quoniam uncie .10 sunt $\frac{10}{11}$ unius pedis; ergo uncie .10. sunt $\frac{2}{4}\frac{4}{1}$ pedis: quare si diuiserimus .20 per regulam de 36., exibunt $\frac{}{}$ unius pedis, ut diximus: similiter duplabis uncias $\frac{1}{2}$ 14, erunt $\frac{10}{10}$ unius pedis; et sic habes in subteriori latere perticas $\frac{1}{4}\frac{1}{4}\frac{1}{4}$ 43, ut hic ostendimus: et pone sexties .6. sub una uirga post $\frac{4}{11}\frac{0}{6}$ sic : [diagram]; et multiplicabis numeros, qui sunt super uirgulis; et integros, qui sunt ante uirgulas, ad modum uij.or figurarum in antea procedendo : uerbi gratia : multiplicabis .8 per 8, qui sunt super primo .6.; et diuides per primum .6.: deinde 8 per 4, et 8 per 3; et diuides per secundum .c.: post hec 8 per 0., et 8 per 1., et 8 per 4; et diuides per tertium 8.; et 8 per 43, et 8 per 16, et 8 per 8, et 4 per .1.; et diuides per quartum .6.; et habebis supra dictas .iiij.or sextas partes tantum unius denarij: deinde multiplicabis .4 per 43, et 4 per 16, et 1. per .0, et diuides per quintum .6.; et habebis super ipsum denarios: deinde multiplicabis .1. per 43, et 0 per 16, et diuides per sextum .6.; et habebis super ipsum .6 medios soldos: ad ultimum multiplicabis perticas .16 per perticas .43., et diuides per $\frac{10}{116}$; et habebis super .11. triplos soldos, et super .6. dupla panora, et ante uirgulam stariora; et sic cum sextis sextorum pedis possumus procedere in infinitum, redigendo fractiones unciarum, que posite in multiplicationibus fuerint in sextis sextarum, si in ipsis ipse fractiones cadere potuerint : et si numerus sextarum unius lateris fuerit minus numero sextarum alterius, supplebis eas cum zefiris super ipsas sextas; hoc est si due sexte sunt in uno latere, et due sint in alio, et si tres tres, et deinceps. | Et si fractiones unciarum minime in sextis sextarum reducere poteris, nequaquam per hunc modum cum ipsis fractionibus operari pateris; sed derelinquas ipsas fractiones; et multiplicabis residuum de ipsis fractionibus , que in sextis sextarum cadere non possunt; et ex ipsis operaberis, secundum quod superius diximus.

In modo secundo.

Potes enim per modum suprascriptum multiplicandi doctrinam reperire modum multiplicandj in alijs regionibus, secundum diuersitates mensurarum ipsarum. Et ut ea, que in hac secunda distinctione promisimus plenarie demonstrentur, quedam huic operi necessaria dignum duximus preponenda. Videlicet *si numerus aliquis diuidatur in quantaslibet partes, et multiplicabitur unaqueque pars per totum numerum summa illarum multiplicationum equabitur quadrato totius numeri,* scilicet multiplicationi ipsius numeri in se. Vt si numerus .ab. diuidatur in quantaslibet portiones, que sint .ag. gd. db. Dico quod si multiplicabitur ag. in .ab., et gd in .ab., et adhuc db. in .ab., erunt ipse multiplicationes in unum coniuncte equales multiplicationi totius numeri .ab. in se. Quotiens enim unitas est in portione .ag., totiens numerus .ab. procreabitur ex multiplicatione ag. in .ab. Similiter quotiens unitas est in .gd., totiens numerus .ab. procreabitur ex multiplicatione .gd. in .ab.: propter eadem ergo quotiens unitas

[margin notes:]
e hic ostendimus : .... et habebis) (fol. 8 recto, lin. 24-27; pag. 13, lin. 16-18).

pertice

61. 8 verso.

x procreabitur .... db., totiens : (fol. 8 verso, lin. 14; pag. 13, lin. 42 — pag. 14, lin. 1).

Fig. 62. Foxed page.

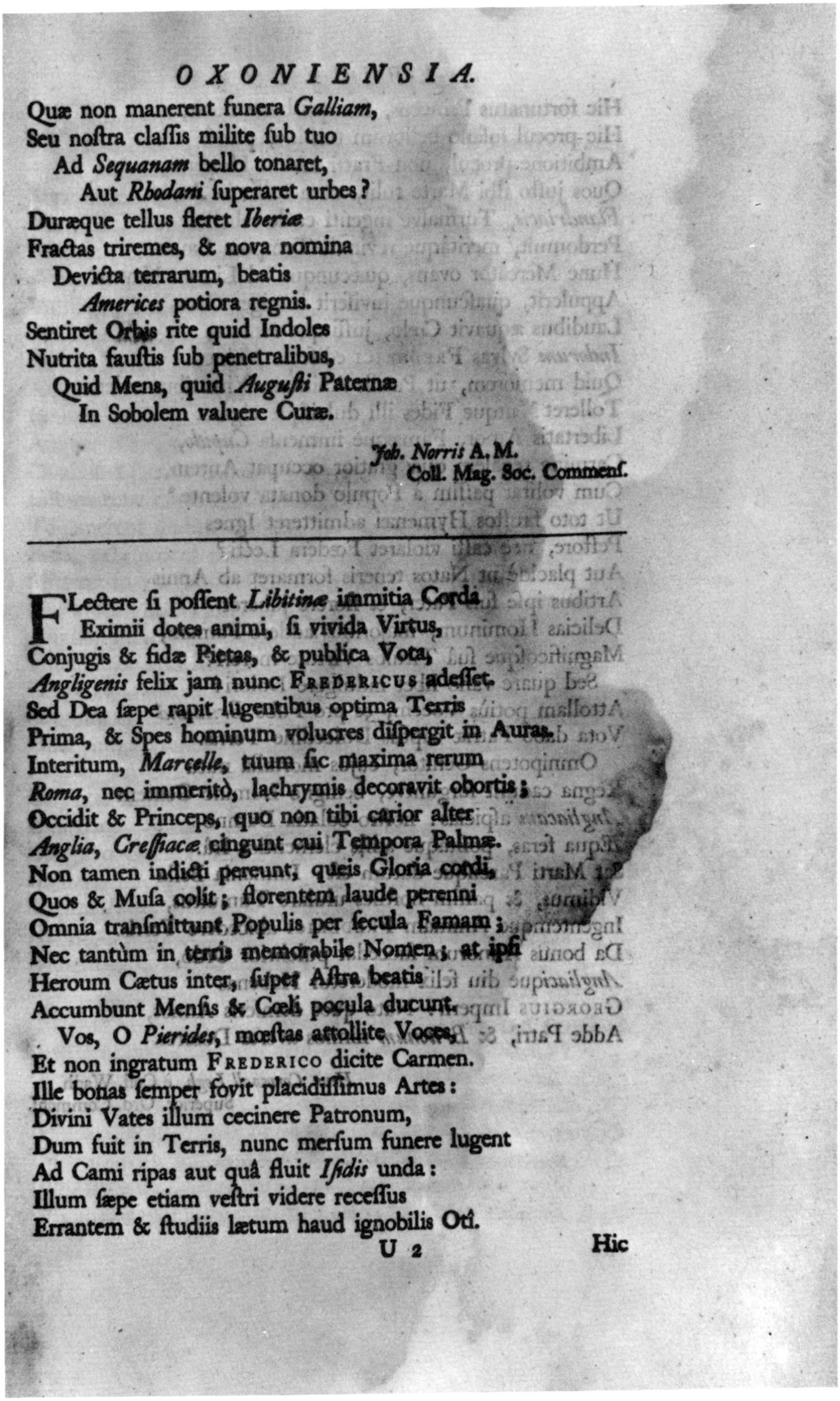

OXONIENSIA.

Quæ non manerent funera *Galliam*,
Seu noftra claffis milite fub tuo
  Ad *Sequanam* bello tonaret,
    Aut *Rhodani* fuperaret urbes?
Duræque tellus fleret *Iberiæ*
Fractas triremes, & nova nomina
  Devicta terrarum, beatis
    Americes potiora regnis.
Sentiret Orbis rite quid Indoles
Nutrita fauftis fub penetralibus,
  Quid Mens, quid *Augufti* Paternæ
    In Sobolem valuere Curæ.

              Joh. Norris A. M.
           Coll. Mag. Soc. Commenf.

FLectere fi poffent *Libitinæ* immitia Corda
  Eximii dotes animi, fi vivida Virtus,
Conjugis & fidæ Pietas, & publica Vota,
Angligenis felix jam nunc FREDERICUS adeffet.
Sed Dea fæpe rapit lugentibus optima Terris
Prima, & Spes hominum volucres difpergit in Auras.
Interitum, *Marcelle*, tuum fic maxima rerum
Roma, nec immeritò, lachrymis decoravit obortis;
Occidit & Princeps, quo non tibi carior alter
Anglia, *Creffiacæ* cingunt cui Tempora Palmæ.
Non tamen indicti pereunt, queis Gloria cordi,
Quos & Mufa colit; florentem laude perenni
Omnia tranfmittunt Populis per fecula Famam;
Nec tantùm in terris memorabile Nomen; at ipfi
Heroum Cætus inter, fuper Aftra beatis
Accumbunt Menfis & Cœli pocula ducunt.
  Vos, O *Pierides*, mœftas attollite Voces,
Et non ingratum FREDERICO dicite Carmen.
Ille bonas femper fovit placidiffimus Artes:
Divini Vates illum cecinere Patronum,
Dum fuit in Terris, nunc merfum funere lugent
Ad Cami ripas aut quâ fluit *Ifidis* unda:
Illum fæpe etiam veftri videre receffus
Errantem & ftudiis lætum haud ignobilis Oti.
          U 2   Hic

Fig. 63. Damp-stained page. Note also the show-through of the text on the reverse side.

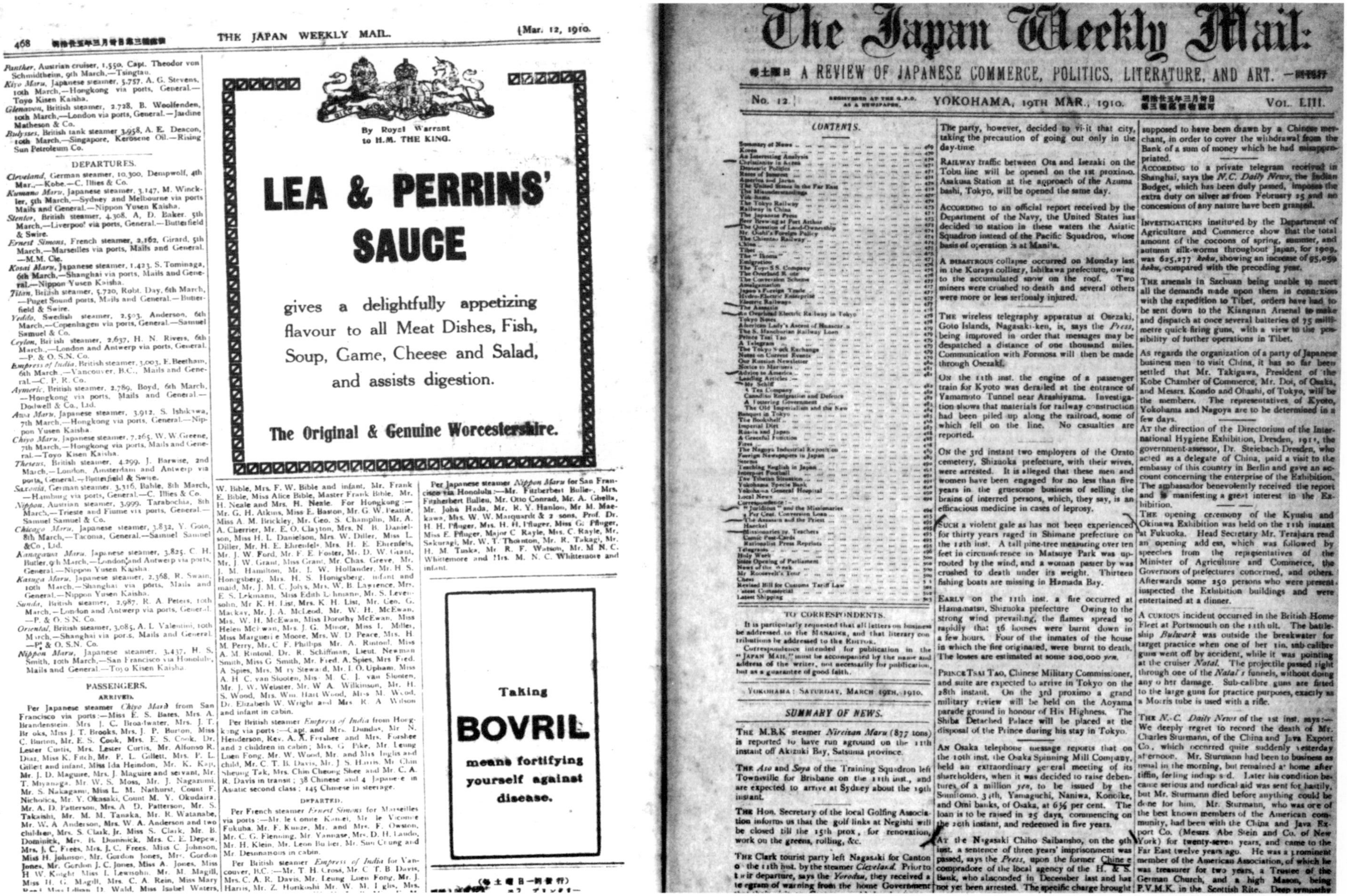

Fig. 64. Facing pages in a newspaper file, one discolored and one not.

The Daily Palo Alto.

Vol. XXXVIII. STANFORD UNIVERSITY, CALIFORNIA, TUESDAY, JANUARY 10, 1911. No. 1.

TWENTY-EIGHT RECORD THEIR FINAL FAILURE

SEVENTY-FIVE OTHERS PLACED ON STRICT PROBATION.

Delinquent Scholarship Committee Compiles Complete Statistics. Several Athletes Affected.

"The scholarship of the past semester shows a marked improvement over that of the same time last year."

This is the statement made by Professor C. H. Gilbert, Chairman of the Faculty Committee on Delinquent Scholarship to a representative of the Daily Palo Alto this afternoon.

A comparison of the statistics given out January 1910 with those presently at hand bears out Chairman Gilbert's statement. Twenty-eight instead of forty-two names have been permanently dropped from Stanford's register because of poor scholarship. Of these twenty-eight, three are women. Seventy-five others have recorded their first failure and are now placed on strict probation. Eight women are recorded among the seventy-five. Only forty-one were on strict probation last year.

Twenty-four, including three women, have a sufficiently low record to be placed on secondary or minor probation. No definite figures as to this class of delinquents were given out in 1910.

As the names of those who failed in their work are withheld, it is not known just how seriously the action of the Scholarship Committee will affect this semester's activities. It is known however, that many prominent students, including some of the Cardinal's best athletes are temporarily or permanently affected.

If the old scholarship ruling of 1909 were yet in effect, the seventy-five on strict probation would not "be among those present," on the campus and undoubtedly more than twenty-eight would be permanently dropped. In January 1909, ninety-one were not permitted to resume their work and fifty-five others were placed on strict probation.

DR. JORDAN PRESIDENT OF ACADEMY OF SCIENCES.

Dr. David Starr Jordan was elected president of the California Academy of Sciences for the coming year at the recent annual election of the association. Professor C. H. Gilbert, of the Department of Zoology, was also honored by being elected to the office of librarian, running successfully against the incumbent.

Works Elected Senator.

John D. Works of Los Angeles was elected United States senator by the legislature today by a large majority. The successful candidate received 92 votes, his nearest competitor, A. G Spaulding of San Diego, polling only 21. The Democrats, with the exception of three, voted for Works.

CARDINAL CAPTURES SERIES FROM CANADIAN PLAYERS

Stanford Aggregation Wins Final Game After a Splendid Exhibition of Rugby Science and Unity of Play.

By I. I. I.

By winning the last two games of the vacation series with Vancouver, the Cardinal players captured the trio of rugby games from the Canadians. A muddy field, together with a new Cardinal rugby lineup, playing together for the first time, lost the first of the series to the Northerners. The two remaining games, however, saw Presley's rugby machine outplaying their opponents and winning the series by a good margin.

Even the most sanguine Cardinal rooter, while believing we would capture the series, looked for a closer score in the winning games. That those seventeen travellers, who after a bare two weeks of practice were made a winning combination, shows perhaps more than anything else could just what George J. Presley's loss, as the Cardinal rugby coach, means. For three years Coach Presley has guided the Cardinal rugby destiny and his ability in selecting and training raw material from which he has developed rugby stars, has placed the Cardinal players in the first rank in the rugby world.

From the time of its arrival until it boarded the "Princess Victoria" to return south, the Cardinal party was entertained royally by its hosts. Hardly an evening passed without a dinner party. New Year's Eve was celebrated by a grand ball in honor of the visitors and during their stay a banquet was given by their hosts after they had been entertained at the theatre. The Canadians were impartial in their rooting at the games and with true sportsmanlike feeling applauded all of Stanford's good plays as heartily as their own.

The first game was played on Monday, December 26th, and was won by Vancouver, score 13-6. The game of Thursday, the 29th was won by the visitors by a score of 10-3 and on Monday, January 2, the Cardinal players ended the series by winning from the Northerners with a 9-0 score.

The first game was played on a muddy field, and being more at home under such conditions, the Canadians followed up their advantage to a clearly earned victory. The game was chiefly confined to dribbling rushes. The Northerners, by a fast following-up of the kickoff, dribbled across for a try. Twice more were they able to duplicate this dribbling rush and added four points more by two conversions.

Similar tactics drove the leather oval across the Vancouver line, Cardinal rallies at midfield being the source of these scores. Geissler and Olmstead shared the honors of chalking up three points apiece by falling on the leather behind their opponents line.

The game of the 29th, saw the Cardinal players at par and their machine-like precision overcame the Northerner's science and Stanford was

Coach George Joseph Presley.

credited with a victory. The Cardinals outclassed their opponents both in the backfield and forward playing. The too strict adherence of Referee McKay to his whistle took away much of the snap that would otherwise have characterized this match.

A. Sanborn, '12, was the Cardinal scorer, first by a spectacular 50-yard run from a midfield excursion and again when he outran Vancouver to score on a dribbling rush. Geissler completed each of these tries by driving the pigskin between the goal posts to tally four points. Vancouver's tally of 3 was made on a penalty kick for Stanford offside.

On a frozen field, covered by an inch of melting snow, the final game and the best exhibition of rugby, during the series, was played. The first half was closely contested and neither fifteen was able to maintain the advantage long enough to advance the ball within speaking distance of its opponent's goal.

The second half saw the Cardinal machine strike through the Canadian's line for three unconverted tries. The scoring was started when Worswick received the ball in a passing rush, via Harrigan and Berryman, and cross kicked to Woodcock, Geissler going across near the side lines to tally 3.

(Continued on page 3)

CAMPUS TO LIVE IN THIRTEENTH CENTURY

MIRACLE PLAYS WILL TRANSPORT US TO DAYS OF YORE.

Mediaeval Scenes of Merrie England Will be Seen in Assembly Hall February 8.

By L. M. Robinson, '12.

Do you believe in miracles? Of course you will answer "No." But before you pass a final judgment, wait and see the Miracles Plays that will be performed in Assembly Hall on the evening of February third. Wait until you hear the voice of the herald bidding all good people come and see the show—a herald clad in shining armor, riding down the road to Paly—and you will behold a wonderful transformation take place upon the campus. The time will be not the present, but the thirteenth century, the arcades of the Quad will be the grim cloisters of a mediaeval monastery, down which jolly old monks will pass along and the campus itself will be the merriest town in all England, because forsooth, it is the day of the show. All this will seem real to you, if you but use an ounce of imagination and trust the rest to the players.

The whole of last semester the English Club was busy preparing for this transformation. Ancient plays were dug up, or gathered from the four corners of the earth and translated from old into modern English. Professor P. Emerson Bassett assumed the responsibilities of coach and has actually found fellows among us who can look the part of saint or monk. Choir boys from the city have been engaged to assist in the anthems, to carry tapers, swing censers and so add to the general enchantment.

Do not fancy from this account that the whole business is but a dreary, churchly procession; for there will be comedy, laughter fairly "holding both its sides." In those days, religion knew how to wink the eye at deviltry. Everything, then, awaits the evening of the third and no little touch that may add to the illusion will be forgotten.

There runs the story that in mediaeval days, when the plays were first presented, the happy crowds that gathered to witness were served with hot cross buns and ale or cider. Do you believe the Stanford public will be so favored? Do you believe in miracles? Well, wait and decide for yourself.

M. E. Society Elects Officers.

Harry Harmon Blee of Santa Ana was elected chairman of the Mechanical Engineering Society for the present semester at its last meeting, and Carl H. Benson will fill the office of secretary. The prosperous condition of the society's treasury led to the authorizing of the expenditure of twenty-five dollars to be used in fitting up its room.

It was also decided to adopt a pin of new design, a tiny gold steam-gauge with the initials of the society around it, making a very distinctive and appropriate emblem.

Four Armory dances were enjoyed by those who remained on the campus during the holidays.

Fig. 65. Half of a newspaper page discolored by exposure to light.

Fig. 66. Variations in size.

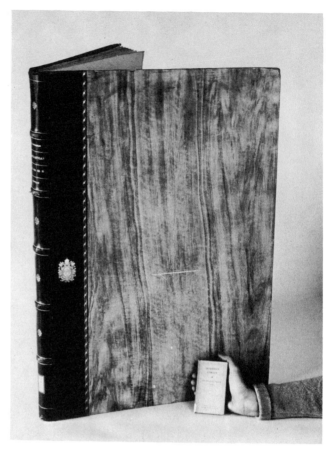

Fig. 67. Extremes of size.

Fig. 68. Variations in shape of bound volumes.

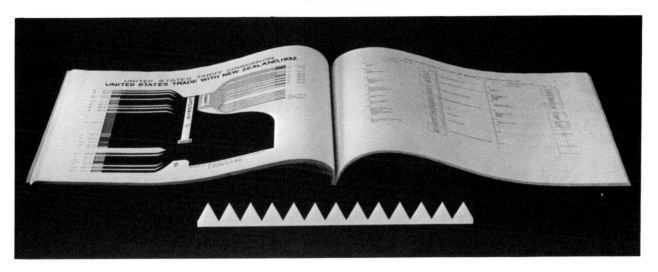

Fig. 69. A horizontal format (wedge points = inches).

Thickness. A third common variable in bound volumes is thickness. The number of pages in a volume may range from very few to thousands. In extreme cases, the thickness of a volume may be its greatest dimension. Thick volumes are difficult to handle when making contact reflex copies on equipment where the book must be handled in an upside-down position. Sometimes the books are too thick to fit conventional book holders. Other expedients, which may be considerably less efficient, may have to be devised to hold the facing pages of thick volumes in plane.

Weight. The range of this factor in bound volumes is very broad. The great weight of some volumes may even limit the choice of copying method to be used. Heavy volumes are, of course, quite difficult to handle in an upside-down position when making contact-reflex copies. Moreover, they are often difficult to handle when using other methods and equipment simply because of their weight and bulk.

Paper characteristics

The physical characteristics of the paper on which a given text is written or printed often create problems in reproduction which may not only require the use of special techniques but may even limit the choice of the method by which certain types of originals can be reproduced.

Paper surfaces. Surfaces range from completely matte surfaces that may have a pronounced texture to very smooth surfaces with a high sheen. Such surface differences will cause differences in reflectance and will affect the exposure used. In copying materials in bound form which are printed on highly calendered or clay-coated stocks, problems in illumination may arise if overbright reflections from curving surfaces are to be avoided.

Fig. 70. Variations in thickness.

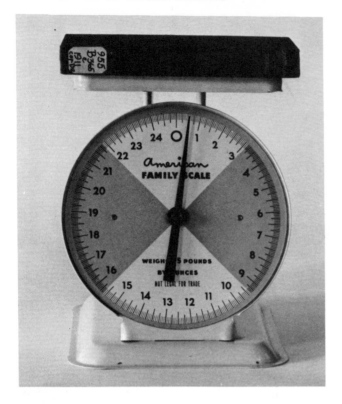

Fig. 71. A nine-ounce volume.

Thin papers. Texts printed on thin papers (e.g., India paper), which have sufficient opacity to prevent show-through, are easily reproduced. However, the thinness of the paper stock may cause problems in handling, since it may be more subject to damage than thicker paper stocks.

Brittle papers. Cheap paper stocks made from wood pulp fibers often become brittle with age, particularly if they are stored in an atmosphere of low humidity where their moisture content is reduced. This is also true of rag-content papers if they have been poorly manufactured. In copying pages from bound volumes in which the paper has deteriorated and become brittle, the greatest care must be used in handling the pages, and many of the techniques ordinarily used in copying cannot be used because of the danger of cracking the paper.

Creased, folded, and wrinkled pages. Creases, folds, and wrinkles may be present because of carelessness, misuse, or accident. Folding, however, may be intentional and frequently appears in serial publications that have been folded and enclosed in a paper wrapper for convenience in

Fig. 72. An eighteen-pound volume.

mailing (Figure 73). Because, in many instances, the wrappers offer but little protection, the publication may also exhibit wrinkles, creases, or other forms of damage by the time it reaches its destination. Creases, folds, and wrinkles seldom impair the legibility of the original but can have a decided effect on its reproducibility. If it is being copied by optical methods (e.g., microfilming, photostating) it may be necessary to remove

methods—is caused by the use of embossing stamps to indicate library ownership.

Still another form of crease is the "river" caused by creases in the paper *before* it is printed. If the crease subsequently is removed, a separation of the letters in the lines of the text will occur.

Folding plates. Another common instance in which the intentional folding of a document can cause problems—and sometimes rather formid-

Fig. 73. A typical bound volume of a serial publication which had been folded for mailing.

creases and wrinkles with a hand iron. Otherwise, their presence may cause shadows which will obscure adjacent portions of the text. If the page is to be copied by contact methods, other techniques may be required, and the problems entailed in making a fully legible copy are usually much greater. In some instances, it may be quite impossible to make a copy at all by contact methods because over-all contact cannot be achieved.

Another intentional condition—one which deforms the paper surface in a way which seriously interferes with the making of copies by contact

able ones—is the presence of folding plates in bound volumes. Not only must the folds be removed (Figure 74), but, in many cases, a problem of sheer size must also be resolved (Figure 75).

Warping. Warped pages are the result of exposure to dampness, but different types of papers respond differently to a humid atmosphere. Some papers are little affected unless the moisture content is excessive, while others will warp quite badly in the presence of relatively little moisture. In bound volumes, the grain of the paper can have a marked effect on the degree of warping. Nor-

Fig. 74. Typical small folding plate.

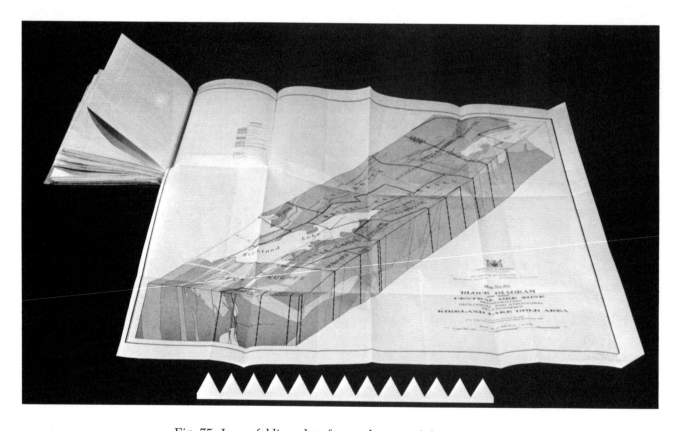

Fig. 75. Large folding plate from volume used for Figure 74.

mally, a book is printed in such a way that, when it is bound, the grain of the paper is parallel to the spine. The presence of moisture will cause some expansion in size, but this expansion is entirely in a lateral direction toward the edge of the page. If the grain of the paper is perpendicular to the spine, expansion from moisture is impeded by the binding threads but not at the outer edges, thus producing a differential in expansion which causes the paper to warp. As with wrinkled and creased pages, warped pages are sometimes impossible to copy by contact methods.

Damaged pages. Damage to pages may be the result of accident or intent and appears in many forms including tears, fraying, indentation of the paper surface, ink-stains, defacement, portions missing, or portions deliberately excised.

Pages which have been damaged, but in which the legibility of the text is not seriously impaired, may still be quite troublesome to reproduce. As is the case with wrinkled pages, damage which affects the flatness of the paper surface, such as indentations, even though the damage may not have occurred in the text area, may still make copying by contact methods difficult or even impossible.

Mended pages. Pages which have been mended with tissues, transparent or translucent tape, or a translucent overlay frequently cause problems in reproduction. Pages mended with colorless transparent tape can usually be copied without difficulty by optical methods. If, however, the tape has a shiny surface, problems with reflections may occur. Further, if the tape is of a kind which becomes yellow or brownish with age, exposure problems can occur. Certain types of mending tape are sufficiently translucent to permit the text to be read easily but create differences in contrast which may make them difficult to reproduce by optical methods. With few exceptions, the presence of mending tape, whether transparent or translucent, interferes seriously with the making of legible contact copies. Documents mended with tape overlays cannot be reproduced by thermographic processes, because the tape acts as an insulating layer which effectively prevents the buildup of sufficient heat in the text beneath the tape to form an image on the sensitized material.

Bindings

The manner in which volumes are bound can pose many problems in reproduction. A full-sewn binding that, when opened, will permit the pages to lie flat (Figure 76) presents the fewest problems, whereas tight, oversewn bindings can be quite difficult to copy either by optical or by contact methods (Figure 77) because of the curvature of the page. Not only does the curvature of the page make coverage difficult in contact copying but it creates a foreshortening of the text at the inner margin when viewed through a camera lens. Furthermore, if the paper has a sheen, the lighting must be arranged in such a way that specular reflections along the curving surface are eliminated. The problem of copying tightly bound volumes becomes even more difficult if the pages have narrow inner margins (Figure 78). In cases in which the inner margin is exceptionally small, the binding threads may actually pierce the text. Rarely, however, does the nature of the binding seriously impair legibility beyond making the reading of the material somewhat less convenient, but satisfactory reproductions are frequently difficult to make and in some cases impossible.

PROBLEMS: OTHER PRINTED ORIGINALS

Technical and physical problems arise in copying certain other printed originals, such as maps, continuous-tone illustrations, and card files.

Maps

Maps exhibit several important characteristics which differentiate them from other types of research materials and which affect their reproducibility. They are often quite large in size and very finely detailed. Because of their size, maps are usually folded, which introduces the additional problem of creases. Because folded maps must be unfolded and refolded each time they are used, damage along the crease lines may also be present. In addition, maps are often printed in several colors. Singly or together, such characteristics can pose unusual problems in reproduction.

Printed continuous-tone illustrations

These illustrations are usually made from photographs and differ from them in two ways. Unless the printing process is of extremely high quality, the tone scale of the printed version will be shorter, i.e., will exhibit fewer gradations of tone, than the photograph from which it was made. Secondly, since such illustrations are printed by means of a screen which breaks the image into a pattern of tiny dots, printed images seldom approach the sharpness and clarity of the original. A typical screen consists of two sheets of optical glass on which a specified number of lines per inch have been engraved and which are then cemented together so that the lines on one sheet are perpendicular to the lines on the other. Image sharpness will depend to a large extent on the size of the dots in the screen used and the surface of the paper on which the image is printed. Newspaper illustrations are usually made with a fairly coarse screen having 60 to 65 lines per inch (Figure 79). High-quality reproductions on shiny,

coated stock are made with screens having 150 to 200 lines per inch (Figure 80). Coarse-screen illustrations do not lend themselves to the making of high-quality enlarged copies, because the enlargement of the dot pattern decreases the number of dots per inch, causing the copy to be very much coarser in appearance than the original (Figures 81 and 82).

Since the tone scale of all but the highest-quality continuous-tone illustrations is rather short, processes or materials of normal contrast must be used if the full tone scale is to be preserved in the copy. The use of high-contrast materials which shorten the tone scale will result in copies which will show a marked loss of both highlight and shadow detail.

Printed card files

If, in copying printed cards such as Library of Congress cards or proof sheets, the purpose is merely to reproduce the information appearing on

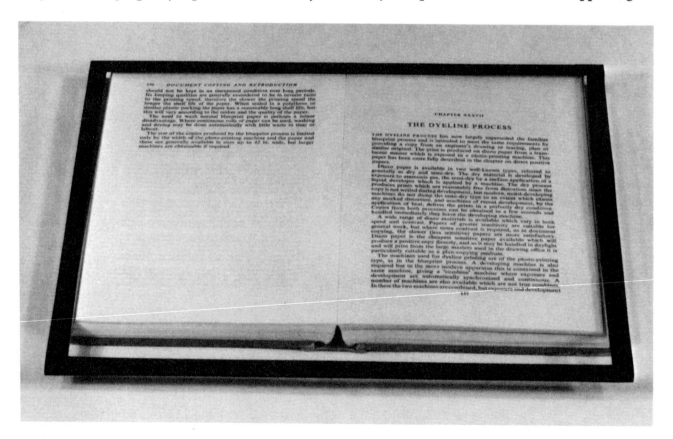

Fig. 76. Full-sewn binding that can be opened flat.

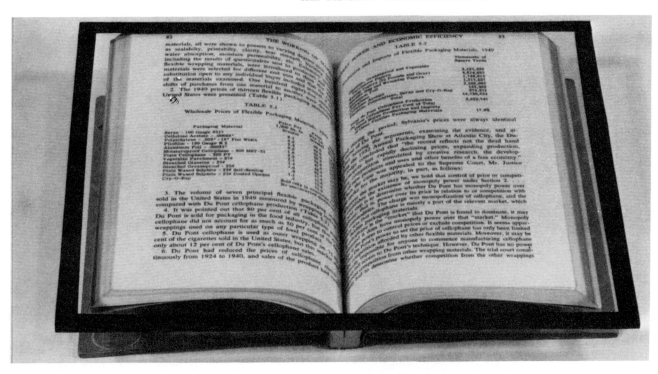

Fig. 77. Page curvature at inner margin caused by oversewn binding.

Fig. 78. Tightly oversewn binding having a narrow inner margin.

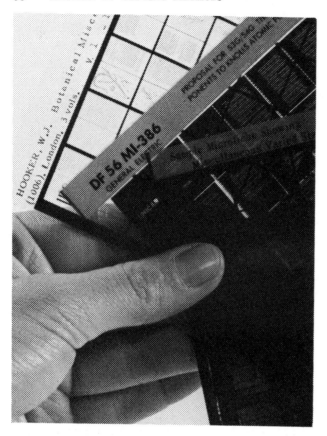

Fig. 79. 65-line halftone.

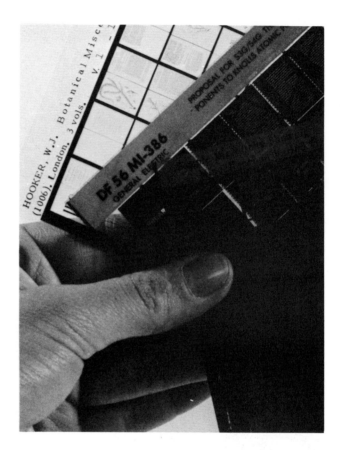

Fig. 80. 200-line halftone.

them, the problems ordinarily encountered are no different from those common to other printed originals. However, card-to-card copying, depending on the process used, will require special equipment and techniques. (Techniques for card copying are described in the fourth part of the *Manual*, "Methods and Techniques." Specific techniques required for particular processes—e.g., Ektafax, xerography—are given in the third part, "Processes.")

PROBLEMS: NON-PRINTED ORIGINALS

Technical and physical problems occur in the copying of non-printed materials, such as manuscripts, typescripts, and photographs.

Many of the basic problems discussed thus far in connection with printed materials—line width, space width, evenness of impression, color, and paper characteristics—also apply to non-printed originals such as manuscripts and typescripts, but

manuscripts in particular exhibit still other characteristics which pose special problems in reproduction.

Manuscripts

It is difficult to make generalizations about manuscripts since the manuscript is the most completely "unstandardized" document the research worker must deal with. Manuscripts appear on any type, size, or color of paper, and on other supports such as papyrus, vellum, or cloth. They may be in the form of bound pages in notebooks with hard (or soft) covers or in the form of unprotected collections of loose sheets. The text may be written with pencil or ink of every conceivable kind, quality, or color, or even with ink that damages the paper. Manuscripts such as journals are frequently written partly in ink and partly in pencil, depending on what writing implement was available at the time. Variations in the quality of the written text extend throughout

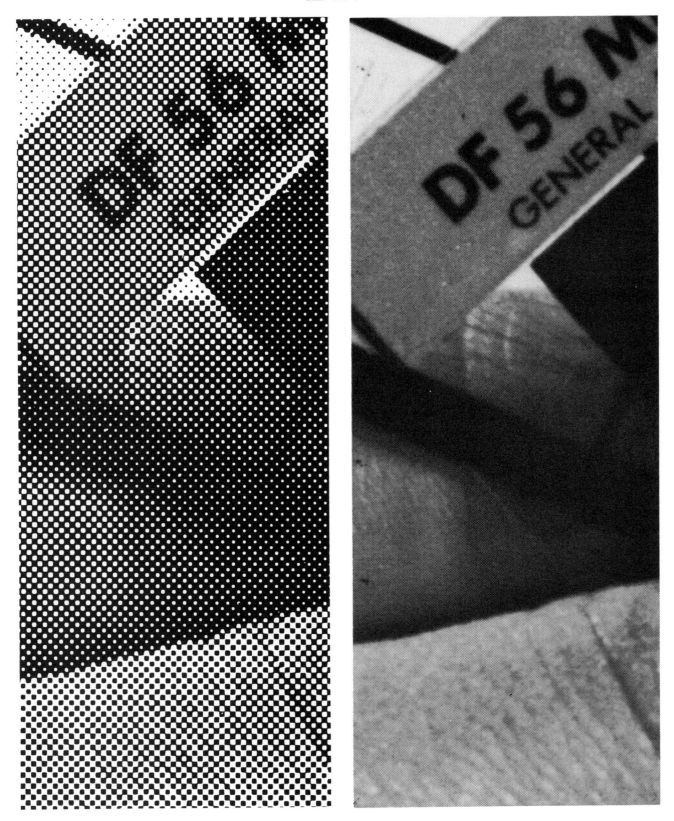

Fig. 81. Five-times enlargement of Figure 79 to show screen pattern.

Fig. 82. Five-times enlargement of Figure 80 to show screen pattern.

every degree of the art of penmanship from the most elegant to the most wretched (Figures 83 and 84). Character height and stroke width range from the very bold to the unbelievably miniscule and fine. The pagination and continuity of the text may be straightforward, highly erratic, or systematically discontinuous, as in letter sheets in which the style of the day dictated a sequence of 1, 3, 4, 2 (Figure 85). Of the eleven principal classes of research materials, manuscripts offer by far the greatest number of problems in reproduction, and often demand unusual procedures and techniques.

Manuscript collections of correspondence are often mounted in albums or on sheets of paper which are then bound to make a volume. It is not unusual in such collections to find that almost every other manuscript page may be of a different size, on paper of a different color, or written in a different ink with a different pen. Even the physical condition of such documents may vary considerably, depending on the conditions under which they were stored before being mounted. Manuscripts thus have the potential of posing a higher proportion of technical and physical problems than any other single class of research materials.

Typescripts

Typescripts, because they are produced partly by mechanical means, do not offer as great a range of problems as manuscripts, but their semi-mechanical method of preparation often poses different kinds of problems. Typescripts done on a manual typewriter may exhibit marked unevenness in impression or tonality if the typist's "touch" is not even. If a typescript is done on a machine with a well-worn ribbon, the impression may be quite faint and lacking in contrast. If a machine is old and worn, or the keys clogged with ink, the impression may be uneven, with marked breaking of fine lines and filling of small spaces. Some typescripts may be second, third, or fourth carbons in which none of the characters are sharp and clearly defined. Another problem that may be encountered in carbon copies is the presence of gray streaks caused by pressure from guide rollers (Figure 86). Additional complications will be present if a typescript has been corrected or annotated in pencil or ink.

Original continuous-tone illustrations

The principal characteristic which differentiates original continuous-tone illustrations from printed ones is their tone scale. An original photographic print of high quality, a pencil or wash drawing, or a painting may have a range and a subtlety of tones greater than that of most printed images and often well in excess of the tone-range capability of most document reproduction processes. The making of good-quality reproductions from such originals requires the use of special materials, close control over each step in the process, and considerable skill on the part of the technician.

Handwritten and typewritten card files

The reproduction of handwritten and typewritten card files often presents many of the problems common to other kinds of documents produced by these methods and, in some cases, additional ones. Consecutive cards in such files often exhibit extreme differences in image quality. A newly made card having good image quality may be adjacent to a much older card which is worn and dirty. Consecutive hand-written cards, made at different times by different persons, may exhibit marked differences in line and space width characteristics and even in the color of the ink used. Similar differences will be found in typewritten card files. Poor-quality cards typed on an old machine with a worn ribbon or by a typist with an uneven "touch" may appear next to cards made on a modern electric typewriter. Reproducing such cards one at a time will be subject to problems in exposure, but the problem becomes much greater if such cards must be reproduced in multiples, since differences in reflectance will cause differences in the quality of the images.

Microforms

There are several different types of microforms, some of which are little used in connection with research materials. Others have come into very extensive use for the acquisition, preservation, and dissemination of research materials of all kinds. Unlike the other types of research materials discussed so far, microforms are reproductions, usually of the first or second generation.

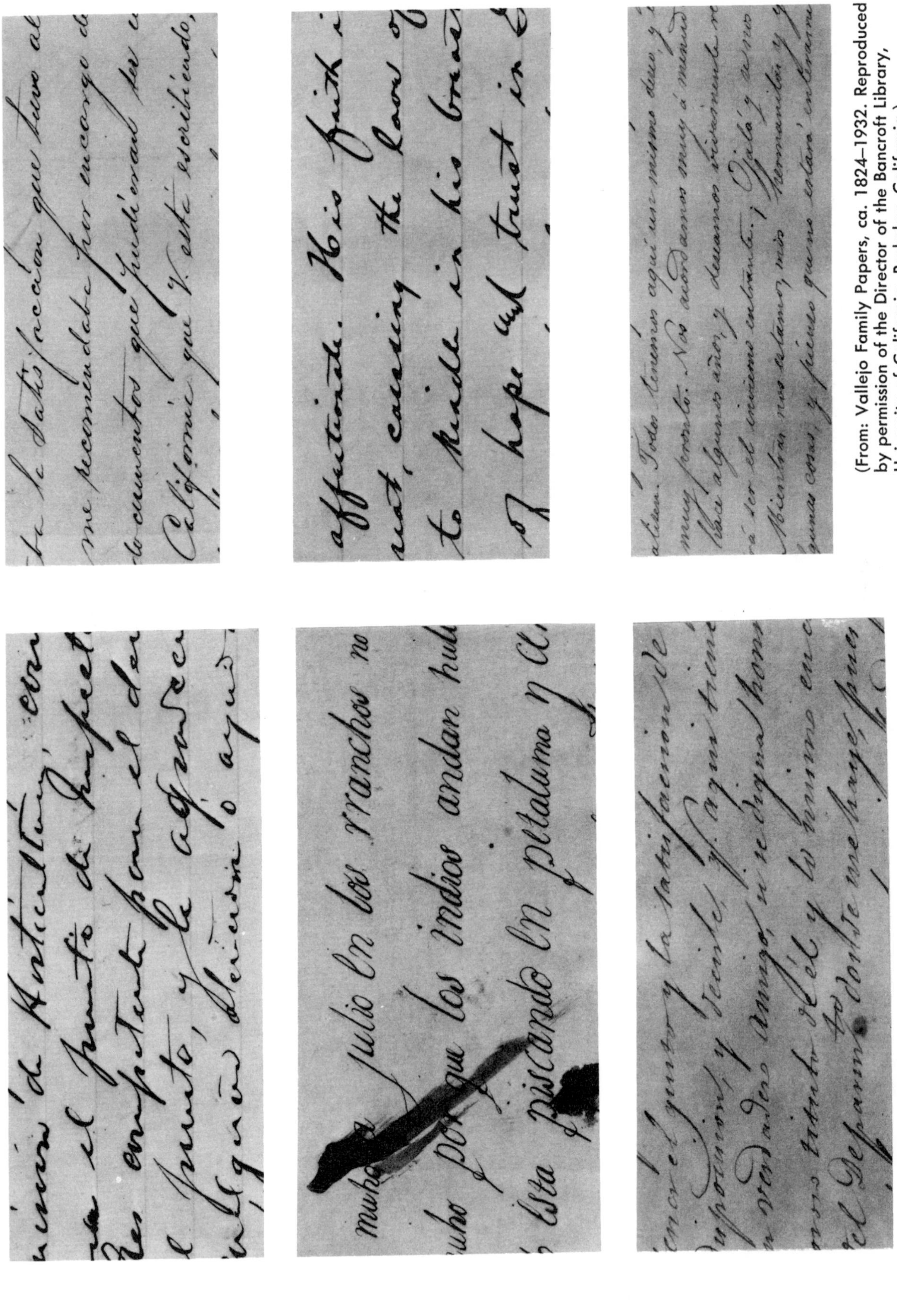

(From: Vallejo Family Papers, ca. 1824–1932. Reproduced by permission of the Director of the Bancroft Library, University of California, Berkeley, California.)

Fig. 83. Manuscript samples.

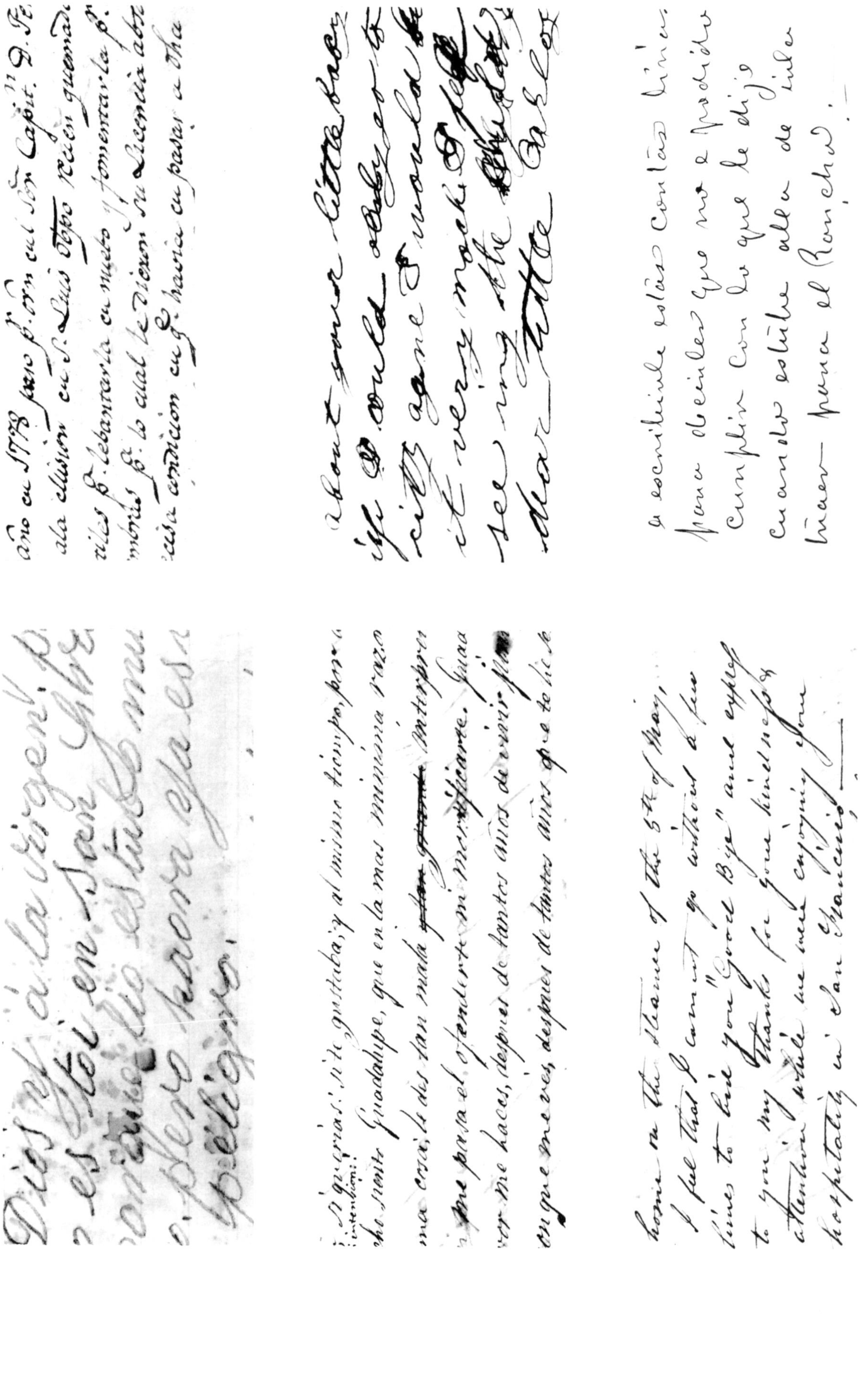

(From: Vallejo Family Papers, ca. 1824–1932. Reproduced by permission of the Director of the Bancroft Library, University of California, Berkeley, California.)

Fig. 84. Manuscript samples.

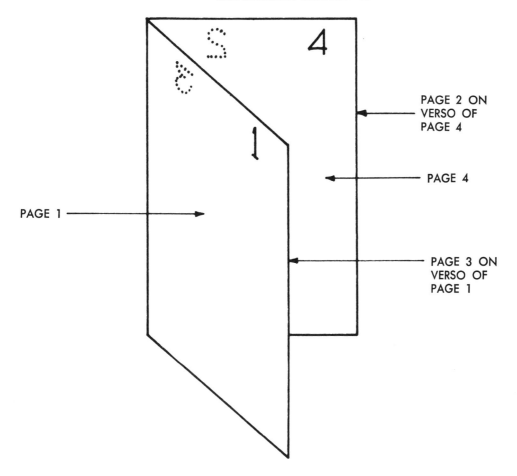

Fig. 85. Letter-sheet pagination.

Microtransparencies. The microform most commonly used in the United States to date is the transparent film. This is produced in roll or ribbon form in lengths up to approximately 100 feet with a width of 35 mm. and no perforations along the edges. Variations of this type include both single- and double-perforated 35 mm. film.

The use of film of this width derives from the fact that early microfilm cameras were designed to accept motion picture film, which was readily available at relatively low cost. The double row of perforations, necessary if the film was to be used in motion picture cameras and projectors, was not necessary for microfilming and imposed undesirable limits on image size. Hence it was that single-perforated and, later, non-perforated film came into use. Also, early 35 mm. cameras used what is called a *double-frame* image size.

The double frame measures 1 by 1½ inches, which is twice the size of the standard motion picture frame (1 by ¾ inches). Thus, a length limitation, quite unnecessary for microfilming purposes, was also derived from early motion picture practice. The frame size which eventually came into standard use[1] for non-perforated 35 mm. film measures 1¼ by 1¾ inches—a gain in area of about 46 percent over the area of the double-frame image (Figure 87). A gain in image size of this magnitude is of great importance in microfilming, because it permits the use of much lower reduction ratios thus providing for higher-quality images. If, for example, a newspaper page 18 inches wide is filmed on the double-frame size, a reduction ratio of 1:18 will be required. The same page

---

[1] *American Standard Specifications for 16-mm. and 35-mm. Microfilms on Reels or in Strips* (PH5.3–1958).

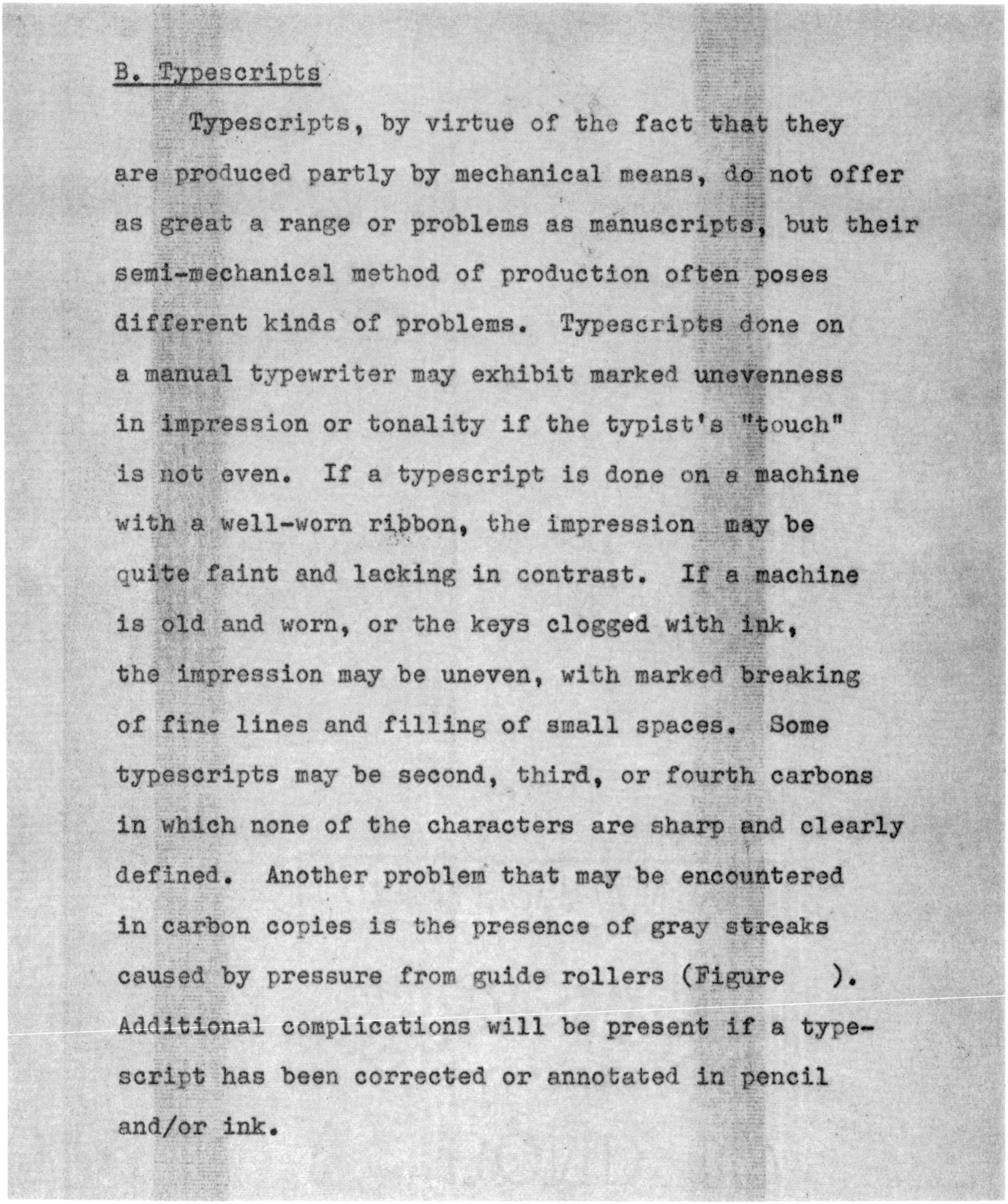

B. Typescripts

Typescripts, by virtue of the fact that they are produced partly by mechanical means, do not offer as great a range or problems as manuscripts, but their semi-mechanical method of production often poses different kinds of problems. Typescripts done on a manual typewriter may exhibit marked unevenness in impression or tonality if the typist's "touch" is not even. If a typescript is done on a machine with a well-worn ribbon, the impression may be quite faint and lacking in contrast. If a machine is old and worn, or the keys clogged with ink, the impression may be uneven, with marked breaking of fine lines and filling of small spaces. Some typescripts may be second, third, or fourth carbons in which none of the characters are sharp and clearly defined. Another problem that may be encountered in carbon copies is the presence of gray streaks caused by pressure from guide rollers (Figure   ). Additional complications will be present if a typescript has been corrected or annotated in pencil and/or ink.

Fig. 86. Guide roller marks on a carbon copy.

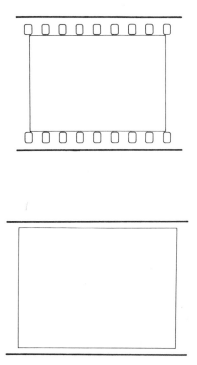

Fig. 87. Frame size of double-perforated and non-perforated 35 mm. film.

mits the length of the image to be varied at will over a range from ⅜ inch up to the maximum length of 1¾ inches (Figure 88).

In addition to 35 mm. roll film, other widths such as 16 mm., 70 mm., and 105 mm. are also used for the microfilming of certain classes of larger documents. The larger sizes were introduced principally for the copying of large engineering drawings and have little applicability in reproducing research materials. Sixteen mm. film, which is extensively used for the microrecording of business records, has been used to only a limited extent for the microrecording of research materials.

A notable exception is its use by the Chemical Abstracts Service of the American Chemical Society. All 3.4 million abstracts which have been published in *Chemical Abstracts* from 1907 to 1965 are available on 16 mm. microfilm in 100-foot rolls either on reels or in cartridges. This microfilm is updated every six months.

While some 35 mm. planetary cameras can be

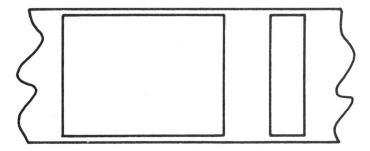

Fig. 88. The maximum and minimum frame sizes of 35 mm. Recordak Micro-File cameras. The largest frame measures 1¾ inches by 1¼ inches; the smallest frame measures ⅜ inch by 1¼ inches.

can be filmed on non-perforated film at a reduction ratio of 1:14.4. If newspaper pages are filmed one page per full frame on non-perforated film, approximately 600 pages can be filmed on a single 100-foot roll of film.

In motion picture practice, all frames must be exactly the same size, but this, too, is undesirable in microfilming where documents of different dimensions and formats are being copied. As a consequence, the cameras developed for this purpose are equipped with a mechanism which per-

adapted to take 16 mm. film, most 16 mm. microfilm cameras are of the "rotary" or "flow" type, which can only be used for recording materials in loose-sheet form. On occasion, such cameras have been used to record collections of typescript and manuscript materials. Sixteen mm. flow cameras equipped with automatic feeding devices have been used for the high-speed recording of library card catalogs. Sixteen mm. film is also used as the intermediate film for the production of catalog cards by Xerox Copyflo printing. Another library use of 16 mm. film, but one which does not entail the recording of research materials, is in photo-charging systems for circulation control.

A new and large-scale application of consider-able importance in the research field was recently announced by the U.S. Patent Office. In addition to printed copies of patents, the Patent Office is now offering on 16 mm. microfilm complete sets of all patents issued annually.

Microfiches. In addition to microtransparen-cies in roll form, there are also *microfiches*. These are sheets of film of various sizes containing series of images arranged in rows. The common sizes in use today are 75 by 125 mm. (3 by 5 inches), 9 by 12 cm., and 105 by 148 mm. (4⅛ by 6 inches). For a short time, 5- by 8-inch microfiches were pro-duced in this country, but this size was abandoned in favor of the 105 by 148 mm. size, which is an

Fig. 89. Microfiches.

international standard size. Microfiches may be prepared either in the form of negatives or positives.

Microfiches only recently have begun to be used in this country, but their use is now growing very rapidly. In Europe, however, microfiches have been in use for more than a quarter of a century. In the United States, there has been a strong impetus toward standardization of frame size, format, and reduction ratio, whereas, in Europe, cameras have been designed which offer a wide choice of image size, format, and number of rows per microfiche, with the reduction ratio varying to suit the characteristics of the material being copied.

Once a microfiche negative has been produced, it can be used for the production of additional, low-cost distribution copies in the form of positive transparencies on silver halide film, duplicate negatives on diazo or Kalvar films, or micro-opaques on silver halide paper.

Not only are microtransparencies reproductions rather than originals, but they are also among the most frequently and widely reproduced of all classes of research materials for three important reasons:

(1) Because they are film transparencies, they lend themselves readily to reproduction by contact printing or projection printing.

(2) Because the reading of microtransparency images requires special equipment, the preferable alternative in many cases is the production of enlargements—*hard copy*—from the microtransparency (a) by conventional photographic enlarging, (b) by xerographic enlarging, (c) by enlarging by the Dry Silver process, or (d) by means of reader-printers.

(3) Because of their size and the relatively low materials costs entailed, large collections of materials in microtransparency form can be duplicated at very low per page costs.

Micro-opaques. Micro-opaques are sheet microforms, similar in format to microfiches. They are produced from microtransparencies either by direct-contact printing onto photosensitive paper or by means of an intermediate photolithographic plate. A fundamental difference between microtransparencies and micro-opaques lies in the eco-

nomics of their production. A roll-form microtransparency of an article or a book can be produced in an edition of one copy quite inexpensively, whereas a micro-opaque cannot. Much more preparation is required for the making of a negative for micro-opaque printing, but, once this is done, the cost of copies is not only low but decreases as the size of the edition increases. Microtransparencies thus lend themselves more readily to inexpensive *copying* applications, whereas micro-opaques are best suited to inexpensive *publishing* applications.

Another important difference between microtransparencies and micro-opaques is the fact that the former are viewed or projected by transmitted light while the latter require reflected light. This has a decided effect on the production of hard copy. Hard copy can easily be made from microtransparencies by a variety of methods but not from micro-opaques. In many large-scale microform programs, micro-opaques are now being supplanted by microfiches because of the relative ease with which hard copy can be produced from the transparent form.

There are three basic micro-opaque formats which are distinguished by their trade names: Microcards, Microlex, and Microprint, and two variants.

(1) Microcards (manufactured by the Microcard Corporation) are 3- by 5-inch micro-opaques made by contact printing from strips of 16 mm. film, or from step-and-repeat camera negatives onto card-weight, silver halide paper. The number of pages on a Microcard will range, on the average, from 24 to 48, depending upon the size of the original and the reduction ratio used in the film master. Microcards have been used extensively for the republication of a vast amount of out-of-print material in many subject fields. (With the increasing popularity of microtransparencies in sheet form—i.e., microfiches—the Microcard Corporation now offers both microfiches and Microcards.)

(2) Microlex is a rather specialized micro-opaque produced by the Lawyer's Co-operative Publishing Company for the republication of materials in the field of law. Microlex sheets measure 6½ by 8½ inches and are produced by contact printing onto sheets of silver halide paper. Each sheet contains 200 pages, and pairs of pages are

Fig. 90. A Microcard.

laminated back to back to form units of 400 pages.

(3) Microprint, a product of the Readex Microprint Corporation, is a photolithographic micro-opaque made by arranging strips of negative film into a master containing ten images in ten rows. From this master negative, a lithographic plate is made which is then used to produce copies by conventional printing techniques. Microprint sheets measure 6 by 9 inches and are printed on one side only. Microprint has been used for the republication of large blocks of research materials, such as the *Sessional Papers* of the British House of Commons for the 19th century.

(4) A variant form of micro-opaque, offered by various microfilm service companies under the trade names of Microstrip or Microtape, consists of a contact print from rolls of 16 mm. film onto silver halide paper which has a pressure-sensitive adhesive backing. The rolls of prints can then be cut into strips and affixed to cards of any size.

(5) A new form of micro-opaque called *Mini-Print* was recently introduced by Mini-Print, Inc., and is, as the name suggests, a form of reduced-size printing. The reduction ratio used in Mini-Print is much lower than that of other micro-opaques, ranging from approximately 1:3 to 1:6, depending on the characteristics of the original. Like Readex Microprint, Mini-Print is produced photolithographically. But, whereas a 6- by 9-inch Readex Microprint sheet contains 100 pages, a Mini-Print sheet the same size contains only 16. Mini-Print can be read with either a low-power, hand magnifier or with specially designed projecting devices. Unlike other micro-opaques, Mini-Print images are not printed on cards but on sheets of paper in signatures just as books are printed.

Copies of originals

Copies of originals, whether made photographically or thermographically, ordinarily differ from the original documents from which they were made in two ways. In most copying processes, a finite loss of definition occurs. With some processes, the loss is relatively small, whereas with others it may be quite noticeable. Secondly, most document copying processes yield copies which are noticeably higher in contrast than their originals. Copies which already show a loss of definition can only be recopied by processes in which definition loss is minimal. High-contrast copies can seldom withstand being recopied by other high-contrast processes.

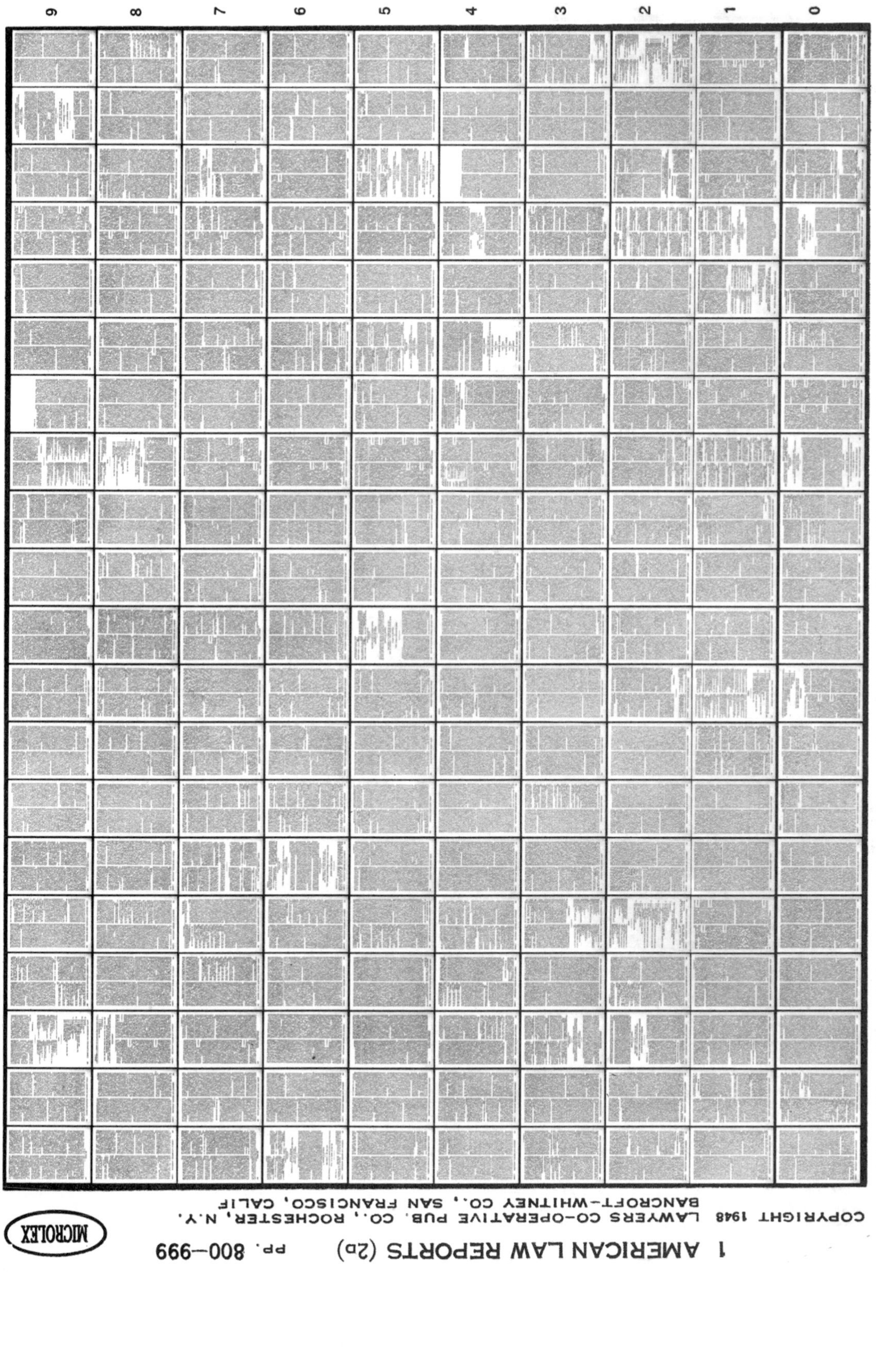

Fig. 91. A Microlex sheet.

1 AMERICAN LAW REPORTS (2d)   PP. 800—999

MICROLEX

Readex Microprint   New York

Fig. 92. A Readex Microprint sheet.

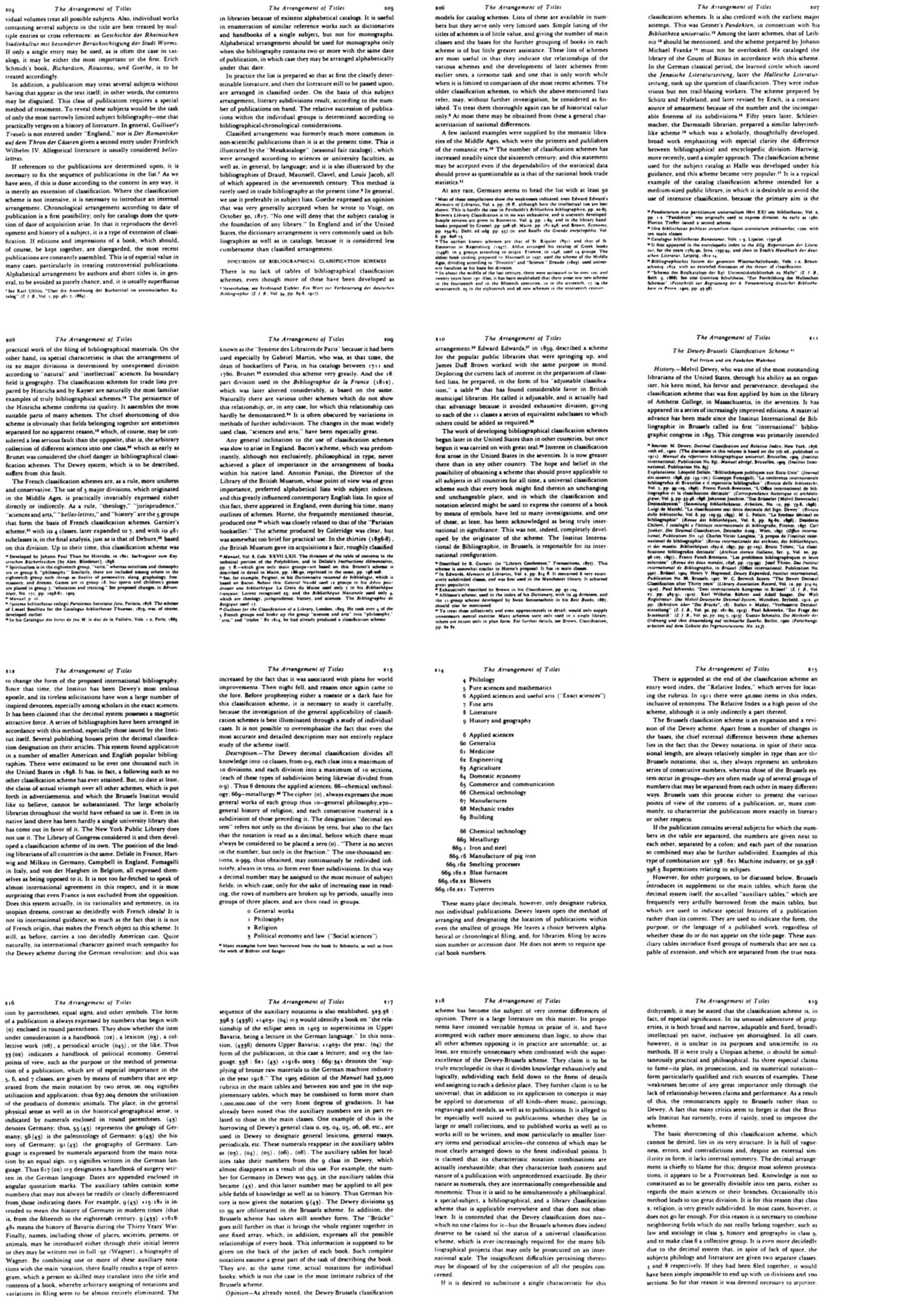

Fig. 93. A Mini-Print sheet.

SUMMARY

The characteristics of the different classes of research materials vary over a wide range, and these characteristics will affect the choice of reproduction equipment, process, method and/or materials and dictate the need for the use of various techniques. While each characteristic may have its individual effect, the presence of more than one or even several influencing characteristics is a commonplace. In a single bound volume, the text may be printed in a small type face having poor line and space width characteristics on paper which has become brittle and discolored. Another volume may have very narrow inner margins, be tightly bound, and contain large folding plates in color. Other combinations of problems are frequently encountered in newspaper files, manuscripts, or typewritten theses. The techniques relating to these problems and combinations of problems are described in Part 4, "Methods and Techniques." It is important to point out, however, that a complete solution to all the problems presented by an original may not be necessary to produce an acceptable copy.

It was mentioned in the discussion of the effects of type size and design on the reproducibility and the legibility of copies that a number of subjective factors enter into any evaluation of what constitutes a satisfactory reproduction from any given original. These are quite apart from any system of numerical measurement of particular characteristics, such as lines per millimeter, density expressed in a logarithmic scale, or contrast as a function of density vs. exposure expressed in the form of a graph.

The ultimate test of the utility of a reproduction of a document is whether or not the information it presents is readily conveyed to the reader. Granted that a perfect reproduction, or one which improves upon the original by enlarging the image or heightening the contrast, may aid in conveying the information contained therein, nonetheless, reproductions which are far from optimum fidelity and clarity are quite satisfactory in terms of the purpose they succeed in serving, which is the conveyance of information. The most common example of a reproduction which has the undesirable characteristics of being fuzzy, and often lacking in contrast as well, is a carbon copy of a typewritten original. Despite their obvious shortcomings when compared to the ribbon copy, carbon copies are universally accepted because they accomplish the required purpose of conveying information. That such relatively poor reproductions can succeed in the business of conveying information is possible only because a number of visual and mental factors are entailed in the conveyance of information by means of graphic symbols. A hierarchy for the factors concerned might be as follows:

(1) Clarity
(2) Recognizability
(3) Interpretability

Where perfect clarity exists in a reproduction, there are no problems of legibility other than those which may have been present in the original itself. Where the reproduction is unsharp, i.e., where the forms of letters and numerals are distorted by the breaking of lines and/or the filling of spaces, clarity is lost, but the individual shapes of letters and numerals may still be unmistakable. Such characters are quite recognizable, despite the poor quality of the reproduction. At the lowest level, the lack of definition of lines and spaces making up the structure of individual characters may be so great as to make characters viewed in isolation unrecognizable but, since words, too, have distinctive shapes, individual characters can be interpreted to be what the shape context of the adjacent letters suggests. Take, for example, the word "spot" in lower-case letters. In Figure 94, the word is first reproduced with perfect clarity and then

Fig. 94. The word "spot" reproduced clearly and unclearly.

with the forms of the letters rough and poorly defined, but clearly recognizable. All that is left is a rough semblance of the shapes of the letters, but, to a reader familiar with the English language in printed form, there can be no mistaking that the word can only be interpreted as "spot." Only one lower-case letter in the alphabet has a descender at the left—the letter "p." No other letter has the particular characteristics of a lower-case "t," with its right-moving hook and straight ascender with a cross stroke. The form of the "s," despite its crudeness, cannot be confused with the form of any other letter. The only letter that might be in doubt is the "o." A lower-case "e" and a lower-case "o" might both appear as a solid black circle, but, at this point, interpretability moves to the contextual level. There is no English word which is spelled "spet," while there is a very common word spelled "spot." Hence only one interpretation is possible.

There are thus no fixed and arbitrary standards of measurement which can be applied to determine whether or not a particular reproduction is "satisfactory." "Utility," to paraphrase a well-known saying, "is in the eye of the beholder." But this is not to suggest that a minimum standard of mere interpretability is enough. While it may barely meet the needs of someone highly conversant in the language used in the document recorded, it would not suffice for a person unversed in the language, a person who must depend on a clear reproduction of every letter in order to look up the meanings of unfamiliar words in a dictionary.

Interpretability and recognizability will serve where the context in which characters appear will support the conveyance of meaning, but where contextual support is absent, i.e., where the signification of each individual character is an entity (as is the case in mathematics or music), then a high standard of clarity must be met. A "3" and an "8" must be unmistakably distinguishable, as must also be a half note and a quarter note in music.

Because subjective factors do enter into the equation, it is well to keep this in mind in any comparison between the characteristics of the different processes described in the following part of this *Manual*. A process which, for example, is superior in resolving power to another may not necessarily be superior for a particular copying application where a high standard of clarity is not really essential.

3. PROCESSES

INTRODUCTION

The year 1950 marked the beginning of a revolution in the photocopying field. In that one year, diffusion-transfer-reversal (DTR), Thermo-Fax, and xerography all became commercially available in the United States. Photocopying was suddenly taken out of the darkroom and the hands of trained technicians and placed in well-lighted offices where clerical personnel without any knowledge of the photographic process were soon making reproductions of documents in seconds at costs measured in pennies instead of dollars. The result of the availability of rapidly and simply produced copies at low cost had a profound effect on the volume of copying being done. By 1955, the total dollar volume of the office copy industry had risen to $50 million and, today, ten years later, it has grown more than tenfold and is steadily climbing toward the $1 billion mark.

With a potential market volume this large, many copying equipment companies have spent large sums in research efforts to make copying still faster, simpler, and cheaper. These efforts have been along two main lines: (a) the improvement of existing processes, and (b) the development of radically different processes. Whereas in 1950 there were only a handful of ways to reproduce a document, there are now more than two dozen, and new processes and new variations on existing ones are appearing at an increasing rate.

Of the processes suitable for the reproduction of research materials described in this section, some have been in use for a number of years; their characteristics are by now well known; and they can be described in a fairly detailed fashion. Other processes, particularly the newer ones, are not so well known. In some cases, manufacturers, understandably enough, are not willing to disclose details about their technological research. In such cases, every attempt has been made to make the description of these processes as complete, from a practical standpoint, as the available information

will allow. A chart summarizing the principal characteristics of copying processes appears on pages 204–205.

Where equipment related to a given process (e.g., Verifax, Kalvar) is made by one manufacturer or very few, the equipment has been listed. In the case of processes for which a wide range of equipment is available from many manufacturers (e.g., diazo, stabilization processing) the equipment of each manufacturer has not been listed, but the names and addresses of a number of the principal domestic and, in some cases, foreign, manufacturers are given. The author and the publisher do not intend that such lists be regarded as complete; no endorsement of these firms or their equipment is implied. In all cases, before selection of equipment is made, local buying guides and equipment directories should be consulted.

The processes described have been rated as to their suitability for reproducing the principal classes of research materials according to the following scale:

Suitable

Generally suitable

Limited

Unsuitable

The terms are intended to be generally indicative of the capabilities of each process for each broad *class* of research materials. There are bound to be exceptions in individual cases. A process rated as "limited" for reproducing manuscripts, might, for a group of manuscripts having the right characteristics, be quite suitable. A true determination of the suitability of a process for reproducing a specific group of documents must take all of the relevant characteristics of the process *and the documents* into account. A chart summarizing the suitability of eighteen processes for copying research materials is shown on page 188.

THE SILVER HALIDE PROCESS

For well over a century, the light-sensitive properties of silver halides have been used for the photographic reproduction of research materials of all kinds. No other copying process yet devised can begin to approach the silver halide process in terms of versatility and in the quality of the results that can be obtained with its use. The silver halide process is capable of producing archivally permanent copies in either negative or positive form. The contrast of copies is controllable and continuous-tone originals can be reproduced with great fidelity. The remarkable resolving power of silver halide coatings is the *sine qua non* of most forms of microrecording. The process is also the basis for most systems of color photography. Silver halide coatings are used extensively for recording phenomena beyond the range of the visual spectrum, such as in X-ray photography. In the document copying field, coatings sensitive to infrared and ultraviolet radiation are used to recover otherwise invisible texts, to detect forgeries, and to reveal palimpsests. But despite its great capabilities, it nonetheless possesses certain drawbacks. The basic process is wet, slow, and relatively expensive. These drawbacks gave impetus to the search for non-silver processes such as thermography, xerography, and Kalvar. They also led to the development of variant silver processes such as DTR, Verifax, stabilization processing, and others, which would at least be faster and simpler, if not substantially cheaper.

So much research has been done in silver halide photography and so much has been written about it that to add still another chapter seems to be a work of supererogation. It is necessary, however, that certain of the main principles and characteristics be set forth briefly once again in the context of this manual if the role of the process, and in particular, variations of the process, are to be understood.

In the basic silver halide process, silver halide grains together with other substances, such as sensitizing dyes, are suspended in a gelatin emulsion. The emulsion is coated onto a support which may be transparent (cellulose acetate film, polyester film or glass) or opaque (paper). If an image is formed on the sensitized coating by means of light, either by contact printing or through a lens, the silver halide grains are invisibly altered by the action of the light and in proportion to the amount of light received. This "latent image" is made visible by immersing the material in a solution containing a "developing agent" and various other chemical substances which reduce the exposed silver grains to black metallic silver. The image thus formed is negative. White areas in the original from which a relatively large amount of light has been reflected appear as black areas, and text areas from which little light has been reflected appear clear or white. When the image has been fully developed, it is then necessary to stop the action of the alkaline developing solution by immersing the copy briefly in a mildly acid "stop bath" and then placing it in a third solution called a "fixing bath." The function of the fixing bath is to dissolve out all of the remaining silver which was not affected by light and which, if allowed to remain *in situ*, would cause the print to gradually darken when exposed to light. Following fixation, the chemicals then remaining in the copy must be removed by a lengthy wash in running water. When all these steps have been completed, the wet copy must be dried.

One of the most important uses of the conventional "wet" silver halide process for reproducing research materials is in microrecording. Other common uses include the production of black and white copies of continuous-tone and half-tone subjects or subjects such as drawings, paintings, and the like, when a high degree of fidelity to the tone scale of the original must be preserved, and for the production of "line" negatives of drawings, maps, graphs, etc. For these purposes, a film negative is usually made which can be used for the subsequent production of either positive prints or a printing plate. Another common use is for the direct camera recording on silver-sensitized paper of documents by means of cameras equipped with prisms, such as "Photostat" or "Rectigraph" equipment. The product of such cameras is a right-reading copy which is usually negative in tonal values.

Since color films such as Kodachrome, Ektachrome, Anscochrome, and others are based on silver halide technology, the process is also widely used for the production of color transparencies for instructional purposes. The great versatility of the silver halide process lends itself to the solution of almost any copying problem, but its use in simple document copying applications where only a legible copy is required has largely been usurped by variant forms of the process and by non-silver processes.

Materials

Silver halide materials are available in a very large range of types and sizes for almost any conceivable document-copying application, from microfilm emulsions capable of recording documents at extreme reductions in size to papers and films which are used to make full-size copies of maps and drawings several square yards in area, or from simple, virtually color-blind coatings for black and white copying to complex coatings for making reproductions in full color. A wide variety of materials is available for copying by all methods—contact, contact reflex, optical copying, and projection printing. A comprehensive listing of all of the available materials by the numerous large manufacturers in various countries would make up a good-sized volume by itself, and would have no place in the present manual. Data on particular products for particular copying applications can be found in the *Photo-Lab Index*[1] or can be obtained from the technical representatives of the various manufacturers.

Contrast

The degree of contrast possible with silver halide materials can be varied over a wide range, from very low to very high. Certain types of coatings on film may be inherently low or inherently high in contrast, whereas other types may offer extensive control over contrast in the development step. Silver halide coatings on paper are also available in a broad range of contrasts or with coatings in which contrast can be controlled by

---

[1] *Photo-Lab Index*, ed. John S. Carroll (Hastings-on-Hudson, New York: Morgan and Morgan). Published in loose-leaf form with quarterly supplements.

means of colored filters. An extensive measure of control is thus possible, since a low-contrast negative can be printed on a *hard* paper to produce a higher-contrast positive, while high-contrast negatives can be printed on a *soft* paper to reduce excessive contrast.

Resolving power

The resolving power of silver halide materials will vary in accordance with the purpose for which the materials are made. Emulsions prepared for applications where high resolution is important—e.g., microrecording—possess resolving power of a high order. A resolution well in excess of 100 lines per millimeter is common. Certain emulsions developed specifically for the highest-possible resolution are capable of resolving several hundred lines per millimeter. A high degree of control over both exposure and processing is necessary if the optimum resolution of which a given emulsion is capable is to be achieved.

Exposure latitude

The exposure latitude of silver halide materials also varies considerably with materials of different types. In copying applications, a general rule of thumb is that the lower the contrast of the material, the greater the exposure latitude will be. With certain very high-contrast materials, such as are used in the graphic arts, exposure latitude is very small.

Speed

Silver halide materials are available with a wide range of speeds to suit particular document reproduction requirements. While very high-speed materials have been developed for recording high-speed events, this is not a condition normally encountered in document reproduction. This is not to say, however, that speed is not, at times, important. In camera work, the use of high-speed materials, other things being equal, permits the use of lower and hence more comfortable levels of illumination; shorter shutter speeds which, under some circumstances, may improve the sharpness of images; or a smaller lens opening, which increases depth of field. In projection print-

TABLE 1
The Silver Halide Process
(Principal Characteristics)

1. The process is:	Wet	X
	Dry	
2. Copies can be made by the following methods:	Contact Copying	X
	Contact-Reflex Copying	X
	Optical Copying	X
	Microcopying	X
	Projection Printing	X
3. The process is capable of producing copies that are:	Positive, from Positives	X
	Negative, from Positives	X
	Positive, from Negatives	X
	Negative, from Negatives	X
4. The process is capable of producing intermediates or masters for subsequent edition printing by:	Diazo	X
	Offset	X *
	Spirit Duplicating	
5. The permanence of copies is:	Archival	X *
	Limited	
	Unknown	
6. The quality of copies of continuous-tone originals is:	Excellent	X
	Fair	
	Poor	
7. The reproduction of fine details (e.g., small type faces, fine lines) is:	Excellent	X
	Fair	
	Poor	
8. The contrast of copies is:	High	X *
	Moderate	X *
	Low	X *

9. The ability of the process to reproduce colored lines is:	Broad	X
	Limited	
10. The paper stock used is:	Plain, Any Color	
	Specially Coated	X
	White	X
	Off-White	X *
11. The tendency of copies to curl is:	High	
	Noticeable	X
	Low	
12. The potential waste factor is:	Considerable	
	Moderate	X
	Low	
13. The approximate time required to make an 8½- by 11-inch copy is: Per linear foot (16 mm. and up in width) is:	See "Notes."	
14. The materials cost per 8½- by 11-inch copy is:	About 4¢ and up, depending on type of material used.	
Per linear foot (11 inches in width) is:	About 6½¢ and up.	
15. Equipment for the process is priced at:	See "Notes."	

16. Other characteristics: Materials are also available for recording by means of infrared and ultraviolet light and X-rays.

*NOTES

4. See "The Autopositive Process," page 99.
5. If copies are properly fixed and washed.
8. Extensive control over contrast is possible with silver halide materials.
10. Stocks having an off-white tint (cream, buff) are available.
13. The time required for making copies varies greatly depending upon the method, the type of equipment, and the procedural steps used. Because of the time required for wet processing, a single copy may take upwards of an hour to make. Substantial numbers of copies, however, either on film or paper, can be processed simultaneously or, by using automated equipment, can be processed in a linear succession at high rates of speed.
15. A great variety of equipment for all methods is available, ranging from very simple equipment for contact printing by the direct method, which may cost a few dollars, to.large, automated equipment for optical copying, which can cost many thousands of dollars.

ing, the use of high-speed materials shortens exposure times and thus speeds up the process. In other applications, materials low in speed are preferable. For contact copying under room light, for example, the material must, on the other hand, be slow enough to withstand exposure to room light without becoming fogged, but at the same time be fast enough to permit relatively short exposures to be used.

The selection of material of appropriate speed (and other characteristics) for a particular kind of equipment is best accomplished by correspondence with any of the major manufacturers of silver-sensitized materials or by consultation with a manufacturer's technical representative.

Color sensitivity

The color sensitivity of silver halide materials for black-and-white recording also varies with the type of material and the purpose for which it is intended. The color sensitivity of films for document copying applications usually falls in one of two broad classifications—orthochromatic or panchromatic. Orthochromatic materials are sensitive to the blue and green portions of the spectrum but not to red. Panchromatic materials are sensitive to light of all colors but not necessarily in the same degree as the response of the human eye to color. Many high-speed panchromatic films are excessively sensitive to red light. Slower-speed panchromatic materials generally exhibit a better balance in the response to color, but, where optimum fidelity in the reproduction of colors as tones of gray is required, correction filters are usually employed.

For the most part, silver halide papers are blue-sensitive or orthochromatic, since paper emulsions are seldom employed directly for copying colored originals. They are used primarily for printing from an intermediate black-and-white negative. A panchromatic emulsion coated on paper is available for use in photostat cameras, because, in this process, the recording is done directly on silver halide paper without the use of an intermediate negative.

Where circumstances demand, a number of different types of papers are available for making prints in full color.

Keeping qualities

Black-and-white silver halide films and papers have a limited shelf life, usually on the order of a year or slightly longer. Color materials have an even shorter shelf life, ranging from six months to one year. Boxes or packages of materials are stamped with an "expiration date" which is the date beyond which the manufacturer will not replace the material should it prove defective. The useful life of stored materials can be extended considerably if they are kept under refrigeration. Conversely, storage under conditions of excessive heat and/or humidity, especially after a package has been opened, can adversely affect the material. The usual recommendations are that the materials be stored in a cool, dry place.

Ideally, silver halide materials should be processed as soon after exposure as possible. With most black-and-white materials, the time interval between exposure and processing is not critical, but, with color materials, a prolonged delay may result in some deterioration of the quality and color of the image.

Permanence

The permanence of silver halide materials is determined by two factors: the permanence of the support on which the emulsion is coated and the removal during processing of any chemical substances which may in time cause deterioration of the image. The cellulose acetate base used for photographic films is a stable material with a very high rating for permanence. The permanence of images on film is, therefore, based on the complete removal of unused silver halides in the fixation step and the thorough washing out of any residual chemicals following fixation. The permanence of silver halide images on paper depends not only on the removal of unused silver halides and residual chemicals in fixation and washing but also on the durability of the paper base. In general, paper bases for photographic emulsions are higher in quality than those ordinarily used for office records and can be expected to have a high degree of permanence, if the processing of the image has been properly carried out. Where durability and permanence of the highest order are required, emulsions coated on 100 percent rag stock paper bases can be used.

Suitability

General note: While the silver halide process has a broader capability than any other process for reproducing research materials of all kinds, materials costs and the labor time required in wet processing will often limit use of this process to copying problems which cannot be successfully dealt with by means of other, less costly, document copying processes.

(1) For bound volumes—suitable.

Pages from bound volumes can be reproduced by either contact or optical methods. Of particular importance in document reproduction are "photostat"-type cameras for direct recording on silver-sensitized paper and cameras for microrecording.

(2) For newspaper files—suitable.

With "photostat"-type cameras, entire pages of newspapers or portions thereof from bound or unbound files can be reproduced full-size or may be enlarged or reduced. The process is also used universally for the microrecording of newspaper files.

(3) For typescripts—suitable.

The process is capable of producing faithful copies of typescripts of all kinds including very poor-quality originals. Extensive use is made of the process for the microrecording of typescripts of doctoral dissertations.

(4) For manuscripts—suitable.

The process is not only suitable for reproducing manuscripts of all kinds but, in addition, through the use of materials sensitized to portions of the invisible spectrum (infrared, ultraviolet and X-rays), can be used for the recovery of faded or obliterated texts, the revealing of palimpsestic writing, and the detection of forgeries. Moreover, the contrast between text and background can often be enhanced by the choice of suitable materials or the use of filters.

(5) For continuous-tone originals—suitable.

The process is eminently well suited to the making of high-quality copies of continuous-tone originals in both black-and-white and color. A number of different types of film are available from the leading manufacturers, which have been coated specifically for this purpose.

(6) For maps—generally suitable.

The only limitation in map copying occurs in the making of black-and-white copies from colored originals. Depending on the color sensitivity of the material used, lines or legends against colored backgrounds may or may not be legible. Dimensionally stable materials are available where exact size or an exact scale ratio must be maintained.

(7) For card files—limited.

The gelatin coating of silver halide materials creates a tendency for even card-weight material to curl. The process, however, is useful for the production of intermediates from which reproductions can be made on card stock by other processes, e.g., xerography.

(8) For copies made by other processes—suitable.

Copies made by all other processes can be satisfactorily reproduced on silver halide materials.

(9) For microforms:

(a) Camera recording—suitable.

Materials of excellent quality in both roll and sheet form are available for high-resolution microrecording. Virtually all microrecording is done on silver halide materials.

(b) Microform duplicating—suitable.

High-speed, high-resolution films are available for microform duplicating.

(c) Eye-legible copies from microforms—suitable.

A variety of silver-sensitized papers including light-weight and translucent stocks can be used for making hard copy from microforms.

Manufacturers

There are a great many manufacturers of equipment for silver halide photography, and the equipment itself is of many types and sizes to suit different purposes. With the exception of 35 mm. hand cameras, of which there are a great many, equipment for the production and use of microforms is listed in Ballou's *Guide.*[2] This includes laboratory equipment as well as microrecording equipment. The principal manufacturers of prism

---

[2] Hubbard W. Ballou, *Guide to Microreproduction Equipment* (Annapolis: National Microfilm Association, 1965, and *Supplement*, 1966).

cameras for the direct recording of images on silver-sensitized paper are listed below. (This list is not comprehensive. No endorsement of these firms or their equipment is implied. Before making selection of equipment, the prospective purchaser should consult local equipment directories or buying guides.)

Anken Chemical & Film Corporation
10 Patterson Avenue
Newton, New Jersey 07860

Itek Business Products
1001 Jefferson Road
Rochester, New York 14623

Xerox Corporation
Midtown Tower
Rochester, New York 14604

A specialized type of prism camera, manufactured by the Anken Chemical & Film Corporation, is the "Photoclerk," which was developed expressly for the purpose of expediting library clerical routines. It is used to reproduce 3- by 5-inch originals at full size and originals up to 4½ by 6½ inches at 66 percent of original size.

Information on other types of cameras and laboratory equipment and on materials is obtainable through industrial photographic supply houses and the technical representatives of the leading manufacturers.

THE STABILIZATION PROCESS

The stabilization process is a departure from conventional silver halide processing, which permits the processing of exposed materials to be carried out very rapidly. The fundamental difference between conventional processing and processing by the stabilization method lies in the different chemical treatment of the exposed and developed silver halide image. To form a permanent, or even semi-permanent image by conventional processing techniques, the silver halides which were not used in the formation of the developed image—and which, if allowed to remain in the print, will rapidly turn dark on exposure to light—are dissolved out of the paper

by means of a fixing bath—the well known "hypo."

In the stabilization process, the unused silver halides are not removed from the print. Instead, they are "stabilized," i.e., chemically converted into substances which are relatively inert and which are not readily affected by the subsequent action of light, heat, or atmospheric conditions. Thus, the classical four-bath method—developing, rinsing, fixing, and washing—which might take from twenty minutes to an hour or more, is reduced to two steps—development and stabilization—which can be accomplished in seconds.

A variant form of stabilization processing used in certain microfilm reader-printers is a "monobath," in which both the image-forming and stabilizing chemicals are contained in a single solution.

Two recent improvements in the stabilization process that have aided in bringing it into prominence have been the incorporation of the developing agent in the light-sensitive coating of the paper itself and the manufacture of compact, efficient processing devices for the rapid processing of exposed prints. By incorporating the developing agent in the paper emulsion instead of having it in the developing solution, chemical life is greatly extended, since deterioration of solution strength because of aerial oxidation of the developing agent has been eliminated.

Stabilization processors consist of two trays— one containing a highly alkaline activator and the other the stabilizing solution—and a series of power-driven rollers which advance the exposed print through the solutions and remove most of the moisture as the print comes out of the machine (Figure 95).

Most stabilization process materials are negative-working. If a positive is required, the first copy must be recopied. This can be done immediately, because the amount of moisture in the paper after processing is not great enough to cause the two sheets to stick together. Unless atmospheric conditions are quite humid, processed prints will become dry enough for easy handling in a few minutes' time.

There are only two steps in the process: (1) exposure of the sensitized material, which can be done with a contact printer, camera, or enlarger, and (2) passing the exposed sheet through a stabilization processor.

Materials

A wide variety of materials coated for stabilization processing are available from several different manufacturers. These include coatings on both film and a variety of paper stocks of different weights and surfaces and are available in various speeds and degrees of contrast. While most stabilization coatings are negative-working, one manufacturer also offers an autopositive material.[3] Stabilization materials can be used for copying by the direct-contact method, the contact-reflex method, by direct optical copying in a camera, or by projection printing. Stabilization process materials can be processed over a solution temperature range of from 65° to 85° F. without significant change in quality.

Contrast

Since stabilization materials are manufactured for general photographic applications as well as for photocopying, coatings having different degrees of contrast or those in which contrast can be controlled by means of filters are available. For ordinary documentary reproduction purposes, such as office copying, most manufacturers of stabilization process materials offer moderately high-contrast coatings on a "document-weight" stock which can be folded for mailing.

In photocopying, the use of low- and medium-contrast materials can be helpful in several ways. When copying finely detailed originals on high-contrast materials, exposure settings are often quite critical. In general, lower-contrast materials have greater exposure latitude than higher-contrast materials, thus permitting a greater margin of error in judging exposure settings. Also, if the field of illumination of a contact-printing device or of a microform reader used to make hard copy is uneven, high contrast tends to exaggerate the unevenness, which often makes exposure times critical, whereas low-contrast materials tend to minimize the unevenness. Low- and medium-contrast materials are particularly useful in reproducing continuous-tone originals, since they are capable of preserving more of the tonal gradations of the original than high-contrast materials.

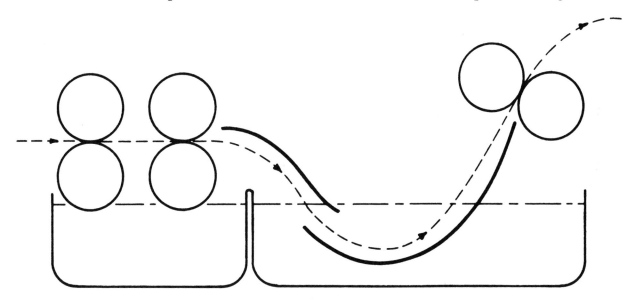

Fig. 95. Schematic diagram of a typical two-bath stabilization processor. Activator is applied by two pairs of rollers which also serve to advance the sheet through the stabilization bath to the squeegee rollers.

---

[3] See "The Autopositive Process," pages 99–104.

TABLE 2
THE STABILIZATION PROCESS
(Principal Characteristics)

1. The process is:	Wet	X
	Dry	
2. Copies can be made by the following methods:	Contact Copying	X
	Contact-Reflex Copying	X
	Optical Copying	X
	Microcopying	
	Projection Printing	X
3. The process is capable of producing copies that are:	Positive, from Positives	X *
	Negative, from Positives	X
	Positive, from Negatives	X
	Negative, from Negatives	X *
4. The process is capable of producing intermediates or masters for subsequent edition printing by:	Diazo	X
	Offset	
	Spirit Duplicating	
5. The permanence of copies is:	Archival	
	Limited	X
	Unknown	
6. The quality of copies of continuous-tone originals is:	Excellent	X *
	Fair	X *
	Poor	
7. The reproduction of fine details (e.g., small type faces, fine lines) is:	Excellent	X *
	Fair	
	Poor	
8. The contrast of copies is:	High	X *
	Moderate	X *
	Low	X *

9. The ability of the process to reproduce colored lines is:	Broad	X
	Limited	
10. The paper stock used is:	Plain, Any Color	
	Specially Coated	X
	White	X
	Off-White	
11. The tendency of copies to curl is:	High	
	Noticeable	X
	Low	
12. The potential waste factor is:	Considerable	
	Moderate	X
	Low	
13. The approximate time required to make an 8½- by 11-inch copy is:	20 seconds and up.	
14. The materials cost per 8½- by 11-inch copy is:	5¢ and up.	
15. Equipment for the process is priced at:	$175.00 and up.	

*NOTES

3. If autopositive stabilization process materials are used.

6. Depending on the contrast of the materials used.

7. Optically produced copies and projection prints on stabilization materials have excellent resolution characteristics. Copies made by contact reflex are somewhat less sharp, but this is inherent in the method, not the materials.

8. Depending on the contrast of the materials used.

Resolving power

The resolving power of stabilization process materials is quite adequate for document reproduction purposes. These include the making of contact, contact-reflex, and optical copies, and prints from line or continuous-tone negatives or microtransparencies. The actual resolving power of the materials in any given application can be affected by several factors such as: contact, contrast, exposure, and, in optical copying or projection printing, the performance characteristics of the lens employed.

Exposure latitude

Exposure latitude is related to the contrast of both the original and the sensitized material and to the fineness of the detail being reproduced. The stabilization process offers somewhat greater exposure latitude than most document reproduction processes because low-contrast materials which have greater exposure latitude can be used.

Speed

The speed of negative-working stabilization process materials ranges from very slow materials for contact and contact-reflex printing, which can be handled under fairly bright room light, to high-speed materials, which can be used for camera recording or for projection printing from continuous-tone negatives, roll-form microtransparencies, or microfiches. Autopositive stabilization materials are very slow and can only be used for contact printing.

Color sensitivity

The color sensitivity of stabilization process materials is orthochromatic, i.e., sensitive to blue and green but not to red light. Colors containing portions of red, such as pink, orange, goldenrod, or salmon, reproduce weakly in a negative copy and as a dark gray tone when recopied to a positive. Documents on paper stocks of these colors require substantially greater exposures to yield a copy with a white or light gray background.

Keeping qualities

As is the case with other silver halide coatings, stabilization process materials stored in a cool, dry place will have a shelf life of a year or more.

Permanence

Since, by the nature of the process, residual chemicals remain in stabilized copies, the permanence of such copies cannot be considered to be archival. Stabilized copies stored in files may exhibit discoloration of the background after only a few months' time. This, however, does not appreciably interfere with legibility. The useful life of stabilized copies which are thoroughly dry and kept in files where they are protected from light and from excessive heat and humidity is presumed to be on the order of several years. Stabilized copies can be rendered permanent if, after they have served the immediate purpose of providing a rapidly produced copy, they are subsequently fixed, washed, and dried.

Suitability

(1) For bound volumes—suitable.

Bound volumes can be copied by the contact-reflex method or optically, by means of a camera. Equipment for both methods is available.

(2) For newspaper files—limited.

While entire pages of unbound newspapers could be copied by the contact-reflex method and recopied to make positives, this procedure would be relatively slow and costly and, for bound files, quite impractical. No optical equipment large enough for copying entire pages of newspapers is available at present.

(3) For typescripts—generally suitable.

If materials of appropriate contrast are used, even typescripts which are faint or markedly uneven can be copied. Typescripts on one side of paper stock which has some degree of translucency can be copied by the direct-contact method to produce right-reading negative copies.

(4) For manuscripts—generally suitable.

As with typescripts, the selection of materials of appropriate contrast can be helpful in reproducing difficult subjects.

(5) For continuous-tone originals—suitable.

A great many types of stabilization process materials are manufactured specifically for reproducing continuous-tone subjects.

(6) For maps—limited.

The contrast and resolving power of stabilization process materials lend themselves well to map reproduction. Where a number of copies are needed, translucent or transparent stabilization process materials can be used to make intermediates for diazo printing. The reproduction of colored maps may be limited, however, by the color sensitivity of stabilization process materials.

(7) For card files—limited.

Card files can be copied with stabilization process materials, but no card-weight material is available for making duplicate card files. Negative or positive stabilization process copies can, however, be used as intermediates to make card-weight copies by contact printing onto silver halide or diazo materials.

(8) For copies made by other processes—generally suitable.

Since copies made by most other processes tend to be relatively high in contrast, the use of moderate contrast stabilization materials can be an advantage in reproducing subjects of this type.

(9) For microforms:

(a) Camera recording—unsuitable.

No stabilization process materials for microrecording are available.

(b) Duplicating—unsuitable.

No stabilization process materials are available for microform duplicating.

(c) Eye-legible copies from microforms—suitable.

Projection-speed stabilization process materials can be used to make hard copy either with darkroom enlargers or with reader-printers. There are a number of the latter on the market.

Manufacturers

The following list is not comprehensive. No endorsement of these firms or their equipment is implied. Before making selection of equipment, the prospective purchaser should consult local equipment directories or buying guides.

Domestic

Carr Corporation
1101 Colorado Avenue
Santa Monica, California 90404

Bell & Howell Company
7100 McCormick Road
Chicago, Illinois 60645

Copease Corporation
10401 Decatur Road
Philadelphia, Pennsylvania 19154

Copia Manufacturing Corporation
1055 Stewart Avenue
Garden City, New York 11533

Documat, Inc.
84 Fourth Avenue
Waltham, Massachusetts 02154

Eastman Kodak Company
343 State Street
Rochester, New York 14608

B. K. Elliot Company
536 Penn Avenue
Pittsburgh, Pennsylvania 15222

Filmotype Corporation
7500 McCormick Blvd.
Skokie, Illinois 60076

Fotorite, Inc.
6901 North Hamlin Avenue
Chicago, Illinois 60645

General Aniline and Film Corp.
140 West 51st Street
New York, New York 10020

J. T. Hellyer, Inc.
Post Office Box 512
St. Charles, Illinois 60174

Ilford, Inc.
37 West 65th Street
New York, New York 10023

Itek Business Products
1001 Jefferson Road
Rochester, New York 14623

Maier-Hancock Sales, Inc.
14106 Ventura Boulevard
Sherman Oaks, California 91403

Pacific Copy Corporation
142 Oregon Street
El Segundo, California 90245

Potter's Photographic Applications Company
160 Herricks Road
Mineola, New York 11501

Robertson Photo-Mechanix, Inc.
250 West Wille Road
Des Plaines, Illinois 60018

Supreme Photo Supply Company, Inc.
1841 Broadway
New York, New York 10023

Foreign

O. L. de Beauvais
50, Rue Truffaut
Paris—17, France

Fuji Photo Film Company
No. 3
2—Chome
Ginza-Nishi Chuo-Ku
Tokyo, Japan

Nederlandsche Fotografische
Industrie N. V. (Dalco)
Soestuinen
Netherlands

ORE Organisation
Otto Reimann
5038 Köln—Rodenkirchen
Weisser Strasse 106
Germany

Polyclair
52 Rue De Ponthieu
Paris VII, France

REVERSAL PROCESSING

Reversal processing is a method which makes possible the production of a positive copy from a positive original or a negative copy from a negative original without the use of an intermediate film. There are nine steps involved in producing an image by reversal processing.

(1) Exposure
(2) Development
(3) Bleaching
(4) Clearing
(5) Re-exposure
(6) Redevelopment
(7) Fixation
(8) Washing
(9) Drying

Following exposure, a negative image (from a positive original) is produced by the first development. The negative image is then removed by bleaching. Since the bleaching bath is acidic, it is followed by a clearing bath which is mildly alkaline. The film is then re-exposed to a strong light source, which exposes the remaining silver halides in the film to form a positive latent image. This image is made visible by a second development step which is followed by fixation, washing, and drying.

Reversal processing is widely used in motion picture work and for certain color processes. In microphotography, it has been used to a limited extent for making duplicate negatives in cases where negative distribution copies are preferable to positives. A common situation in which this is true is where positive hard copy is to be made from distribution copies. Ordinarily, duplicate negatives are made from intermediate positives and are, therefore, of the third generation. Reversal processing thus offers the advantage of eliminating one printing generation. Films of several types suitable for reversal processing are available from a number of manufacturers of photographic film.

AUTOPOSITIVE PROCESSES

The term "autopositive" has been in use for many years to denote a process for producing a direct-positive image, which is based on a phenomenon known as the *Herschel Effect*. In recent years, several other processes for producing direct-positive images have been developed. Although they differ greatly from the Herschel Effect process, they are nonetheless referred to in popular usage as autopositive processes and their materials as autopositive materials. The word "autopositive" has, therefore, become a class word which now includes several processes. In addition to the Herschel Effect process and stabilization processing of Herschel Effect materials, a wash-off method and a method for making direct-positive offset masters are described here. The Diaversal process is another process which is classed as autopositive, but, because it is a variant form of diffusion-transfer-reversal, it is described in the section on DTR processes.

THE AUTOPOSITIVE PROCESS (HERSCHEL EFFECT)

In 1839, Sir John Herschel observed that exposure to red light bleached out the image on silver chloride printing-out papers. This bleaching effect has since been known as the Herschel Effect and is the basis for the autopositive process. Autopositive papers are papers which have been pre-exposed to light of an appropriate wave length and, if processed without further exposure, will develop out to an over-all black. If, however, such papers are exposed to yellow light, the effect of pre-exposure is destroyed, thus producing a positive copy from a positive original. The autopositive process may therefore be classed as a subtractive direct-positive process, since the action of yellow light prevents the material from darkening on development. The spectral response of autopositive materials is such that, not only will yellow light destroy the image-forming ability of the coating, but exposure to white light will restore it. Because of this reversibility phenomenon, autopositive materials can also be used to make negatives from positives and positives from negatives. By appropriate masking techniques, it is possible to produce images in which one part is negative and the other positive.

With the exception of stabilization process materials, the procedures entailed in copying with autopositive materials are the same as those used in conventional silver halide copying—exposure, development, rinsing, fixing, washing, and drying.

Materials

Autopositive coatings are available on both paper and film supports and on glass plates as well, and can be used for copying by both the direct-contact and the contact-reflex methods, by direct optical copying in a camera, or by projection printing.

Contrast

The contrast of autopositive materials ranges from moderate to high, depending on the type of coating and the particular copying application for which it is intended.

Resolving power

Autopositive materials for making eye-legible copies by all methods have good resolution characteristics equivalent to those of normal silver halide materials used for the same purpose.

Exposure latitude

Like other silver halide materials, the exposure latitude of autopositive materials is related to contrast and to the characteristics of the original being reproduced. If high-contrast materials are used to reproduce finely detailed originals, exposure latitude is quite small.

Speed

Autopositive materials are available in a wide range of speeds, from very slow materials which can be handled under room light to very high-speed materials which can be exposed in a camera or used for projection printing.

Color sensitivity

The color sensitivity of Herschel Effect types of autopositive materials is limited, of course, since the formation of positive-to-positive or negative-to-negative images is accomplished by exposure to yellow light.

Keeping qualities

Autopositive materials, like other silver halide coatings, have a shelf life of a year or more if stored in a cool, dry place.

Permanence

Like that of other silver halide materials, the permanence of autopositive materials depends on fixation and washing. Autopositive materials which have been thoroughly fixed and washed will have archival permanence.

Suitability

Autopositive materials are used principally for the reproduction of engineering drawings and for

TABLE 3
THE AUTOPOSITIVE PROCESS (HERSCHEL EFFECT)
(Principal Characteristics)

1. The process is:	Wet	X
	Dry	
2. Copies can be made by the following methods:	Contact Copying	X
	Contact-Reflex Copying	X
	Optical Copying	X
	Microcopying	
	Projection Printing	X
3. The process is capable of producing copies that are:	Positive, from Positives	X
	Negative, from Positives	X *
	Positive, from Negatives	X *
	Negative, from Negatives	X
4. The process is capable of producing intermediates or masters for subsequent edition printing by:	Diazo	X
	Offset	X *
	Spirit Duplicating	
5. The permanence of copies is:	Archival	X *
	Limited	
	Unknown	
6. The quality of copies of continuous-tone originals is:	Excellent	
	Fair	X *
	Poor	
7. The reproduction of fine details (e.g., small type faces, fine lines) is:	Excellent	X
	Fair	
	Poor	
8. The contrast of copies is:	High	X
	Moderate	
	Low	

9. The ability of the process to reproduce colored lines is:	Broad	
	Limited	X
10. The paper stock used is:	Plain, Any Color	
	Specially Coated	X
	White	X
	Off-White	
11. The tendency of copies to curl is:	High	
	Noticeable	X
	Low	
12. The potential waste factor is:	Considerable	
	Moderate	X
	Low	
13. The approximate time required to make an 8½- by 11-inch copy is:	15 seconds and up.*	
Per linear foot (6 inches and up in width) is:	15 seconds and up.*	
14. The materials cost per 8½- by 11-inch copy is:	6¢ and up.	
Per linear foot (10 inches in width) is:	7¢ and up.	
15. Equipment for the process ranges in price from:	$225.00 to $2,450.00.*	

*NOTES

3. See process description.
4. See the Photo-Direct and Project-A-Lith systems, page 102.
5. If properly fixed and washed.
6. Autopositive materials are designed principally for the reproduction of line originals and range from moderately high to high in contrast. This limits their ability to reproduce continuous-tone originals.

13. If stabilization processing is used. (See Kodak Q-System, page 102.) Normal processing may require 30 to 45 minutes or more.
15. Autopositive materials are used with conventional silver halide equipment or diazo printers. The prices shown are for the two pieces of equipment manufactured specifically for use with autopositive-stabilization materials.

various applications in the graphic arts. While they are potentially suitable for the reproduction of certain classes of research materials, they have been little used for this purpose. With the exception of recently introduced autopositive materials which can be quickly processed by stabilization, the principal drawback to their use is the slowness of wet processing. For most classes of research materials, their utility must, therefore, be considered as unsuitable or, at best, limited.

There are no autopositive materials for the production and duplication of microforms, but autopositive materials which can be processed by stabilization can be classed as suitable for the production of hard copy from microtransparencies, since materials of this kind are now being used in reader-printers.

Variant autopositive processes

(1) The Kodak Q-System: This system is a combination of two processes—autopositive and stabilization—and was designed principally for the reproduction of engineering drawings by contact printing. The autopositive material used is a room-light-speed coating known as Kodagraph Autopositive Q Paper Ultra-Thin QA1. This material is used in conjunction with a two-bath stabilization processor known as the Kodak Auto-Processor Model Q33-T, which handles paper up to 33 inches wide and of any length. The processor operates at a speed of 10 feet per minute (2 inches per second).

A smaller processor, also used for processing autopositive materials by two-bath stabilization, called the Duostat, is manufactured in England by Kodak Limited but is not available in the United States. The Duostat handles paper up to 14 inches in width and also operates at a rate of 10 feet per minute. Both the Duostat and the Kodak Auto-Processor Model Q33-T can be used for the processing of negative-working stabilization process materials as well as autopositive materials.

(2) Kodak Positive Process Paper: Still another combination of the autopositive and stabilization processes is Kodak Positive Process Paper (manufactured by Kodak for Itek Business Products) for use in stabilization process Itek reader-printers.

(3) Wash-off autopositive: Another method for producing an autopositive image, used in making film transparencies of engineering drawings, employs a "wash off" method of processing which is radically different from normal silver halide processing. In the wash-off system, the silver halide coating includes a developing agent which, when placed in an alkaline activating solution, not only makes visible the latent image but also hardens the coating in the image area. Non-image areas which remain very soft are then entirely removed simply by washing the film in warm water (80° to 100° F.). A duplicate of an engineering drawing made on this film serves as a second original, since the film has a matte surface which can be drawn on. In addition, the physical characteristics of the photographically produced lines that make up the image are such that they can be erased with a moistened felt tip or a soft eraser.

(4) The "Photo-Direct" and "Project-A-Lith" systems: "Photo-Direct" and "Project-A-Lith" are trade names of the Addressograph-Multigraph Corporation and Itek Business Products for materials manufactured by the Eastman Kodak Company for making direct-positive offset masters. The masters have two sensitized coatings—a pre-exposed coating on top of an unexposed layer. In addition, a developing agent is also incorporated in the coating (Figure 96). When an image of a document is formed through a lens on the surface of a direct-positive offset master, light from the white background areas passes through the pre-exposed upper layer to the light-sensitive layer beneath. Following exposure, the master is placed in an activating solution which causes the developing agent to reduce the exposed silver in the lower layer. The concentration of developer in the emulsion is carefully balanced to develop only the exposed silver in the lower layer, at which point it becomes exhausted and hence cannot develop any of the exposed silver in the upper layer. In the image areas, however, where no light has reached the lower layer, the developing agent diffuses through this layer to the pre-exposed layer to form a positive image. The developer not only produces a visible image but at the same time hardens the gelatin in the image areas in the pre-exposed

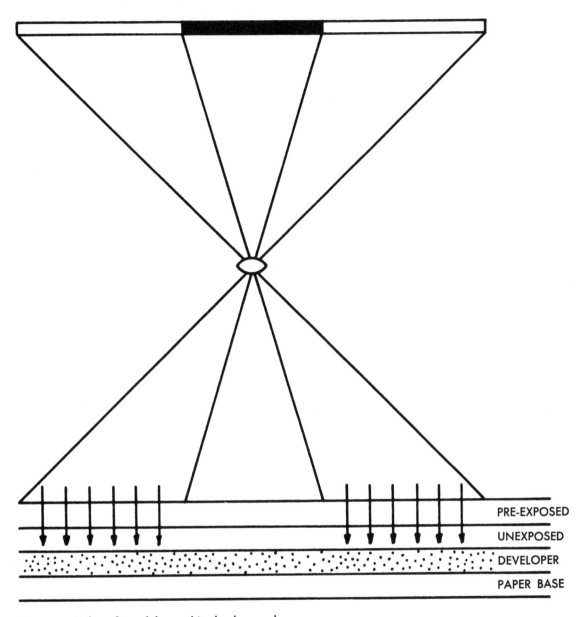

PRE-EXPOSED

UNEXPOSED

DEVELOPER

PAPER BASE

Exposure: Light reflected from white background
areas passes through the pre-exposed layer and creates
a latent image on the unexposed layer.

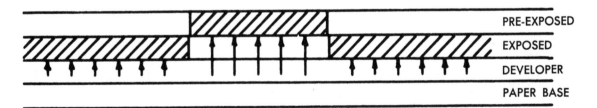

PRE-EXPOSED

EXPOSED

DEVELOPER

PAPER BASE

Development: When the exposed sheet is placed in an
activator solution, developer in the developer layer reduces
the silver in the exposed areas but exhausts itself before
it reaches the pre-exposed layer. Where no exposure has
occurred, developer passes through the unexposed layer
and reduces the silver in the pre-exposed layer.

Fig. 96. Schematic diagram of the formation of a positive image on a direct-positive
offset master.

layer. The composition of the pre-exposed layer is such that the background area is water receptive and the hardened image areas are ink receptive when treated with a stop-bath solution. Approximately two minutes are required to make a master.

Manufacturers

Contact-speed, Herschel Effect autopositive materials can be exposed with conventional contact printers of either the flat-bed or rotary types and projection speed materials in conventional photographic enlargers or cameras, and are obtainable from leading manufacturers of silver-sensitized materials. Following exposure, the processing steps (and equipment used) are the same as for other types of silver halide papers—developing, rinsing, fixing, washing, and drying. Although the Kodak Q33-T and Duostat processors were designed specifically for use with autopositive materials, they can also be used for processing other types of stabilization materials.

Special equipment is used for the production of "Photo-Direct" and "Project-A-Lith" offset masters and is supplied by:

Manufacturer	Equipment
Addressograph-Multigraph Corp. 1200 Babbitt Road Cleveland, Ohio 44132	A-M Model 705 Camera Processor
Itek Business Products 1001 Jefferson Road Rochester, New York 14623	Platemaster

THE GELATIN-DYE-TRANSFER PROCESS

The gelatin-dye-transfer process, best known by the trade-names of "Verifax" and "Readyprint," is essentially a process whereby a soft gelatin image containing developed silver halides and dye is used as a printing matrix, from which prints can be obtained by physical transfer of the soft gelatin.

A Verifax copy is made by (a) exposing the light-sensitive Verifax matrix paper for a few seconds, by the contact-reflex method, while in contact with the subject to be copied; (b) "activating" the exposed matrix in an alkaline solution for a period of 20 seconds; and (c) transferring the image to a sheet of Verifax copy paper under squeegee or roller pressure. Additional copies may be made by briefly reinserting the matrix in the activator and repeating the transfer step. Single-sided copies can also be exposed by the direct-contact method.

Important characteristics of the Verifax process are its ability to produce a number of copies from a single matrix and the fact that the copies are on a plain, uncoated paper stock which is quite inexpensive.

The Readyprint process is quite similar to the Verifax process; it has essentially the same characteristics, and the procedural steps in making a copy are the same. However, only a single copy can be made from the Readyprint matrix. A different type of activator is used with Readyprint matrices, and both the exposure and activating times for Readyprint matrices are shorter than those required for Verifax copying. While Verifax equipment can be used to expose Readyprint matrices, they must be processed in a Readyprint Copier. While a single-copy Verifax matrix is also available, Readyprint matrices have the advantage of being cheaper.

Since the Verifax process has been designed primarily for the copying of office records, the materials available are in standard office record sizes ranging from 5½ by 8½ inches to 11 by 17 inches.

Materials

Verifax Matrix Paper has a visible coating on one side which is pale gray in color. A two-inch uncoated tab at one end of the sheet is used for handling the matrix during processing. The coating consists of a gelatin emulsion containing silver halides, dye-forming components, and a non-diffusing developing agent. Since the developing agent is incorporated in the emulsion itself, development is accomplished by soaking the matrix in an alkaline activating solution. When a matrix is placed in the activator, the exposed (background) areas become hardened while the unexposed (image) areas become softened. When the matrix is then rolled or squeegeed in contact with a sheet of Verifax Copy Paper, a thin layer of the soft gelatin containing dye, reduced silver, and other silver compounds is transferred to the copy paper.

Three types of matrices are available—one which yields only a single copy and two which yield multiple copies. When multiple-copy matrices are used, the matrix, following the transfer of the first copy, is reinserted in the activator for a moment and a second copy pulled. Each successive copy is somewhat fainter than its predecessor. The number of copies which can be made from a single matrix will be governed primarily by three factors:

(1) The contrast and boldness of the lines and characters of the original;

(2) The accuracy of the exposure; and

(3) The speed and skill of the operator.

The number of copies per matrix will also vary with different models of Verifax equipment, since some are better designed than others for rapidity of handling.

The reason why speed on the part of the operator is important arises from the fact that, while the paper base of the matrix is of fairly heavy stock, it becomes increasingly soft and limp from being repeatedly soaked in the activator solution, eventually becoming too soft to work with. From a good original, runs as high as twelve are not uncommon, but the average is closer to five or six.

Only a single type of matrix is manufactured for Readyprint copying and is available in three sizes—5½ by 8½, 8½ by 11, and 8½ by 14 inches.

The copy paper ordinarily used for routine copying applications is an uncoated paper having sufficient absorbency to take up the right amount of image dye from the matrix with each transfer. The dye is actually taken into the paper and therefore will not rub off. The copy paper is the same size as the matrix—8½ by 13 inches for making 8½- by 11-inch copies. The excess two-inch tab is trimmed off after the transfers have been made.

Since the copy paper does not have the continuous coating of gelatin common to conventional photographic papers, the tendency to curl is low. The surface, being similar to that of ordinary office stationery, although slightly less smooth, readily accepts pencil, ink, typing, or rubber stamp impressions. Images can be transferred to either side of the copy paper, or both, when two-sided copies are desired.

In addition to the copy paper which is available in a variety of standard office stationery sizes and, for color-coding purposes, in seven colors as well, card-weight, translucent, transparent, and offset master stocks are also available. The offset master stock, which is known as Kodak Type EV, comes in a variety of standard sizes and slottings to fit various offset presses. Offset masters can also be made on presensitized offset plates by using a Type CS matrix in lieu of a film negative.

Only a single type of copy paper, which is quite similar to Verifax Copy Paper, is available for use with the Readyprint process.

Contrast

The contrast of Verifax materials is fairly high and the scale of tonal gradations quite short. At maximum density, the tone of the image is a dark shade of gray rather than black. Each successive image pulled from multiple-copy matrices is lighter in tone than its predecessor, the last acceptable copy being quite pale and lacking in contrast. Continuous-tone illustrations, for the most part, reproduce quite poorly, since the lack of tonal gradation causes extensive losses of both highlight and shadow detail. In a relatively short time, the dye in the image changes color from gray to brownish gray, but no progressive change in the appearance of the image occurs thereafter.

Resolving power

The maximum resolution which can be obtained at an optimum exposure is on the order of 3.5 to 4.0 lines per millimeter (90 to 100 lines per inch).

Exposure latitude

The exposure latitude of Verifax materials varies with the fineness of the details in the original being copied and with the number of copies being made from the matrix. When making only single copies of finely detailed originals,

TABLE 4
THE GELATIN-DYE-TRANSFER PROCESS (VERIFAX AND READYPRINT)
(Principal Characteristics)

1. The process is:	Wet	X
	Dry	
2. Copies can be made by the following methods:	Contact Copying	X
	Contact-Reflex Copying	X
	Optical Copying	
	Microcopying	
	Projection Printing	
3. The process is capable of producing copies that are:	Positive, from Positives	X
	Negative, from Positives	
	Positive, from Negatives	
	Negative, from Negatives	
4. The process is capable of producing intermediates or masters for subsequent edition printing by:	Diazo	X
	Offset	X
	Spirit Duplicating	
5. The permanence of copies is:	Archival	
	Limited	X *
	Unknown	
6. The quality of copies of continuous-tone originals is:	Excellent	
	Fair	
	Poor	X
7. The reproduction of fine details (e.g., small type faces, fine lines) is:	Excellent	
	Fair	X
	Poor	
8. The contrast of copies is:	High	X
	Moderate	
	Low	

9. The ability of the process to reproduce colored lines is:	Broad	X
	Limited	
10. The paper stock used is:	Plain, Any Color	X *
	Specially Coated	
	White	
	Off-White	
11. The tendency of copies to curl is:	High	
	Noticeable	X
	Low	
12. The potential waste factor is:	Considerable	
	Moderate	X
	Low	
13. The approximate time required to make an 8½- by 11-inch copy is:	For single copies—30 seconds. For 6-copy sets—8 to 10 seconds per copy.	
14. The materials cost per 8½- by 11-inch copy is:	Single copies—9¢ to 12¢. Multiple copies—as low as 2½¢.	
15. Equipment for the process ranges in price from:	$187.50 to $395.00.	

*NOTES

5. See "Permanence," page 108.
10. While the copy paper has no coating, it does have special absorbency characteristics and is available in seven colors.

exposure latitude is approximately ± 10 percent of the base exposure. With originals which are bolder, exposure latitude ranges from approximately minus 30 percent to plus 60 percent. When multiple copies of finely detailed originals are being made, exposure latitude is almost zero, and four copies may be the maximum obtainable. With bolder originals, the exposure latitude for five-copy sets is approximately ± 30 percent.

The fact that each successive copy pulled from a matrix is lighter than the preceding one can be used to advantage when only one or two copies are needed. If, for example, a matrix is underexposed and the first copy is too dark and filled for easy legibility, the second and third copies will be lighter and may be legible. Estimates of exposure for one or two copies should, therefore, tend toward underexposure, because underexposures, if not excessive, can often be saved simply by pulling additional copies.

Speed

The speed of Verifax matrices is such that they can be safely handled under fairly bright conditions of room illumination, but care should be taken to prevent unnecessary or prolonged exposure of the emulsion surface to light. A slight degree of overexposure can reduce the number of copies that can be made from a matrix. Extensive overexposure will, of course, result in the total loss of the image. The light sources used in Verifax equipment are bright enough to keep exposures for average documents within a controllable range of a few seconds without giving off excessive heat.

Color sensitivity

Verifax materials have a good over-all sensitivity to color with a high degree of sensitivity to yellow light and a lower sensitivity to red and blue. Even at substantial underexposures to favor line density, lemon or canary yellows do not reproduce. Colors made up of yellow and another color, such as yellow-orange and yellow-green, reproduce much better because of the added red and blue content, respectively. With most processes, colored paper stocks reproduce with a grayish background which will vary in density accord-

ing to the color sensitivity of the materials used. To eliminate background tone, the exposure must be increased. With Verifax materials, only a slight increase in exposure is required for most pastel tints to produce copies which have a white background.

Keeping qualities

Verifax matrix materials have a shelf-life of approximately one year if stored in a cool, dry place.

Permanence

An extensive study of the permanence of Verifax copies was conducted by Ennis and Hulswit[4] and the results published in 1963. On the basis of the accelerated aging method they employed, it was stated that "the copy paper can be expected to retain a practical level of durability for periods of time in excess of a century" and, further, that "If the aging model is correct, a properly prepared Verifax copy kept in normal storage conditions should retain substantially all its original legibility to the point of physical disintegration."

Suitability

(1) For bound volumes—limited.

Only one Verifax copier currently being manufactured—the *Regent* model—can be used for bound-volume copying by the contact-reflex method, and it has a maximum exposure area of 8½ by 11 inches.

(2) For newspaper files—unsuitable.

The available equipment limits copying newspaper materials to clippings or portions of loose sheets up to the size of the exposure area of the particular Verifax equipment being used.

(3) For typescripts—generally suitable.

Because the Verifax process was designed principally for the copying of office records which are chiefly typewritten, its performance with such originals is generally satisfactory. Because of the relatively high contrast of the materials, markedly

[4] John L. Ennis and Frank T. Hulswit, "The Permanence of Verifax Copies," *Photographic Science and Engineering*, Vol. 7, No. 3 (May–June, 1963), pp. 145–56.

uneven typescripts may not reproduce well nor will poor-quality carbon copies.

(4) For manuscripts—generally suitable.

The color response of Verifax materials to inks of various colors aids in reproducing manuscript materials. Problems may be encountered, however, in reproducing either ink or pencil writing which is markedly uneven in line width and density.

(5) For continuous-tone originals—unsuitable.

The tone scale of Verifax materials is too limited for the reproduction of continuous-tone originals. Considerable losses in both highlight and shadow detail occur.

(6) For maps—limited.

Maps in general tend to be finely detailed and are often larger than the maximum exposure area of Verifax equipment. Also, the presence of color in maps presents problems. While the appearance of bold texts against a colored background can be improved by increasing the exposure, fine lines tend to break if exposure is increased.

(7) For card files—limited.

A card-weight Verifax copy paper is available which makes it possible to do card-to-card copying in small editions at relatively low cost. Small cards, e.g., library catalog cards—can be copied four at a time on 8½- by 11-inch matrices, but the difficulty of accurately registering successive images pulled from the same matrix may require hand cutting of two sides of each card. An accessory card-holding device is available for use with the Verifax *Signet* copier.

(8) For copies made by other processes—limited.

The main problem in reproducing from copies made by other processes is contrast. Many copying processes are inherently high in contrast. The heightened contrast which occurs in recopying with Verifax materials often causes breaking and filling of fine lines and spaces with a resulting loss in legibility.

(9) For microforms—unsuitable.

The Verifax process is limited to the making of eye-legible copies.

Manufacturer

Verifax equipment is manufactured by the Eastman Kodak Company, 343 State Street, Rochester, New York 14608, and is available through Kodak dealers.

Equipment

Model	Maximum Copy Size (in inches)
Signet, Model C-K	8½ by 14
Signet, Model BD (for direct current)	8½ by 14
Regent	8½ by 11
Regent, Model FG (3-wire grounding)	8½ by 11
Auto-Twin	11 by 17
Cavalcade	8½ by 14

Accessories:

Verifax Actimeter Unit, Model 1-K (a device which provides automatic maintenance of activator supply to machine).
Verifax Offset Adapter, Model 2 (a device for transferring an image from a matrix directly to a Kodak EV offset plate).
Matrix and copy paper dispensers.
Card holder (for 3- by 5-, or 4- by 6-inch cards) for Signet Copier.
Card-holder kit for Signet Copier.

THE EKTALITH PROCESS

The Ektalith process is a variant form of the Verifax process, which employs camera-speed, Verifax-type materials for optical copying. The principal use of the process is the rapid production of high-quality, low-cost offset masters. It can also be used, however, for making multiple copies on a copy paper similar to Verifax copy paper, negative intermediates for printing on pre-sensitized offset plates, translucent copies for diazo printing, or transparencies for use on overhead projectors. The steps in the process are the same as for Verifax—exposure, activation, and transfer.

TABLE 5
THE EKTALITH PROCESS
(Principal Characteristics)

1. The process is:	Wet	X
	Dry	
2. Copies can be made by the following methods:	Contact Copying	
	Contact-Reflex Copying	
	Optical Copying	X
	Microcopying	
	Projection Printing	
3. The process is capable of producing copies that are:	Positive, from Positives	X
	Negative, from Positives	X
	Positive, from Negatives	
	Negative, from Negatives	
4. The process is capable of producing intermediates or masters for subsequent edition printing by:	Diazo	X
	Offset	X
	Spirit Duplicating	
5. The permanence of copies is:	Archival	
	Limited	X *
	Unknown	
6. The quality of copies of continuous-tone originals is:	Excellent	
	Fair	
	Poor	X
7. The reproduction of fine details (e.g., small type faces, fine lines) is:	Excellent	X
	Fair	
	Poor	
8. The contrast of copies is:	High	X
	Moderate	
	Low	

9. The ability of the process to reproduce colored lines is:	Broad	X
	Limited	
10. The paper stock used is:	Plain, Any Color	X *
	Specially Coated	
	White	
	Off-White	
11. The tendency of copies to curl is:	High	
	Noticeable	
	Low	X
12. The potential waste factor is:	Considerable	
	Moderate	
	Low	X
13 The approximate time required to make an 8½- by 11-inch copy is:	For single copies—one minute. For 10-copy sets—about 10 seconds per copy.	
14. The materials cost per 8½- by 11-inch copy is:	Single copies—17¢. Multiple copies—about 2½¢.	
15. Equipment for the process ranges in price from:	$565.00 to $1,650.00, without camera.*	

*NOTES

5. See "The Verifax Process, Permanence," page 108.

10. While the copy paper has no coating, it does have special absorbency characteristics.

15. The Ektalith units manufactured by the Eastman Kodak Company are processing units designed only to be used in conjunction with process cameras of various types and sizes.

Materials

Ektalith materials are of three types: image-forming materials, transfer materials, and the activator solution.

(1) Image-forming materials: The principal material used in the Ektalith process is a sheet of medium-weight paper having a sensitized coating on which the image is formed. It is known as Ektalith Transfer paper. It is quite similar in many of its characteristics—contrast, resolving power, exposure latitude, color sensitivity, and keeping quality—to Verifax Matrix paper. Its speed, however, is much higher. The resolution of Ektalith copies also is higher than Verifax copies, because the image is formed optically rather than by the contact-reflex method. Presumably, copies made by the Ektalith process would have the same degree of permanence as Verifax copies.

In addition to the Ektalith Transfer paper, another type of sensitized material, known as Ektalith Negative Material, is available. This material consists of a coating on a translucent paper stock. The material is exposed and activated to produce a visible image, but the image is not transferred. Following activation, the soft gelatin in the image areas is removed by wiping the surface with wet cotton. The negative image thus formed can then be used as an intermediate for printing on pre-sensitized offset masters or other types of light-sensitive material.

(2) Transfer materials: These include (a) Ektalith Copy paper which is used for making up to 10 copies from a single sheet of Ektalith Transfer paper, (b) a transparent receiving sheet for subsequent diazo printing, and (c) Kodak EV offset masters, which are available in a variety of standard sizes and slottings to fit various types of offset presses.

(3) Activator solution: In addition to the activator solution used to develop the latent image, a replenisher known as Ektalith Copy Additive is also supplied.

Suitability

(1) For bound volumes—limited.

While, as far as its capability goes, the Ektalith process might be classed as suitable for bound-volume copying and the copying of typescripts and manuscripts, the process of copying is relatively slow, and the materials costs are higher than those used in other optical copiers employing other processes such as xerography, Electrofax, or stabilization. The Ektalith process was designed principally for the making of low-cost, offset mats and not simply as a copying process for the making of individual use copies.

In cases in which the making of a number of copies of typescript or manuscript originals or printed materials in bound form is required, the Ektalith process can be rated as suitable.

(2) For newspaper files—limited.

Ektalith materials have a maximum size of 12 by 18 inches. Clippings or portions of pages can be copied within the limitations noted above. Because the Ektalith process is an optical process, pages larger than 12 by 18 inches can be reduced in size to fit the materials.

(3) For typescripts—limited (see (1) above).

(4) For manuscripts—limited (see (1) above).

(5) For continuous-tone originals—unsuitable.

Because of the high contrast of the process, extensive losses in highlight and shadow detail occur.

(6) For maps—limited.

In addition to the limitations described for other types of eye-legible originals, the copying of maps is limited by the size of the materials available and, in reproducing colored maps, by the color sensitivity of the process.

(7) For card files—suitable.

While no card-weight material is available for direct card-to-card copying, the ability of the process to produce offset masters lends itself to card reproduction where the volume is great enough to justify the costs of both Ektalith and offset equipment.

(8) For copies made by other processes—limited.

Along with its other limitations, the high contrast of the Ektalith process limits its ability to reproduce copies made by most other photocopy processes.

(9) For microforms—unsuitable.

The Ektalith process is limited to the making of eye-legible copies.

Manufacturer

With the exception of cameras, of which there are a number of makes and models which can be used for exposing Ektalith Negative Materials, all Ektalith process equipment is manufactured by:

Eastman Kodak Company
343 State Street
Rochester, New York 14608

and distributed by Eastman Kodak Company dealers with offices in principal cities.

Equipment

Ektalith Loader-Processor, Model 2—A room-light unit for storing, handling, and processing Ektalith Transfer Paper up to 12 by 18 inches, Ektalith Negative Material up to 11 by 18 inches, and offset masters up to 12 by 18 inches. The unit can be operated in conjunction with office-type copying cameras.

Ektalith Processor, Model 10-K—A darkroom processor for Ektalith Transfer paper and Ektalith Negative Material up to 9 by 14 inches. Images can be transferred to offset masters up to 10 by 15 inches.

Ektalith Processor, Model 20-K—A darkroom processor for Ektalith Transfer paper up to 12 by 18 inches and Ektalith Negative Material up to 11 by 18 inches. Images can be transferred to masters up to 15¼ by 20½ inches.

Ektalith Copy Unit, Model 1—A unit for making multiple copies on Ektalith Copy paper or on transparent receiving sheets up to 9 by 14 inches.

Ektalith Actimeter, Model 100-K—A device for automatic solution replenishment for use with the Model 2 Loader-Processor and, by means of adaptors, with the Model 10-K and Model 20-K Processors.

Accessories—include a storage cassette for the Model 2 Loader-Processor, Transfer paper holders for various sizes of Transfer paper, and Transfer paper dispensers.

Cameras—Any of a number of types of room-light or darkroom copying cameras can be used to expose Ektalith sensitized materials. One camera —the Kenro 10-15 Console—has been designed specifically for use with the Ektalith process and includes in a single unit both a camera and the Ektalith Loader-Processor. It provides for size control in a continuous range from 100 percent of original size to 50 percent. It employs a traveling light source with automatic speed control to compensate for necessary changes in exposure at different degrees of reduction.

DIFFUSION-TRANSFER-REVERSAL

The diffusion-transfer-reversal process (usually abbreviated as DTR)[5] provides a method for the simultaneous production of both a reverse-reading negative *and* a right-reading positive. Moreover, this is accomplished with only a single processing step which can be performed in less than a minute under ordinary room-light conditions.

A simple schema of what occurs in the production of an image by the DTR process is as follows:

When a sheet of silver halide negative material is exposed in contact with a document and subsequently developed, the silver salts in the background area which have been exposed are converted, in the process of development, to black metallic silver. The text area which has not received any exposure thus still contains unexposed, undeveloped silver salts which, in ordinary photographic processes, must subsequently be removed by the action of a fixing bath. In DTR processing, the negative plus a positive receiving sheet are processed simultaneously in a simple machine that first keeps the sheets separated long enough for their surfaces to become moistened by the developer, and then forces them into contact by means of a pair of rollers which carry the sheets out of the machine. In the course of this brief processing (20 to 30 seconds), a great many complex chemical events occur. Essentially, however, the presence of a solvent for silver halides causes the undeveloped silver salts in the text areas to transfer by diffusion into the positive sheet, in the course of which they become reduced to black metallic silver to form the positive image (see Figure 97). The two sheets are then separated.

---

[5] In Great Britain, the process is also known as the "Chemical Transfer" process.

TABLE 6
THE DIFFUSION-TRANSFER-REVERSAL PROCESS
(Principal Characteristics)

1. The process is:	Wet	X
	Dry	
2. Copies can be made by the following methods:	Contact Copying	X
	Contact-Reflex Copying	X
	Optical Copying	X
	Microcopying	
	Projection Printing	X
3. The process is capable of producing copies that are:	Positive, from Positives	X
	Negative, from Positives	X *
	Positive, from Negatives	X *
	Negative, from Negatives	X
4. The process is capable of producing intermediates or masters for subsequent edition printing by:	Diazo	X
	Offset	X
	Spirit Duplicating	X
5. The permanence of copies is:	Archival	
	Limited	X
	Unknown	
6. The quality of copies of continuous-tone originals is:	Excellent	
	Fair	
	Poor	X
7. The reproduction of fine details (e.g., small type faces, fine lines) is:	Excellent	X
	Fair	
	Poor	
8. The contrast of copies is:	High	X
	Moderate	
	Low	

9. The ability of the process to reproduce colored lines is:	Broad	X
	Limited	
10. The paper stock used is:	Plain, Any Color	
	Specially Coated	X
	White	X
	Off-White	X *
11. The tendency of copies to curl is:	High	
	Noticeable	X
	Low	
12. The potential waste factor is:	Considerable	
	Moderate	X
	Low	
13. The approximate time required to make an 8½- by 11-inch copy is:	30 seconds and up.	
14. The materials cost per 8½- by 11-inch copy is:	About 6¢ and up.	
15. Equipment for the process ranges in price from:	$49.00 to $650.00.	

Upon emerging from the processing machine, the sheets are somewhat damp but become dry in a few minutes on exposure to air.

In the DTR process, no control over the quality of copies in the processing step is possible. If a copy is incorrectly exposed, the entire copying procedure must be repeated at a different exposure.

Materials

The materials required for making DTR copies are: (1) a negative sheet; (2) a positive sheet; and (3) developer solution.

Negative materials are available in a variety of speeds ranging from contact-speed, room-light materials to materials fast enough to be used in a

STAGE 1—The exposed but undeveloped negative.

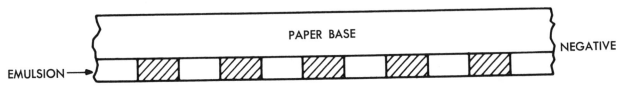

STAGE 2—Processing. The exposed (background) areas of the negative are developed. Transference of a positive image by diffusion from the text areas begins to take place.

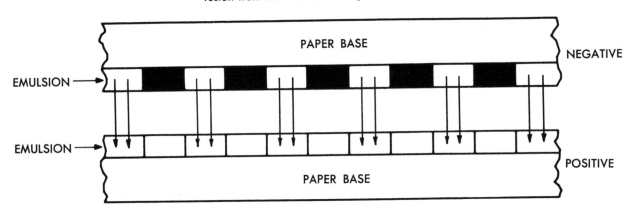

STAGE 3—The image after transference is completed and the two sheets have been separated.

Fig. 97. Three stages in the formation of a DTR image.

camera or for projection printing. Negative coatings are also available on a waterproof base as well as on an ordinary paper base. Some manufacturers supply materials from which more than one positive copy can be transferred. The materials are available in all standard paper sizes up to 18 by 24 inches and in rolls of various widths and lengths.

Positive coatings are available on a great variety of paper and film stocks including a standard weight white or tinted stock, a lightweight stock, a tissue, stock coated on both sides, and card stock. Film stocks include both translucent and transparent materials on acetate and polyester bases. A waterproof translucent stock is also available. In addition, special materials are available for making spirit masters and aluminum offset plates.

Developer solutions are of two kinds. The first is a highly energetic solution containing developing agents and other substances and it has a relatively limited life. A quart of this solution will process approximately one hundred 8½- by 11-inch copies, but, if left in the tray of the processing apparatus for a few days, it rapidly becomes weakened through aerial oxidation and must be replaced. To reduce oxidation effects, many manufacturers devised "cartridges" into which the developer could be drained and stored away from contact with air when the copier was not in use.

A second type of developer solution, recently introduced in conjunction with a new type of DTR material, is called an "activator." It does not need to be replaced but can be merely replenished to maintain the proper solution level in the developer tray. The use of the term "activator" suggests that, like certain other types of photocopy materials, the developing agent is no longer contained in the developer solution but is incorporated into the paper coating. For optimum results, DTR developers should be kept within a temperature range of 70° to 80° F., but can be used at temperatures which are considerably lower or higher.

Recently, several manufacturers of DTR materials have offered new materials which are advertised as "dry." This is misleading; the copies are certainly not dry in the true sense of the word. What is meant here is that copies are dry enough to write on immediately and can be folded without sticking.

Contrast

DTR copies are high in contrast. Faint images are often materially strengthened in DTR copies. Gradations of tone in both highlight and shadow areas of continuous-tone illustrations do not reproduce well.

Resolving power

When used for contact-reflex copying, the resolving power of DTR materials is approximately 4.5 lines per millimeter (115 lines per inch). The resolving power of optically produced copies is much higher.

Exposure latitude

Because the contrast of DTR materials is high, exposure latitude is largely a function of type size in terms of line and space width. With type faces which are bold and have good line and space width characteristics, exposure latitude is fairly broad. With small type faces which have a delicate line structure, exposures become critical.

Speed

Materials for contact-reflex copying are usually supplied in two speeds—slow and medium. Slow materials can be used under quite bright conditions of room illumination, including fluorescent light, provided they are protected from unduly long exposure to ambient light. Exposure to daylight from windows and skylights must, however, be avoided. Medium-speed materials are best handled under incandescent illumination. Materials for camera use or for projection printing must be handled in photographic darkrooms under appropriate safelights as recommended by the manufacturer.

Color sensitivity

DTR materials are low in sensitivity to the red-orange portion of the spectrum. Lines of these colors record as strong blacks. Texts on pink, salmon, orange, or goldenrod paper stocks require substantial increases in exposure to eliminate background tone. Fine or faint lines on paper stocks of these colors may be impossible to reproduce, because the amount of overexposure required may cause such lines to break or even to disappear. With the exception of light blue and yellow, colored lines can be recorded.

Keeping qualities

DTR materials have a shelf life of approximately one year, but, if stored in a cool, dry place, their useful life may be considerably longer.

Permanence

No provision is made in the DTR process for the removal of residual chemicals from the paper. There are a number of fragmentary and inconclusive statements in the literature regarding the effect of these chemical products on the permanence of DTR copies. There is presumptive evidence to suggest that their presence will, in time, be deleterious to the image. Until more exhaustive testing has been carried out, DTR copies cannot be recommended for copying applications where archival permanence is an important factor.

Suitability

(1) For bound volumes—limited.

The process itself is generally suitable for copying from bound volumes, but a limitation is imposed by the fact that most of the available equipment for use with the process is for copying by the contact-reflex method.

(2) For newspaper files—limited.

Although there are DTR copiers large enough for copying entire pages of newspapers, copying from bound files would be too cumbersome and difficult to be practical.

(3) For typescripts—generally suitable.

Most typewritten materials can be copied satisfactorily with DTR materials. Where both very faint and very bold typing appears on a single document, fully legible copies may be difficult to make because of the high contrast of DTR materials.

(4) For manuscripts—generally suitable.

Provided that line density is fairly even, manuscript pages generally reproduce well. In some cases, the legibility of copies is better than that of originals due to the heightening of contrast introduced by DTR copying. As with typescripts, fine or faint lines appearing together with bold ones may be difficult to copy. Certain combinations of colored inks and colored paper stocks also may not reproduce well.

(5) For continuous-tone originals—limited.

The high contrast of DTR materials causes considerable loss of both highlight and shadow detail in continuous-tone originals. Copies from originals of moderate contrast may be recognizable but are far from being faithful copies.

(6) For maps—limited.

Loose-sheet, black-and-white maps up to the maximum size of the equipment available can be reproduced. Copying fold-out maps by the contact-reflex method from bound volumes is seldom practical. Copies of colored maps may suffer from the low sensitivity of DTR materials to the red-orange portion of the spectrum and the fact that dissimilar colors may reproduce as identical shades of gray.

(7) For card files—limited.

While card-weight DTR materials are available, the materials have a tendency to curl and the unit costs of copies, compared with certain other processes, are relatively high.

(8) For copies made by other processes—limited.

The high contrast of DTR materials makes them unsuitable for recopying high-contrast positive copies made by other processes or high-contrast negatives, particularly if there is any veiling of the lines. Copies made by processes which are relatively low in contrast can usually be copied satisfactorily.

(9) For microforms:

    (a) Camera recording—unsuitable.

No materials are available for microrecording.

    (b) Duplicating—unsuitable.

No materials are available for microform duplicating.

    (c) Eye-legible copies from microforms —limited.

The principal drawback in using DTR for making hard copy from microforms is the high contrast of the materials. Microforms themselves are high in contrast. When such high-contrast originals are reproduced by a process as high in contrast as DTR, any unevenness in line density or in the illumination system used is accentuated. Fine lines in positive copies tend to break or disappear and small spaces within and between text characters in negative copies tend to fill.

Manufacturers

The following lists are not comprehensive. No endorsement of these firms or their equipment is implied. Before making selection of equipment, the prospective purchaser should consult local equipment directories or buying guides.

Among the principal manufacturers of DTR *materials* are:

Agfa-Gevaert, Inc.
275 North Street
Teterboro, New Jersey 07608

Anken Chemical & Film Corporation
10 Patterson Avenue
Newton, New Jersey 07860.

American Photocopy Equipment Company
2100 West Dempster Street
Evanston, Illinois 60202

Mitsubishi Paper Mills Ltd.
Products distributed by:
Pacific Copy Corporation
142 Oregon Street
El Segundo, California 90245

Some of the leading manufacturers and distributors of both domestic and foreign DTR *equipment* which can be used for copying research materials are:

A. B. Dick Company
5700 West Touhy Avenue
Chicago, Illinois 60648

American Photocopy Equipment Company
2100 West Dempster Street
Evanston, Illinois 60202

Anken Chemical & Film Corporation
10 Patterson Avenue
Newton, New Jersey 07860

Continental Copy Products
Pacific Copy Corporation
142 Oregon Street
El Segundo, California 90245

Copease Corporation
10401 Decatur Road
Philadelphia, Pennsylvania 19154

Copy-Craft, Inc.
105 Chambers Street
New York, New York 10007

Dokuphot-Apparatebau
Weidenbornstrasse 9
62 Wiesbaden, Germany

Intercop
International Copying Machines
Company m.b.H.
Danziger Strasse 35a (Artushof)
2 Hamburg 1, Germany

Meteor Apparatebau
Paul Schmeck GMBH
Frankfurter Strasse 27
59 Siegen, Western Germany

Nashua Corporation
Office Copy Division
44 Franklin Street
Nashua, New Hampshire 03060

Nord Photocopy & Business Equipment Corp.
New Hyde Park, Long Island, New York
   11040

Pacer International Corporation
375 Park Avenue
New York, New York 10022

Pacific Copy Corporation
142 Oregon Street
El Segundo, California 90245

Ravenna Bürotechnik Friedrich Brante
4801 Borgholzhausen
bei Bielefeld
Western Germany

SCM Corporation
410 Park Avenue
New York, New York 10022

Hermann Wolf GMBH
Kieler Strasse 33
56 Wuppertal-Elberfeld, Germany

THE DIAVERSAL PROCESS

The diaversal process is a variant form of diffusion-transfer-reversal in which both the negative and the positive image forming layers, which are on separate supports in ordinary DTR, are coated on a single support. The composition of the negative layer, which is coated on top of the positive layer, is such that when an exposed sheet of diaversal material is developed to form both the negative and positive images, the negative layer may then be readily washed off, leaving only the positive image on the support.

Materials

Diaversal materials are often listed as auto-positive materials, despite the fact that the process is quite different from the autopositive process based on the Herschel effect. Diaversal coatings are available on both paper and film supports and can be used for copying by the direct-contact method, by direct optical copying in a camera, or by projection printing. Unlike other materials which produce a direct-positive copy and which require all of the processing steps common to silver halide materials—development, rinsing, fixing, and washing—diaversal materials require only development followed by the wash necessary to remove the negative layer.

Contrast

Diaversal materials are designed for line copying and are high in contrast.

Resolving power

The resolving power of diaversal materials is equivalent to the resolving power of other types of silver halide materials. Excellently detailed copies can be made by any of the methods indicated.

Exposure latitude

Because of the high contrast of diaversal coatings, exposure latitude is quite limited.

Speed

Diaversal materials are high in speed and must be handled in a photographic darkroom. Materials for projection printing are fast enough to permit the use of very short exposures at small lens openings.

Color sensitivity

Diaversal materials have orthochromatic sensitivity similar to DTR materials—i.e., they are sensitive to blue and green areas of the spectrum but not to red. Because of their speed, they must be handled under a red safelight in a darkroom.

Keeping qualities

The keeping qualities of diaversal materials are similar to those of other silver halide materials used in photocopying. Under reasonable conditions of temperature and humidity, the shelf life of the material is a year or more.

Permanence

Because the chemistry of the diaversal process is similar to DTR, although diaversal copies are washed after development, presumably they would be superior in permanence to ordinary DTR copies which are not washed. Whether adequately washed diaversal copies would be equivalent in permanence to properly processed silver halide copies has not been indicated by manufacturers of diaversal materials.

Suitability

(1) For bound volumes—suitable.

If prism-type cameras are used, diaversal materials are suitable for bound-volume copying.

(2) For newspaper files—suitable.

Prism-type cameras can be used to record portions of or entire pages of newspapers in either bound or unbound form.

(3) For typescripts—generally suitable.

Ribbon copies or carbon copies, which are fairly even in tone, copy satisfactorily. Unevenly typed originals may fail to reproduce legibly because of the high contrast of the materials.

(4) For manuscripts—limited.

The high contrast of diaversal materials makes the copying of manuscripts in which fine or faint lines appear together with bold ones difficult. Also, certain combinations of colored inks and colored paper stocks may not reproduce well.

(5) For continuous-tone originals—unsuitable.

Diaversal materials are too high in contrast to yield satisfactory reproductions of continuous-tone originals.

(6) For maps—limited.

While black-and-white maps can be reproduced by using prism-type cameras, the high contrast and color-sensitivity characteristics of diaversal materials limit its utility for copying colored maps.

(7) For card files—unsuitable.

No materials for direct card-to-card copying are currently available.

(8) For copies made by other processes—limited.

The high contrast of diaversal materials makes them unsuitable for recopying high-contrast copies made by other processes. Copies made by processes which are relatively low in contrast can usually be copied satisfactorily.

(9) For microforms:

(a) Camera recording—unsuitable.

No materials are available for microrecording.

(b) Duplicating—unsuitable.

No materials are available for microform duplicating.

(c) Eye-legible copies from microforms —limited.

The high contrast of diaversal materials when used for printing from high-contrast microforms makes exposures quite critical and can cause breaking of fine lines.

Manufacturers

The following list is not comprehensive. No endorsement of these firms or their equipment is implied. Before making a selection of equipment, the prospective purchaser should consult local equipment directories or buying guides.

Prism-type cameras for use with diaversal materials are manufactured by:

Anken Chemical & Film Corporation
10 Patterson Avenue
Newton, New Jersey 07860

Itek Business Products
1001 Jefferson Road
Rochester, New York 14623

Diaversal materials are manufactured by the Eastman Kodak Company for Itek Business Products and by the Anken Chemical & Film Corporation.

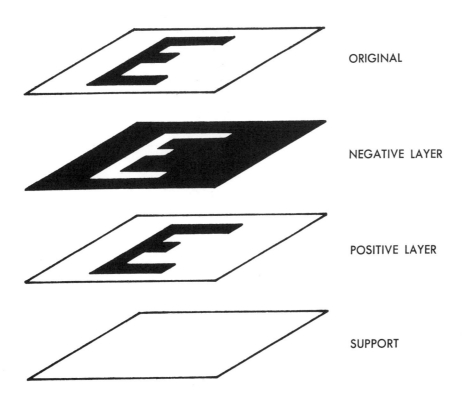

ORIGINAL

NEGATIVE LAYER

POSITIVE LAYER

SUPPORT

Fig. 98. Schematic diagram of diaversal layers.

TABLE 7
The Diaversal Process
(Principal Characteristics)

1. The process is:	Wet	X
	Dry	
2. Copies can be made by the following methods:	Contact Copying	X *
	Contact-Reflex Copying	
	Optical Copying	X
	Microcopying	
	Projection Printing	X
3. The process is capable of producing copies that are:	Positive, from Positives	X
	Negative, from Positives	
	Positive, from Negatives	
	Negative, from Negatives	X
4. The process is capable of producing intermediates or masters for subsequent edition printing by:	Diazo	X
	Offset	
	Spirit Duplicating	
5. The permanence of copies is:	Archival	
	Limited	
	Unknown	X
6. The quality of copies of continuous-tone originals is:	Excellent	
	Fair	
	Poor	X
7. The reproduction of fine details (e.g., small type faces, fine lines) is:	Excellent	X
	Fair	
	Poor	
8. The contrast of copies is:	High	X
	Moderate	
	Low	

9. The ability of the process to reproduce colored lines is:	Broad	X
	Limited	
10. The paper stock used is:	Plain, Any Color	
	Specially Coated	X
	White	X
	Off-White	
11. The tendency of copies to curl is:	High	
	Noticeable	X
	Low	
12. The potential waste factor is:	Considerable	
	Moderate	X
	Low	.
13. The approximate time required to make an 8½- by 11-inch copy is:	See "Notes."	
14. The materials cost per 8½- by 11-inch copy is:	About 10¢ and up.	
15. Equipment for the process is priced at:	See "Notes."	

*NOTES

2. The intensity of the light source of the contact printer must be reduced if projection-speed materials are used.

13. Although only development and washing are required, the fact that the process is wet and prints must subsequently be dried makes the process relatively slow. The making of a single copy may require as much as a half hour, but the simultaneous processing and drying of a number of prints would reduce the time considerably.

15. Diaversal materials can be used with a wide variety of standard photographic equipment including contact printers, enlargers, and prism-type cameras such as "Photostat," "Rectigraph," and "Dexigraph" cameras.

THE POLAROID PROCESS

The Polaroid process is a variant form of DTR developed by Dr. Edwin Land of the Polaroid Corporation.[6] The Polaroid process extends the range of DTR far beyond the document copying field and into a long list of applications, including color photography, which formerly were the exclusive province of conventional silver halide photography.

In conventional DTR as it is used for document copying, an exposed negative sheet is placed in contact with a positive receiving sheet and the two sheets are processed by passing them through a solution which produces both a negative and a positive image simultaneously in a few seconds' time. In the Polaroid process, a "package" system is used consisting of the negative and positive materials and a pod of a chemical reagent which produces the negative and positive images. The design of the film-holding mechanism of Polaroid equipment is such that, after an exposure is made, a tab is pulled which advances the sensitized material out of the camera between two pressure rollers. The pressure rollers break the pod and spread a very thin layer of the reagent uniformly over the surface of the negative and positive materials. After a few seconds, the negative and positive materials are peeled apart as in conventional DTR. Schematically, therefore, the Polaroid process is quite similar to the DTR process used in document copying devices but, chemically, it is quite different because Polaroid materials are high-speed materials designed for use in a camera to produce high-quality images of subjects having an extended tone range.

With the exception of one type of Polaroid material, the negative material is not reusable for making additional positives.

Materials

A variety of different types of materials are available for photography by the Polaroid process including panchromatic black-and-white materials, a high-speed recording material, an infrared

sensitive material, two types of materials for making lantern slides from either line or continuous-tone originals, a color film, and one type of material (designated as Type 55P/N) which produces both a positive print and a reusable negative.

Developing time for most films is in a range of from 10 to 20 seconds. The color film requires a 50-second developing time, and the film for making continuous-tone lantern slides requires a developing time of two minutes.

Polaroid materials are available in roll form and film packs and range in size, depending upon the type of material and its purpose, from 2¼ by 2¼ inches to 4 by 5 inches.

Although a small amount of moisture is present in the viscous reagent used to develop the latent image, most Polaroid copies can be considered as dry. The materials used for slide making must be given an after-treatment in a liquid hardener which also prevents fading and discoloration. The Type 55P/N film negative must be washed and dried before it can be used for making additional prints.

Contrast

Polaroid materials range in contrast from normal to high depending on the purpose the different types of materials are intended to serve.

Resolving power

The resolving power of Polaroid materials is high. Polaroid Type 55P/N film, for example, according to the manufacturer, is capable of a resolution of approximately 150 lines per millimeter (3,810 lines per inch) and the print transferred from it is capable of a resolution of 28 to 30 lines per millimeter (approximately 700 to 750 lines per inch).

Exposure latitude

The exposure latitude of Polaroid materials is comparable to that of silver halide materials having similar characteristics but, with the exception of Type 55P/N film, no control to correct the quality of the prints because of under- or overexposure can be interposed.

---

[6] "Polaroid" is a registered trademark of the Polaroid Corporation.

Speed

The speed of Polaroid materials ranges from 50 to 10,000 ASA. The color film has a speed of 75 ASA.

Color sensitivity

The color sensitivity of most black-and-white Polaroid material is panchromatic.

Keeping qualities

Black-and-white Polaroid materials have a shelf life of approximately ten months. The color film has a shelf life of approximately six months if the materials are stored in a cool, dry place. Shelf life can be extended if the materials are kept under refrigeration.

Permanence

In a leaflet issued by the Polaroid Corporation entitled "How To Be Sure Your Polaroid Black & White Land Pictures Are Permanent," the following statement on permanence appears:

"Polaroid black and white Land pictures are permanent only if properly coated with the Print Coater packed in every box of film. This is true for both roll and pack film types. If the pictures are coated, and handled and stored as suggested in this folder, their lasting properties are as good as those of carefully processed conventional prints." Detailed instructions are given in the leaflet on coating, storing, and handling.

Suitability

The Polaroid process cannot be classed as essentially a document-copying process. Hence its suitability for reproducing most types of research materials is limited. The process is primarily an optical copying process designed for camera recording on materials which at present have a maximum size of 4 by 5 inches. Also, the materials are relatively expensive when compared with those of a number of other processes designed specifically for document-copying applications. The process does, however, offer advantages in certain applications which are unequalled by any other process.

In the first place, because Polaroid materials are capable of a tone range equivalent to continuous-tone silver halide materials, they are suitable for the copying of continuous-tone and half-tone subjects. Furthermore, the processing of the exposed materials yields a positive print in less than a minute. With Polaroid Type 55P/N film, it is possible to produce both a negative and a positive print having a maximum size of 4 by 5 inches, but the negative can then be used to make enlarged prints to any desired size. The photographic service at the Widener Library at Harvard University, for example, uses a Polaroid MP-3 camera and stand with Type 55P/N film to provide a low-volume service for reproducing continuous-tone and half-tone subjects on a much more rapid and economical basis than would be possible with conventional silver halide materials requiring wet processing.

Another application in which the Polaroid process is useful is in the making of lantern slides. Using Types 46L and 146L Projection Films, 3¼- by 4-inch slides of line originals, such as maps, graphs, drawings, or portions of text, can be produced with great rapidity.

At the present time, there are no applications of the process in the field of microforms.

Manufacturer

The manufacturer is:

Polaroid Corporation
Cambridge, Massachusetts 02139

Equipment

In addition to a number of hand cameras for both amateur and professional work in black-and-white and color, the Polaroid Corporation also manufactures two pieces of equipment which are useful in copying applications.

Polaroid Copymaker Model 208—This unit consists of a baseboard and easel, a calibrated column and camera arm, an electric timer for controlling exposure and development, and two fluorescent lights mounted on arms. The easel is marked off into several field sizes for different camera height settings. The maximum-size original which can be copied is 11 by 14 inches.

Polaroid MP-3 Industrial View Camera—This unit consists of a view camera equipped with both a Polaroid camera back and a standard camera back

TABLE 8
The Polaroid Process
(Principal Characteristics)

1. The process is:	Wet	
	Dry	X *
2. Copies can be made by the following methods:	Contact Copying	
	Contact-Reflex Copying	
	Optical Copying	X
	Microcopying	
	Projection Printing	
3. The process is capable of producing copies that are:	Positive, from Positives	X
	Negative, from Positives	
	Positive, from Negatives	
	Negative, from Negatives	X
4. The process is capable of producing intermediates or masters for subsequent edition printing by:	Diazo	
	Offset	
	Spirit Duplicating	
5. The permanence of copies is:	Archival	X *
	Limited	
	Unknown	
6. The quality of copies of continuous-tone originals is:	Excellent	X
	Fair	
	Poor	
7. The reproduction of fine details (e.g., small type faces, fine lines) is:	Excellent	X
	Fair	
	Poor	
8. The contrast of copies is:	High	X *
	Moderate	X *
	Low	

9. The ability of the process to reproduce colored lines is:	Broad	X
	Limited	
10. The paper stock used is:	Plain, Any Color	
	Specially Coated	X
	White	X
	Off-White	
11. The tendency of copies to curl is:	High	
	Noticeable	X
	Low	
12. The potential waste factor is:	Considerable	
	Moderate	X
	Low	
13. The approximate time required to make a 4- by 5-inch copy is:	2 minutes and up.*	
14. The materials cost per 4- by 5-inch copy is:	About 55¢ and up.	
15. Equipment for the process is priced at:	$59.95 and up.	

*NOTES

1. See "Polaroid Materials," page 124.
5. See "Permanence," page 125.
8. Depending on the type of film used.
13. The developing time for most Polaroid materials is in a range from 10 to 20 seconds and, for color film, about 50 seconds. The total time to make a copy will vary, however, with the time required to arrange the camera set-up plus the developing time.

for 4- by 5-inch Polaroid or conventional silver halide films, a column and camera arm, a baseboard, and four lamps mounted on arms. Films smaller than 4 by 5 inches can be used by employing adaptors. The MP-3 is available in two sizes. The Standard Model has a 38-inch column and a 19- by 24-inch baseboard. A larger model, designated as Model XL, has a 56-inch column and a 24- by 27-inch baseboard. The camera can also be pivoted 90° for photographing wall-mounted subjects too large for the baseboard. A variety of accessories are available for special applications.

THE DRY SILVER PROCESS

The Dry Silver process is a negative-working process employing a coating which can be either on a paper or a film base. It contains light-sensitive substances which, following exposure, can be developed to form a visible image by the action of heat. The process is thus completely dry.

Materials

The only Dry Silver material currently available is a coating on a lightweight paper stock which is used for the production of hard copy from microtransparencies. It is designated as type 770 Dry Silver microfilm copy paper.

Contrast

The contrast of Type 770 Dry Silver paper is relatively high.

Resolving power

The resolving power of Type 770 Dry Silver paper is excellent and well in excess of the resolution requirements for hard copy produced from microtransparencies.

Exposure latitude

No data available.

Speed

The speed of Type 770 Dry Silver paper is high enough for the rapid production of hard copy. The total print production time in one type of Dry Silver printer—the Microcard Corporation's Model EL-4 Microfiche Enlarger-Printer—is five seconds per print.

Color sensitivity

While the spectral response of the process is stated to be broad, the use of Type 770 Dry Silver paper is limited to the making of copies from black-and-white microtransparencies.

Keeping qualities

No data available.

Permanence

Permanence is questionable because Dry Silver copies show a marked tendency to darken with age.

Suitability

The Dry Silver process, at the present stage of development, is not suitable for the making of eye-legible copies directly from originals such as bound volumes, newspapers, typescripts, manuscripts, continuous-tone originals, maps, card files, or eye-legible copies made from other processes (Classes 1 through 8). Its only use is for the making of hard copy from microtransparencies.

(9) For microforms:

(a) Camera recording—unsuitable. No equipment or materials are available for microrecording uses.

(b) Microform duplicating—unsuitable. No equipment or materials are available for duplicating uses.

(c) Eye-legible copies from microforms —generally suitable.

Type 770 Dry Silver microfilm copy paper is manufactured specifically for the production of hard copy from microtransparencies. Where continuous-tone illustrations are present, these may suffer because of the relatively high contrast of the process.

Manufacturers

Dry Silver equipment is manufactured by:

3M Company
2501 Hudson Road
St. Paul, Minnesota 55101

Microcard Corporation
365 South Oak Street
West Salem, Wisconsin 54669

Equipment

3M Quadrant Dry Silver Printers—The first Quadrant Printer was introduced in 1964 and was the first device to employ the Dry Silver process. It is a specialized piece of equipment designed for producing 8½- by 11-inch hard copy from microtransparencies of size "A" engineering drawings filmed in groups of four on full-frame, non-perforated 35 mm. microfilm mounted in aperture cards. Print production time is approximately ten seconds.

A second Quadrant Printer has subsequently been brought out which prints from aperture card microfilms having eight instead of four images. *The Microcard Corporation's Model EL-4 Microfiche Enlarger-Printer*—The EL-4 Enlarger-Printer is an automatic printer designed to produce hard copy on Type 770 Dry Silver process paper of the entire contents of microfiches made in accordance with *Federal Microfiche Standards* (see Appendix D). It operates at a production rate of 5,000 prints per eight-hour shift. Prints produced on the EL-4 Enlarger-Printer are slightly reduced in size.

THE THERMO-FAX PROCESS

The Thermo-Fax process, a product of the 3M Company,[7] was the first successful document copying process employing heat to form an image. In this process, the sensitized material consists of a thin sheet of paper containing certain chemical compounds which, when subjected to heat of an appropriate temperature, form colored substances. When a sheet of this material is placed in contact with a document and exposed to infrared (heat) radiation, the infrared rays pass through the non-infrared absorbing sensitized material to the document where they are absorbed by the metallic or carbon content of the text. The text is thus actually heated up to a temperature high enough to convert the chemical compounds in the sensitized layer to colored substances to form a visible image. The Thermo-Fax process, therefore, requires no development step to make visible a latent image. A direct image is formed by exposure alone.

---

[7] "Thermo-Fax" is a registered trade mark of the 3M Company.

The composition of Thermo-Fax coatings is such that the sensitized layer is relatively opaque while the support material is relatively translucent. This makes it possible to produce right-reading rather than reverse-reading copies in a single step by the contact-reflex method.

An essential requirement, if documents are to be reproduced by the Thermo-Fax process, is that the text be written or printed with a pencil or ink which contains a substance which rapidly absorbs sufficient infrared radiation to create the elevated temperature pattern needed to affect the heat-sensitive coating. Most colored inks, which are manufactured from dyestuffs, do not, and hence are not reproducible by thermographic means.

Because heat cannot be transmitted through a lens in the same manner that light can, nor transmitted efficiently through most paper stocks because of their relatively high infrared absorption, Thermo-Fax copying is limited largely to the making of copies by the contact-reflex method described.

Materials

Materials for Thermo-Fax copying are manufactured not only by the 3M Company but also by a number of other paper manufacturers and are of two types. One type consists of a colored base material coated with an opaque but thin waxy substance. Heat formed in the image areas melts this coating to expose the colored base thus rendering the heat-formed image visible. In the second type, heat formed by the image causes a chemical change in the sensitized coating from a colorless to a colored state. There is a disadvantage in the first type: not only is the material somewhat pressure sensitive—i.e., will mar if subjected to pressure from a hard object such as a paper clip or a fingernail—but it also behaves as carbon paper. If annotations are made on it, the pressure of pen or pencil causes the colored coating to adhere to whatever surface may be beneath it.

Materials of several different kinds to suit different purposes are available. For ordinary copying applications, an inexpensive, lightweight buff or off-white shade of paper is generally used. White stocks and stocks of other tints such as

TABLE 9
The Dry Silver Process
(Principal Characteristics)

1. The process is:	Wet	
	Dry	X
2. Copies can be made by the following methods:	Contact Copying	
	Contact-Reflex Copying	
	Optical Copying	
	Microcopying	
	Projection Printing	X *
3. The process is capable of producing copies that are:	Positive, from Positives	
	Negative, from Positives	X
	Positive, from Negatives	X
	Negative, from Negatives	
4. The process is capable of producing intermediates or masters for subsequent edition printing by:	Diazo	
	Offset	
	Spirit Duplicating	
5. The permanence of copies is:	Archival	
	Limited	
	Unknown	X *
6. The quality of copies of continuous-tone originals is:	Excellent	
	Fair	X
	Poor	
7. The reproduction of fine details (e.g., small type faces, fine lines) is:	Excellent	X
	Fair	
	Poor	
8. The contrast of copies is:	High	X
	Moderate	
	Low	

9. The ability of the process to reproduce colored lines is:	Broad	X *
	Limited	
10. The paper stock used is:	Plain, Any Color	
	Specially Coated	X
	White	
	Off-White	X
11. The tendency of copies to curl is:	High	
	Noticeable	X
	Low	
12. The potential waste factor is:	Considerable	
	Moderate	
	Low	X
13. The approximate time required to make an 8½- by 11-inch copy is:	5 to 10 seconds.	
14. The materials cost per 8½- by 11-inch copy is:	2¢.	
15. Equipment for the process ranges in price from:	$1,795.00 to $18,000.00.	

*NOTES

2. While the process may be capable of producing copies by other methods, the only materials and equipment currently available are for projection printing from microtransparencies.

5. Copies progressively change from buff to a brownish color, even when stored in files protected from light.

9. Although broad spectral response is claimed for certain formulations, the process is at present limited to making hard copy from black-and-white microtransparencies.

TABLE 10
THE THERMO-FAX PROCESS
(Principal Characteristics)

1. The process is:	Wet	
	Dry	X
2. Copies can be made by the following methods:	Contact Copying	
	Contact-Reflex Copying	X
	Optical Copying	
	Microcopying	
	Projection Printing	
3. The process is capable of producing copies that are:	Positive, from Positives	X
	Negative, from Positives	
	Positive, from Negatives	
	Negative, from Negatives	X
4. The process is capable of producing intermediates or masters for subsequent edition printing by:	Diazo	
	Offset	X
	Spirit Duplicating	X
5. The permanence of copies is:	Archival	
	Limited	X
	Unknown	
6. The quality of copies of continuous-tone originals is:	Excellent	
	Fair	
	Poor	X
7. The reproduction of fine details (e.g., small type faces, fine lines) is:	Excellent	
	Fair	
	Poor	X
8. The contrast of copies is:	High	X *
	Moderate	X *
	Low	

| 9. The ability of the process to reproduce colored lines is: | Broad | |
| | Limited | X |

10. The paper stock used is:	Plain, Any Color	
	Specially Coated	X
	White	
	Off-White	X

11. The tendency of copies to curl is:	High	
	Noticeable	X
	Low	

12. The potential waste factor is:	Considerable	
	Moderate	X *
	Low	

13. The approximate time required to make an 8½- by 11-inch copy is:	4 seconds.
14. The materials cost per 8½- by 11-inch copy is:	About 4¢ and up.
15. Equipment for the process ranges in price from:	$379.00 to $575.00.

16. Other characteristics: Since the background (non-text) areas of copies retain their sensitivity to heat, additional information can be recorded on these areas at a later time.

*NOTES

8. Depending on whether moderate or high-contrast materials are used.

12. Waste with high-contrast materials is greater than with moderate-contrast materials.

yellow, green, and pink are also available but are somewhat more expensive. In addition, there are ledger-weight and bond-weight stocks, a gummed stock for making labels (which may be obtained either perforated or non-perforated), an offset-master stock, and a spirit-master stock similar in its characteristics to Eichner process materials (q.v.). The spirit-master stock is supplied in sets consisting of a spirit master and a thin, cellophane-like sheet coated with a purple dye, which is placed in contact with the document to be copied. Heat from the original melts the dye and causes it to transfer to the spirit master.

Offset masters can be made thermographically but only from copy typewritten on a special paper stock called "Z" paper. The "Z" paper image can then be transferred to a "Z" plate by running it through a Thermo-Fax machine. Several "Z" plates can be made from a single "Z" paper master at one time, or the "Z" paper master can be retained and additional plates made at a later time. "Z" plates are capable of runs of 2,000 copies or more.

Contrast

The contrast of materials for Thermo-Fax copying varies with the type of material and the manufacturer and ranges from moderate to high. In general, the greater the contrast, the blacker the image will be.

Resolving power

The resolving power of materials for Thermo-Fax copying is somewhat limited by the nature of the process. At normal exposures, fine lines do not reproduce well because they do not absorb and dissipate sufficient heat. If the duration of exposure is increased to strengthen the appearance of fine lines, broader lines tend to widen and spaces between them tend to fill. Not only does this make the reproduction of small type faces difficult and sometimes impossible but, in borderline cases, exposure latitude for reproducing small type faces is virtually nil.

Exposure latitude

The exposure latitude of materials for Thermo-Fax copying varies principally with the contrast of the materials and the fineness of the detail being reproduced. Fairly bold originals copied on moderate-contrast materials can be reproduced satisfactorily over a range of settings. With more finely detailed subjects, there is little exposure latitude on moderate-contrast materials and none at all on high-contrast materials.

Speed

The response of materials for Thermo-Fax copying to heat given off from the text being copied is very rapid. Documents eleven inches long passing the tubular lamp, which acts as the heat source in a Thermo-Fax office copier, are reproduced in four seconds or less.

Color sensitivity

The term "color sensitivity" does not apply because exposure is accomplished by means of heat rather than light from any visible portion of the spectrum. Lines or areas printed in colored inks usually cannot be reproduced, not because of their color but because most colored inks do not contain substances which absorb heat.

Keeping qualities

Materials for Thermo-Fax copying have an indefinite shelf life if they are protected from sunlight or heat.

Permanence

Because heat is the agency which darkens the substances forming the image, heat is the one condition from which the materials must be protected both before and after use. Because the materials are permanently sensitive to heat, the heat of a lighted cigarette held too close to a copy can cause the paper to darken. It should be remembered, however, that under ordinary conditions of storage and use, temperatures high enough to cause copies to darken to a point where they are no longer useful as records are seldom encountered. But, where archival permanence is an important consideration, it is highly doubtful that Thermo-Fax copies, because of their sensitivity to elevated temperatures, could be considered suitable.

Suitability

(1) For bound volumes—unsuitable.

At the present time, there is no Thermo-Fax equipment which can be used for the making of copies from bound material.

(2) For newspaper files—unsuitable.

Thermo-Fax equipment is limited to the making of letter- or legal-size copies of originals in loose-sheet form.

(5) For continuous-tone originals—unsuitable.

The contrast and limited tone scale of Thermo-Fax materials make them unsuitable for the copying of continuous-tone originals.

(6) For maps—limited.

Maps up to 8½ by 14 inches in size which have a fairly broad line structure can be reproduced, but finely detailed maps reproduce poorly.

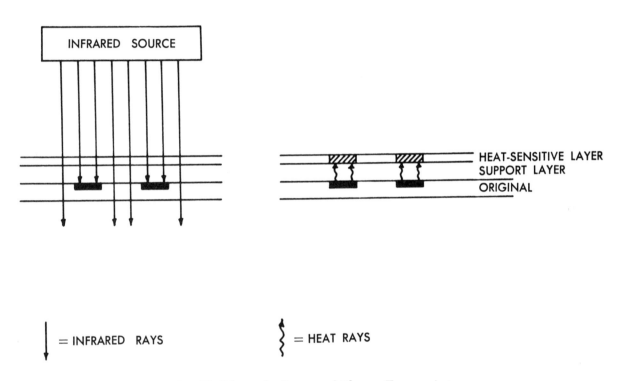

Fig. 99. Schematic diagram of Thermo-Fax copying.

(3) For typescripts—generally suitable.

The process is capable of reproducing materials typewritten with ribbons or other materials having a carbon content. Most colored typewriter ribbons will not reproduce.

(4) For manuscripts—limited.

Manuscripts written with pencil or ink containing a carbon or metallic compound may reproduce, but most colored pencils and inks will not. In addition, fine lines (which occur frequently in manuscript materials) may not absorb enough heat to reproduce.

(7) For card files—limited.

Cards can be reproduced on ordinary Thermo-Fax materials but not onto card-weight stock.

(8) For copies made by other processes—limited.

Copies made by silver processes such as DTR (which have a metallic content) can be reproduced, but dye-formed copies (diazo, Ektafax, etc.) cannot. Furthermore, because copies made by other processes tend to be high in contrast, the added contrast introduced in Thermo-Fax copying may result in copies which are not fully legible. Caution should be used in copying Xerox copies onto Thermo-Fax materials. If slow Thermo-Fax materials are used and if several copies are required, a reaction occurs between the thermoplastic powder making up the Xerox image and the support material of the Thermo-Fax paper, which causes the support material to adhere to the Xerox image.

(9) For microforms—unsuitable.

The Thermo-Fax process is limited to the making of eye-legible copies from original documents. *Rare, valuable, fragile, or brittle documents, or documents in which either the paper support or image might in any way be adversely affected by heat, should not be copied by the Thermo-Fax process.*

Manufacturers

The following lists are not comprehensive. No endorsement of these firms or their equipment is implied. Before making selection of equipment, the prospective purchaser should consult local equipment directories or buying guides.

Thermo-Fax copiers are manufactured by:

3M Company
2501 Hudson Road
St. Paul, Minnesota 55101

They are distributed by 3M Business Products Sales, Inc., with offices in principal cities in the United States and abroad.

Equipment

Model Number	Name	Maximum size copy (in inches)	Features
45	Secretary	8½ by 14	Without exposure compensating device.
47	Statement Machine	8½ by 14	With exposure compensating device.
50	Major	15 inches wide by any length	Without exposure compensating device.
50AFW	Major	15 inches wide by any length	With exposure compensating device.

Thermo-Fax *materials* are manufactured and distributed by the 3M Company. Other types of thermal copy papers which can be used with Thermo-Fax copiers are manufactured by the following companies:

American Stencil Manufacturing Company
4290 Holly Street
Denver, Colorado 80216

Continental Copy Products
Pacific Copy Corporation
142 Oregon Street
El Segundo, California 90245

Copy-Craft, Inc.
105 Chambers Street
New York, New York 10007

Frankel Carbon & Ribbon Company
285 Rio Grande Boulevard
Denver, Colorado 80223

Interchemical Corporation
Copying Products Division
417 East Seventh Street
Cincinnati, Ohio 45202

Labelon Corporation
10 Chapin Street
Canandaigua, New York 14424

A. P. Little, Inc.
1185 Scottsville Road
Rochester, New York 14624

Nashua Corporation
Office Copy Division
44 Franklin Street
Nashua, New Hampshire 03060

Old Town Corporation
750 Pacific Street
Brooklyn, New York 11238

Orchard Paper Company
3914 Union Boulevard
St. Louis, Missouri 63115

Perry-Sherwood Corporation
257 Park Avenue
New York, New York 10010

THE EICHNER PROCESS

The Eichner process is a variant form of thermographic copying developed in Germany by the firm of Eichner Drycopy, GMBH, in which a "thermocarbon"—a sheet coated with a heat-sensitive dye—is used as an intermediate for the formation of an image by the action of heat.

The process is dry, rapid, and inexpensive and can be used to transfer an image to a variety of supports, such as translucent or transparent materials, spirit and offset master stock, and to ordinary paper stocks of various weights and colors as circumstances may require. As is the case with other thermographic copying processes, the Eichner process is limited to the copying of texts written or printed in inks or other substances which are capable of absorbing and dissipating heat. Non-infrared absorbing materials such as most colored pencils and inks cannot be reproduced.

In making a copy of a document, a receiving sheet of plain paper is placed between a thermocarbon sheet and the document to be copied (Figure 100). Infrared radiation is then passed through the thermocarbon and the receiving sheet to the face of the document being copied where it is absorbed by the text and dissipated in the form of heat at a temperature high enough to cause the coating on the thermocarbon to soften and adhere to the receiving sheet. Copies of one-sided originals can also be made using the direct-contact method by placing the thermocarbon face down over the receiving sheet and placing the document face up over the thermocarbon (Figure 101). A disadvantage of this method lies in the fact that it is limited to copying originals which are thin enough or sufficiently transparent to infrared radiation to produce a heat-formed image. Also, the thicker the paper stock of the original, the poorer the definition of the copy will be.

Materials

The principal material used in the Eichner process is the thermocarbon sheet which is available from most suppliers in either blue or black and in standard office document sizes. Because the process can be used to transfer images to spirit masters, offset masters, clear acetate, and other supports, these materials are usually supplied in paired sets consisting of a receiving sheet and a thermocarbon.

Contrast

The contrast of Eichner process thermocarbons is high. In copying texts which are uneven, fine or weak lines tend to reproduce poorly or not at all. Copies of continuous-tone illustrations exhibit extensive losses of both highlight and shadow detail.

Resolving power

As is the case with other thermographic processes, resolving power is somewhat limited by the nature of the process itself. When copying by the method shown in Figure 100, the dissipation of heat through the thickness of the receiving sheet causes the image to be slightly fuzzy. In copying by the method shown in Figure 101, definition loss increases with the thickness of the paper stock of the original being copied. Also, fine lines are difficult to reproduce at normal exposures because they do not absorb and dissipate sufficient heat. Increasing the exposure to produce a stronger image causes broader lines to thicken and hence to close up small spaces within and between letters.

Exposure latitude

Because the contrast of the materials is relatively high, exposure latitude is fairly narrow. Slight underexposure causes breaking of fine lines, while slight overexposure causes filling of spaces within and between letters.

Speed

The response of Eichner process materials to heat is quite rapid thus permitting exposures of only a few seconds' duration.

Color sensitivity

As is the case with other thermographic processes, the term "color sensitivity" is inapplicable, because exposure is accomplished by means of heat rather than light. Most colored pencil images and inks cannot be reproduced because they do not contain substances which absorb heat.

TABLE 11
The Eichner Process
(Principal Characteristics)

1. The process is:	Wet	
	Dry	X
2. Copies can be made by the following methods:	Contact Copying	X
	Contact-Reflex Copying	X
	Optical Copying	
	Microcopying	
	Projection Printing	
3. The process is capable of producing copies that are:	Positive, from Positives	X
	Negative, from Positives	
	Positive, from Negatives	
	Negative, from Negatives	
4. The process is capable of producing intermediates or masters for subsequent edition printing by:	Diazo	X
	Offset	X
	Spirit Duplicating	X
5. The permanence of copies is:	Archival	
	Limited	
	Unknown	X *
6. The quality of copies of continuous-tone originals is:	Excellent	
	Fair	
	Poor	X
7. The reproduction of fine details (e.g., small type faces, fine lines) is:	Excellent	
	Fair	
	Poor	X
8. The contrast of copies is:	High	X
	Moderate	
	Low	

9. The ability of the process to reproduce colored lines is:	Broad	
	Limited	X
10. The paper stock used is:	Plain, Any Color	X *
	Specially Coated	
	White	
	Off-White	
11. The tendency of copies to curl is:	High	
	Noticeable	
	Low	X
12. The potential waste factor is:	Considerable	
	Moderate	X
	Low	
13. The approximate time required to make an 8½- by 11-inch copy is:	15 seconds.	
14. The materials cost per 8½- by 11-inch copy is:	2.4¢ and up.	
15. Equipment for the process ranges in price from:	$240.00 to $300.00.	

*NOTES

5. No data is available on the stability of the image-forming substances.

10. In copying by the method shown in Figure 100, a very thin receiving sheet is used to minimize definition loss. In copying by the method shown in Figure 101, image transfer can be made to a variety of different supports.

Keeping qualities

Eichner process materials stored in a cool, dry place have an indefinite shelf life.

Permanence

Although permanence is claimed for Eichner process copies, particularly if images are transferred to high-quality paper stocks, no data are available regarding the stability of the image-forming material used in the thermocarbons.

Suitability

(1) For bound volumes—unsuitable.

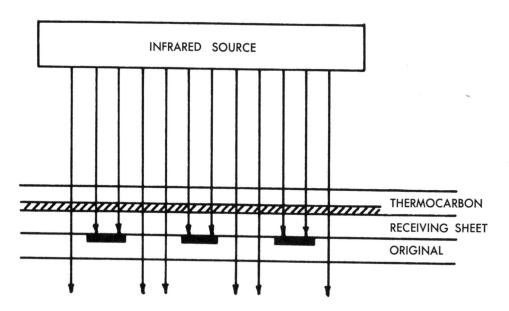

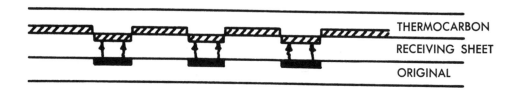

Fig. 100. Schematic diagram of contact-reflex copying with Eichner process materials.

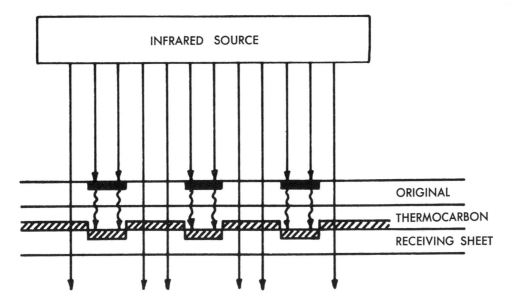

| = INFRARED RAYS | = HEAT RAYS |

Fig. 101. Schematic diagram of direct-contact copying with Eichner process materials.

Eichner process materials and equipment are, in general, limited to the copying of originals in loose-sheet form. One machine—the Ditto Master-fax—is capable of copying from pamphlets or thin bound originals.

(2) For newspaper files—unsuitable.

Only portions of newspaper pages in loose-sheet form up to a maximum size of 8½ by 14 inches can be copied.

(3) For typescripts—limited.

Typescripts with even impressions reproduce satisfactorily, but uneven originals may show marked breaking and filling of fine or weak lines and small spaces. Typescripts in non-infrared absorbing inks cannot be reproduced. Lack of sharpness in carbon copies is accentuated in Eichner process copies.

(4) For manuscripts—limited.

Manuscripts exhibiting fine or weak lines do not reproduce well and manuscripts written in non-infrared absorbing materials do not reproduce at all.

(5) For continuous-tone originals—unsuitable.

The high contrast of Eichner process materials causes extensive losses of tonal gradation in copies of continuous-tone originals.

(6) For maps—limited.

The relatively low resolution of Eichner process copies and the inability of the process to record lines printed in most colored inks severely limit its ability to reproduce maps.

(7) For card files—limited.

While images can be transferred to card-weight stock, small type faces in printed cards show a definition loss, unevenly typed originals do not reproduce well, and non-infrared absorbing inks do not reproduce at all.

(8) For copies made by other processes—limited.

The high contrast of the process, the relatively low resolution of copies, and the inability of the process to record non-infrared absorbing (e.g., dye) images limit its ability to reproduce copies made by other processes.

(9) For microforms—unsuitable.

The Eichner process is limited to the making of eye-legible copies. *Rare, valuable, fragile, or brittle documents, or documents in which either the paper support or image might in any way be adversely affected by heat, should not be copied by the Eichner process.*

Manufacturers

Eichner process equipment, under a variety of trade names (shown at the right of the respective manufacturers' names in the following list), is available from the following companies. This list is not comprehensive. No endorsement of these firms or their equipment is implied. Before making selection of equipment, the prospective purchaser should consult local equipment directories or buying guides.

ABM Dryfax Corporation   "Dryfax"
387 Park Avenue, South
New York, New York 10016

Addo-fax   "Addo-fax"
300 Park Avenue
New York, New York 10022

Columbia Ribbon and Carbon   "Transofax"
Manufacturing Company, Inc.
Glen Cove, New York 11542

Ditto, Inc.   "Masterfax"
6800 McCormick Road
Chicago, Illinois 60645

Viewlex, Inc.   "Viewfax"
Holbrook, Long Island,
New York 11741

THE EKTAFAX PROCESS

The Ektafax process is a thermographic process which makes possible the making of multiple copies of documents on plain paper or on other materials. It is based on heat-induced chemical reactions in a polymeric substance, which, in company with a dye, is coated on an intermediate sheet called a master.

The steps entailed in making a copy are as follows:

(1) A master is placed with its coated side in contact with the document to be copied.

(2) The two sheets are passed through a thermographic exposing unit such as a Thermo-Fax "Secretary" office copier. The heat absorbed by the text causes a chemical change in the polymer in the text areas.

(3) The master is then placed in contact with a sheet of plain paper.

(4) These two sheets are then passed through a device called an Ektafax Transfer Unit, in which heat and considerable pressure cause some of the dye in the text area of the master to transfer to the receptor sheet.

(5) The copy and master are separated and the master placed in contact with a second receptor sheet to make a second copy. Up to a dozen legible copies can be made from a good-quality original.

Materials

The principal materials used with the Ektafax process are the masters, of which two types are available: "K" masters for the making of multiple copies, and "E" masters for single copies. When successive copies are made from "K" masters, the image becomes progressively lighter as the dye in the master becomes used up. With the "E" master, only a single copy can be made, but the "E" master possesses the unusual property of being able to rejuvenate itself. After a period of "rest," an "E" master can be re-used to copy an entirely different original. This process can be repeated about a dozen times. Although an Ektafax image can be transferred to plain paper, a stock especially well suited for the process is supplied under the name of Ektafax Copy paper. This is a highly calendered paper stock which makes it possible to get the maximum number of copies from "K" masters. Both types of masters and the copy paper are supplied in a number of standard paper and card sizes up to 8½ by 14 inches. In addition, an offset-master stock is also supplied. Runs of up to 10,000 copies are claimed for these masters.

The optimum machine temperature for using "E" and "K" masters differs somewhat—147° F. for the former and 158° for the latter, ±3°. Some temperature latitude is important when using "K" masters because the successive feeding of sheets of copy paper which are at room temperature tends to cool the rollers slightly. If, at the time of installation, the Ektafax Transfer Unit is set at the temperature for "K" masters, "E" masters can also be used, but the rejuvenation period becomes fairly long. If the rejuvenation period is not long enough, a "ghost" image of the document which was copied when the master was previously used will appear on the new copy. If extensive use of "E" masters is required, the thermostat setting on the Ektafax Transfer Unit can be set to the lower temperature.

Contrast

The contrast of Ektafax copies is also affected by the thermostat setting of the machine. In general, the higher the temperature, the greater the contrast. If the temperature setting is too high, contrast will be strong and some background tone will appear before the maximum number of copies is obtained. If the temperature is too low, the copies will be grayish and lacking in contrast, and fewer copies will be obtained from a single "K" master. Because of the difference in operating temperature for "E" and "K" masters, "E" masters will have greater contrast than "K" masters at any given setting.

Ektafax copies produced within acceptable temperature limits show a considerable increase in contrast over that of the original. Any unevenness in the printing or the typing of the original being copied becomes emphasized in the copy. Bold lines reproduce strongly, while faint lines appear fainter on the copy or may not reproduce at all. Because of the effect of temperature on contrast, this effect is more pronounced when using "E" masters than it is with "K" masters.

In copying continuous-tone originals, the increase in contrast causes the tone scale to become exaggerated with a consequent loss of both highlight and shadow detail. This effect also, at any given temperature setting, is more marked when "E" masters are used.

Resolving power

"K" masters exposed at optimum settings are capable of a maximum resolution of approximately 5 lines per millimeter. "E" masters, because of their higher contrast, show a greater degree of breaking and filling of fine lines and spaces which limits resolving power to a maximum of approximately 3 lines per millimeter.

Exposure latitude

As with most high contrast, heat-sensitive materials, the exposure latitude of Ektafax masters is limited, but the design of thermal exposing units takes this factor into account by providing adequate controls for slight changes in exposure. The length of time required for an 11-inch document to pass through a Thermo-Fax Model 45 copier at the slowest usable setting is approximately 4 seconds, and at the fastest setting, 2 seconds. This range of 2 seconds is divided, however, into ten settings on the exposure dial with ample room for in-between settings as well. Exposure latitude, using "K" masters, for small and delicately structured type faces is slightly greater than ± one full interval on the exposure dial. With larger faces having greater evenness of line width, exposure latitude is ± approximately three full intervals. With "E" masters, exposure latitude is considerably narrower, ranging from ± one-half of an interval to ± two full intervals.

While acceptable copies can be made with "K" masters over a wider range of settings, exposure settings must be close to optimum if the maximum number of copies is to be obtained from each "K" master.

Speed

The response of Ektafax materials to heat is very rapid. "E" masters are slightly slower than "K" masters but exposure times for 8½- by 11-inch originals with either type are on the order of five seconds or less.

TABLE 12
The Ektafax Process
(Principal Characteristics)

1. The process is:	Wet	
	Dry	X
2. Copies can be made by the following methods:	Contact Copying	
	Contact-Reflex Copying	X
	Optical Copying	
	Microcopying	
	Projection Printing	
3. The process is capable of producing copies that are:	Positive, from Positives	X
	Negative, from Positives	
	Positive, from Negatives	
	Negative, from Negatives	X
4. The process is capable of producing intermediates or masters for subsequent edition printing by:	Diazo	X
	Offset	X
	Spirit Duplicating	
5. The permanence of copies is:	Archival	X *
	Limited	
	Unknown	
6. The quality of copies of continuous-tone originals is:	Excellent	
	Fair	
	Poor	X
7. The reproduction of fine details (e.g., small type faces, fine lines) is:	Excellent	
	Fair	X
	Poor	
8. The contrast of copies is:	High	X
	Moderate	
	Low	

9. The ability of the process to reproduce colored lines is:	Broad		
	Limited		X
10. The paper stock used is:	Plain, Any Color		X *
	Specially Coated		
	White		
	Off-White		
11. The tendency of copies to curl is:	High		
	Noticeable		
	Low		X
12. The potential waste factor is:	Considerable		
	Moderate		
	Low		X
13. The approximate time required to make an 8½- by 11-inch copy is:	First copy—25 seconds. Additional copies—15 seconds each.		
14. The materials cost per 8½- by 11-inch copy is:	Single copies—2¼¢. Multiple copies—As low as 2¢ each.		
15. Equipment for the process is priced at:	$157.50.* Can also be rented for $8.00 per month.		

16. Other characteristics: Partially used "K" masters can be stored and re-run at a later time.

*NOTES

5. Ektafax copies have archival permanence if transferred to archival-quality paper stocks.

10. Images can also be transferred to light-weight stocks such as onion skin, to card stocks up to approximately 0.020 inch in thickness, to translucent stock for diazo printing, or to transparent stock for use on an overhead projector. For maximum number of copies from "K" masters, highly calendered paper stock should be used.

15. Does not include the cost of thermographic copier (from $379.00 to $429.00 for outright purchase, or $35.00 per month rental.)

Color sensitivity

Since most colored lines and texts are produced with inks which do not absorb infrared radiation, they cannot be reproduced by the Ektafax process. However, when copying texts which are printed on paper stocks of different colors, this lack of response to color can work to the user's advantage since no adjustment of the exposure setting of the thermographic unit needs to be made to compensate for the color differences.

Keeping qualities

According to the manufacturer, the shelf life of Ektafax materials is unlimited.

Permanence

The manufacturer states that Ektafax copies are unaffected by heat and light and will last as long as the paper they are printed on.

Other characteristics

Since an image from an Ektafax master can be transferred to a variety of different supports, the process can be used to make transparencies for overhead projectors, tissue-weight copies, color-coded copies, or masters for subsequent diazo printing. For maximum sharpness in diazo printing, reverse reading images can be produced simply by turning the master over so that the coated side is facing up and the backing side is in contact with the surface of the document to be copied. Images can also be readily transferred to card stock. The process thus lends itself to the reproduction of sets of library catalog cards from typed or printed originals.

Another characteristic of Ektafax "K" masters is that the image does not deteriorate on standing. If, for example, only three copies of a document are needed at a given time but more may be required later, the master can be filed and additional copies made as needed at some future time.

If two-sided originals are being copied, two-sided copies can be made by successively preparing masters of each side and then placing the masters on each side of a sheet of copy paper and running the three sheets through the Ektafax Transfer Unit at one time.

Another characteristic of the Ektafax image, relatively unusual in copying processes, is that the image can be erased to about the same degree that a typewritten image can be erased. If the receptor sheet used is an erasable bond, the image can be erased quite easily.

If an Ektafax copy should become torn or if Ektafax copies are used for paste-ups, clear cellulose tape can be used but should be applied to the backs of copies only. If the tape is applied to the surface of the Ektafax image, the image will gradually bleed into the adhesive coating and become illegible.

Suitability

(1) For bound volumes—unsuitable.

There is no Ektafax equipment currently on the market with which it is possible to make copies of pages from bound volumes.

(2) For newspaper files—limited.

Clippings up to 8½ by 14 inches in size reproduce well, provided that the text is not printed with a colored dye-based ink or that such an ink is not used to form a colored background for white lettering.

(3) For typescripts—generally suitable.

Ribbon copies or good-quality carbon copies are heightened in contrast but usually copy well. Typescripts made with dye-colored ribbons cannot be reproduced. Uneven ribbon copies or carbons yield copies which accentuate the unevenness.

(4) For manuscripts—limited.

Manuscripts written with infrared absorbing inks or pencil exhibiting fairly uniform line width and density can be reproduced satisfactorily. Manuscripts written with colored ink or pencil images which do not absorb infrared cannot be reproduced. Because of the relatively high contrast of the process, manuscripts exhibiting weak or uneven line width and density may not reproduce legibly.

(5) For continuous-tone originals—unsuitable.

The high contrast of the process exaggerates the tone scale of continuous-tone subjects. Copies exhibit a substantial loss of both highlight and shadow detail. If the contrast of the original is low, the results are recognizable but are not of good quality.

(6) For maps—limited.

Black-and-white maps up to 8½ by 14 inches in size can be reproduced if the line width and type size employed are within the resolving-power limitations of the process. Maps having backgrounds printed in color with inks that do not absorb infrared will reproduce in black-and-white outline. If map lines or legends are printed in non-infrared absorbing inks, they will not reproduce.

(7) For card files—generally suitable.

Since the Ektafax image can readily be transferred to card stocks, the process is quite suitable for the production or duplication of card files from printed or typewritten originals, especially if a number of copies from each original is required. Printed cards such as Library of Congress catalog cards and proof slips reproduce well in moderate quantities (usually 4 to 5 copies) depending upon the type of card stock used and the user's judgment of acceptable image quality. Similar results can be obtained from typewritten cards if the typed image is sharp and even. Variations in the strength of individual letters caused by uneven typing pressure on manual machines are accentuated in the copies. Reproductions of such cards are often unsightly or even illegible. Handwritten cards written with non-infrared absorbing inks will not reproduce.

(8) For copies made by other processes—limited.

The principal limitations in the use of the Ektafax process for reproducing copies made by other processes are its inability to reproduce non-infrared absorbing images, its resolving power limitations, and its relatively high contrast. The Ektafax process is incapable of making copies from Ektafax copies, or from copies made by Thermo-Fax, the Eichner process, or spirit-duplicated copies. It is also limited in its ability to reproduce diazo copies. Since most photocopies are fairly high in contrast, the added contrast introduced in Ektafax copying frequently causes breaking and filling of fine lines and spaces.

(9) For microforms—unsuitable.

The Ektafax process is limited to the making of eye-legible copies.

Rare, valuable, fragile, or brittle documents, or documents in which either the paper support or image might in any way be adversely affected by heat, should not be copied by the Ektafax process.

Manufacturers

Exposing units are manufactured by the 3M Company, 2501 Hudson Road, St. Paul, Minnesota 55101, and are distributed by 3M Business Products Sales, Inc., both in this country and abroad. The transfer unit is manufactured by and is available through offices of the Recordak Co., Business Systems Markets Division of the Eastman Kodak Company, 343 State Street, Rochester, New York 14608.

Equipment

Exposing Units

Thermo-Fax "Secretary" Model 45
(Without exposure compensating device)

Thermo-Fax "Secretary" Model 47
(With exposure compensating device)

Transfer Unit

Ektafax Transfer Unit Model 10

ELECTROSTATIC PROCESSES

One of the most radical departures from conventional silver halide photocopying was the development of electrophotographic methods for the formation of an image. These methods are based on physical and electrical, rather than on chemical, phenomena. The underlying principles of electrophotography are those of photoconductivity and electrostatics.

Electrostatic attraction is the familiar phenomenon which occurs when two appropriate substances are rubbed together to produce a static charge capable of attracting small objects the way a magnet attracts metal filings. In earlier times, electrostatic attraction was thought to be a form of magnetism.

Photoconductors may be briefly described as substances which become more conductive in the light than they are in the dark. If a sheet of material coated with a photoconductive substance is given a uniform electrostatic charge in the dark and is then exposed through a lens to the projected image of a document, light reflected from the white background areas of the document causes the electrostatic charge in the corresponding areas of the photoconductive surface to dissipate. However, in the image areas, where no light has been received, the charge remains, creating what is called an *electrostatic latent image*. If the photoconductive surface is then cascaded with suitable, finely divided, black powder, the powder will cling to the image areas by electrostatic attraction, thus producing a visible image. To render this powder image usable in the form of a copy, it must either be transferred to or formed directly on a sheet of paper or other suitable support where it can be made stable by fusing it to the support through the application of heat, vapor, or solvents.

There are two electrophotographic processes in wide use for document reproduction purposes which, although based on essentially the same principles, differ in the materials and methods used. The first of these—*xerography* (from the Greek words *xeros,* dry, and *graphein,* to write)—employs a selenium coating on a metal plate as the photoconductor. The image formed on this plate is then transferred to a sheet of plain paper. The second—*Electrofax*—employs as the photoconductor a thin layer of zinc oxide coated on the paper which becomes the copy. Xerography may be thus described as *transfer* electrophotography and Electrofax as *direct* electrophotography.

XEROGRAPHY

There are five steps entailed in the making of a xerographic copy (Figure 102):

(1) Plate charging: The photoconductive selenium plate or drum is exposed to a corona discharge in the dark which imparts a uniform electrostatic charge to its surface.

(2) Exposure: The photoconductive surface is exposed through a lens to the projected image of a document. Light from the white background areas dissipates the charge, but, in the image areas, the charge remains.

(3) Development: A black powder called the developer, consisting of carrier and toner particles, is cascaded over the photoconductive surface where the toner particles adhere by electrostatic attraction to the image areas.

(4) Image transfer: A sheet of paper is placed over the photoconductive surface and the toner image is transferred to it by imparting an electrical charge of the opposite polarity to the paper surface.

(5) Fusing: The toner image is fused to the paper by the application of heat.

Because all of the toner does not transfer to the paper, a sixth step—the cleaning off of residual toner—must be done before the photoconductive surface can again be used.

In the first xerographic copiers which appeared on the market in 1950 and which are still used, principally for the production of offset plates, the successive steps were performed manually by the operator. In various types of xerographic copiers which have appeared since then, all of the steps have been completely automated.

Materials

Three materials are employed in xerographic copying:

(1) The selenium photoconductor;

(2) The toner; and

(3) The paper or other support to which the toner image is transferred.

While the selenium coating is reusable, it has been classed as a material because (a) its characteristics govern, to a large extent, the characteristics of xerographic copies, and (b) it has a fairly long but nonetheless limited life and must be replaced from time to time. Its surface is quite delicate and care must be exercised to ensure that no foreign objects or finger marks from careless handling mar its surface.

The toner is made up of two components—the toner particles themselves and much larger *carrier* particles, which are used to give the toner particles a charge opposite to that of the latent image, thus improving the electrostatic attraction between the image and the toner.

The paper to which xerographic images are most commonly transferred is a bond-weight, white stock. However, other supports are used including most of the papers in common use, such as light-weight, card-weight, or translucent stocks, and 100 percent rag or other durable stocks where permanence is desired. In addition, xerographic images can be transferred to spirit masters, paper or metal offset masters, or transparent plastic stocks

Contrast

While the relative contrast of xerographic copies is high, visual contrast is moderate. Lines of text reproduce as a grayish black. Ordinarily, the relative contrast of a process can be most readily seen by comparing a copy of a continuous-tone illustration with the original. This is not possible with most xerographic copies, because the photoconductive coating does not have the ability to hold an electrostatic charge over a broad area and thus the tonal areas making up such illustrations record in outline only. Continuous-tone copies can be made on Xerox standard equipment by means of an accessory developing unit called a *tone tray*. With the Model 914 and Model 813 copiers, some improvement in copies of continuous-tone illustrations or solid areas can be accomplished by interposing an acetate half-tone screen between the original and the exposing surface.

Resolving power

Since the xerographic process employs an optical method, the factors affecting image sharpness are the quality of the optical system employed and the size of the toner particles used to form the image. In commercially available xerographic equipment, these factors have been taken into account to ensure optimum image sharpness. Eye-legible copies made directly from originals or by projection printing from microtransparencies made at relatively high reduction ratios show excellent resolution characteristics well in excess of 100 lines per inch. The resolution obtained in prototype microxerographic recording equipment (see "Variations on the xerographic process," page 152) is reported to be approximately 130 lines per millimeter.

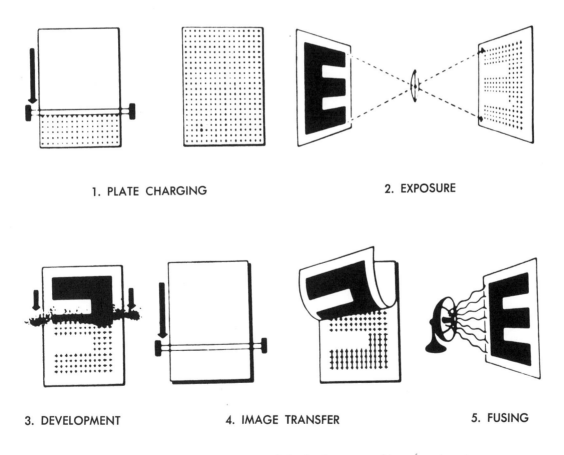

1. PLATE CHARGING

2. EXPOSURE

3. DEVELOPMENT

4. IMAGE TRANSFER

5. FUSING

Fig. 102. Schematic representation of the basic xerographic processing steps.

TABLE 13
THE XEROGRAPHY PROCESS
(Principal Characteristics)

1. The process is:	Wet	
	Dry	X
2. Copies can be made by the following methods:	Contact Copying	
	Contact-Reflex Copying	
	Optical Copying	X
	Microcopying	X
	Projection Printing	X
3. The process is capable of producing copies that are:	Positive, from Positives	X
	Negative, from Positives	
	Positive, from Negatives	X
	Negative, from Negatives	
4. The process is capable of producing intermediates or masters for subsequent edition printing by:	Diazo	X
	Offset	X
	Spirit Duplicating	
5. The permanence of copies is:	Archival	X *
	Limited	
	Unknown	
6. The quality of copies of continuous-tone originals is:	Excellent	
	Fair	
	Poor	X *
7. The reproduction of fine details (e.g., small type faces, fine lines) is:	Excellent	X
	Fair	
	Poor	
8. The contrast of copies is:	High	X *
	Moderate	
	Low	

9. The ability of the process to reproduce colored lines is:	Broad	X
	Limited	
10. The paper stock used is:	Plain, Any Color	X
	Specially Coated	
	White	
	Off-White	
11. The tendency of copies to curl is:	High	
	Noticeable	
	Low	X
12. The potential waste factor is:	Considerable	
	Moderate	
	Low	X
13. The approximate time required to make an 8½- by 11-inch copy is:	1½ seconds and up.*	
Per linear foot (5 inches and up in width) is:	4 seconds.	
14. The materials cost per 8½- by 11-inch copy is:	About 1¢ and up.*	
Per linear foot (11 inches in width) is:	About 2¢ (Copyflo).	
15. Equipment for the process is priced at:	See "Xerographic equipment," page 156.	

*NOTES

5. If paper having archival permanence is used.
6. The inability of most xerographic copiers to hold an electrostatic charge over an area makes for poor-quality continuous-tone copies. Some improvement can be effected by using a special dot-pattern screen supplied by the Xerox Corporation. Better results are obtained with Xerox standard equipment if a special developing unit accessory called a "Tone tray" is used.

8. Although the maximum density of Xerox images is a tone of gray well below the maximum black of silver halide photocopies, the tone scale is nonetheless quite short.
13. Depending on the type of Xerox equipment used.
14. Depending on the type of Xerox equipment used and the volume of copying.

Exposure latitude

The exposure latitude of the xerographic process is fairly broad. Xerographic copiers which operate at a fixed exposure setting produce satisfactory copies from originals which vary widely in their reflectance. Xerographic microfilm enlargers produce satisfactory hard copy over a broad range of densities.

Speed

The xerographic process has ample speed for copying directly from originals, for projection printing, and for microrecording.

Color sensitivity

Lines of most colors record quite strongly on xerographic copies, but light blues tend to be faint. Very pale blue lines may not record at all. This can sometimes be used to advantage in making annotations on originals which are not wanted on copies.

Copies of texts on colored paper stocks will vary in quality depending on the particular color and the degree of color saturation. Texts on pale blue paper record without noticeable background tone. Background tone is strongest in shades containing red such as orange, goldenrod, salmon, and pink. The fact that the photoconductive coating does not hold a charge over a broad area is an advantage in copying pastel shades since it greatly reduces the amount of background tone that otherwise would be present. This phenomenon is also quite noticeable in copying texts on papers having a high color saturation, but texts against backgrounds in the orange-red region reproduce only faintly or not at all.

Keeping qualities

All of the materials used in the xerographic process are quite stable and, if kept under reasonable storage conditions, should have an indefinite shelf life.

Variations of the xerographic process

Microxerography. The use of xerography for microphotography of documents has been under investigation for some time by the Micro-Data division of the Bell and Howell Corporation under a grant from the Council on Library Resources. The purpose of this investigation was to develop a camera which, by employing xerography, would make possible the rapid, inexpensive, and on-site production of microcards or microfiche of research materials without the delays attendant upon laboratory processing.

At the present time, a prototype camera has been built and is now undergoing field testing at the John Crerar Library in Chicago. This machine, known as *Midax,* is capable of copying pages from bound volumes, including half-tones, at a fixed reduction ratio of 1:12 on either a 3- by 5-inch transparent film or opaque card. At this reduction ratio, the capacity of a film or card is limited to 12 images. A second camera, however, is now being designed which will operate at a reduction ratio of 1:20. Approximately 30 seconds is required to produce each microxerographic image.

Of particular importance is the fact that the xerographic process makes it possible to add images at any time, up to the capacity of the film sheet or card. For example, a four-page article may be copied at one time and an eight-page article added to the same film at another time. The design of the equipment is such that the film can be easily positioned for the recording of additional images at any desired location on its surface.

The resolving power of microxerographic images produced with the prototype camera is approximately 130 lines per millimeter.

LDX (long distance xerography). LDX is a facsimile transmission system which employs xerography as the recording medium. In the LDX system, three components are employed—a transmitter, a receiver, and a transmission facility which may be a leased telephone line, a coaxial cable or a microwave system.

In the transmitter, a very small spot of light from a cathode ray tube is focused on the document to be copied where it rapidly scans across the face of the document in a successive series of very fine lines. As this light beam passes alternately over the letters of the text and the spaces between the letters, differences in the reflectance of the light occur. These different intensities of light are converted into electrical impulses of different strengths which are then transmitted to the receiving unit. The receiving unit also employs a cathode ray tube which projects a small spot of light onto an electrostatically charged selenium drum. The function of the receiving unit is to reconvert the electrical impulses of different strengths into variations in the intensity of the light spot focused on the selenium drum. As this light spot traverses the surface of the drum in the same fashion in which the scanner spot traversed the original document, variations in light intensity result in variations in exposure to form a latent electrostatic image which can then be developed, transferred to a sheet of paper, and fused by conventional xerographic techniques.

The speed of transmission and the quality of the copies is related. At a speed of 3½ letter-size (8½ by 11 inches) documents per minute, resolution is approximately 250 lines per inch. At a speed of 16 letter-size documents per minute, the resolution is approximately 100 lines per inch. Copies made by the receiving unit may be either on ordinary paper or paper offset mats. As with other types of xerographic equipment, low unit costs can only be obtained if the volume of copying is quite high.

The LDX transmitter is capable of handling graphic materials in loose-sheet form in widths up to 8½ inches and lengths of up to 5 feet. At the present time, the equipment is not capable of transmitting images from bound materials or from microforms.

Xerox Copyflo. There are four Xerox Copyflo printers, two of which produce hard copy from roll-form microtransparencies, one which copies only from originals, and one which is capable of both functions. The Copyflo 11 Model 1 is an automatic continuous enlarger widely used for reproducing research materials. It produces hard copy on rolls of paper stock from either 16 or 35 mm. roll film. Prints can be produced on paper stock ranging in width from 4½ to 18 inches. The operating speed of the machine is 20 linear feet per minute. Ten magnification ratios may be used in enlarging from 35 mm. film—7, 7½, 8½, 9, 9½, 11, 12, 13, 14, and 15. Five additional magnification ratios—17, 18, 19, 22, and 24—may be used for enlarging from 16 mm. film. Copyflo prints can be made on ordinary bond paper, translucent stock, card stock, 100 percent rag stock, and offset masters.

It is possible with the Copyflo 11 Model 1 to make positive enlargements from positive microtransparencies by changing the polarity of the electrostatic charge and by using a developer which has carrier particles of the opposite electric potential. Because of the time and costs entailed in changing the printer over from a negative-positive to a positive-positive operation, the usual procedure is to make a duplicate negative film from the positive and print from that.

Detailed information on the preparation of microtransparencies for Copyflo printing is given in the section entitled "Eye-legible copies from microforms," pages 287–94.

Permanence

The toner particles which form the image are quite stable. If the image is properly fused to a high-quality paper support, such copies would have archival permanence.

Suitability

See list of equipment, page 156.

(1) For bound volumes—generally suitable.

Pages from bound volumes up to 9 by 14 inches in size can be copied on the Xerox 914 Copier. Smaller volumes can often be copied two pages at a time. The depth of field of the lens on the 914 Copier is relatively small and may make the copying of tightly bound volumes having narrow inner margins difficult or in some cases impossible.

(2) For newspaper files—limited.

Clippings or portions of newspaper pages can be copied on the Xerox 813 and 914 Copiers. While entire pages of newspapers could be copied on the Xerox 1860 Copier, the limited demand for this type versus the high rental cost of the unit would make this impracticable.

(3) For typescripts—suitable.

Both the 813 and 914 Copiers were designed principally for the copying of office records in which typewritten materials are a commonplace. Such materials can also be copied with either the Number One or Number Four Cameras and processing equipment.

(4) For manuscripts—generally suitable.

Manuscripts written in pencil or ink generally reproduce satisfactorily, but the weakness of the xerographic process in reproducing pale blues may make it impossible to reproduce manuscripts written in light blue ink.

(5) For continuous-tone originals—limited.

Most xerographic equipment is incapable of reproducing continuous-tone originals except in outline. A slight improvement in tone quality can be achieved with the 813 and 914 Copiers if a special screen supplied by the Xerox Corporation is used. Results of better quality can be obtained with the Number One or the Number Four Cameras if the accessory tone tray is used in processing.

(6) For maps—limited.

Maps up to 9 by 14 inches in size can be copied on the 914 Copier. Some colored maps can be reproduced, but maps having areas which are orange or orange-red may not reproduce. Light blue lines such as are used in coast and geodetic survey maps to indicate ocean depths, or the blue lines used on land maps to indicate rivers, lakes, and canals may not reproduce. While large maps could be reproduced on the 1860 Copier, the volume of map reproduction would have to be very high to justify the rental cost of the equipment.

(7) For card files—suitable.

There are a number of ways in which card files can be reproduced with xerographic equipment. Direct card-to-card reproduction can be done with the 914 Copier; cards can be reproduced singly or in groups of 4, 6, 8, or more via microfilm and Copyflo printing; larger cards (e.g., 4 by 6 inches) can be reproduced at a smaller size (e.g., 3 by 5 inches) via microfilm and Copyflo printing; editions of cards can be produced xerographically by copying them on offset mats, by using the Number One or Number Four Camera, or the 813 or 914 Copier, or by producing offset mats from microfilm by Copyflo printing. Book catalogs of card files can also be made by shingling the cards in columns, microfilming them, and printing offset mats by Copyflo from the microfilm.

(8) For copies made by other processes—generally suitable.

Copies made by most other reproduction processes reproduce satisfactorily. The one exception to this is found in negative originals which are fairly dense and finely detailed such as blue-prints, stabilization-process negatives, or negative photostats.

(9) For microforms:

(a) Camera recording—limited.

The microxerographic recording method described under "Variations of the xerographic process" is an experimental development which is not yet commercially available.

(b) Duplicating—unsuitable.

No xerographic equipment for roll-to-roll or sheet-to-sheet duplicating has thus far been developed.

(c) Eye-legible copies from microforms —suitable.

Except for the weakness of the xerographic process in reproducing continuous-tone illustrations, inexpensive, high-quality hard copy can be made from roll microforms by means of Copyflo equipment, the 1824 Printer, and a newly developed experimental printer for automatically producing hard copy from microfiches.

Catalog card reproduction

Where the volume of catalog card reproduction is large, a combination of xerography and offset printing can be used to advantage. A typical system employs the Xerox Number One Camera and a jig having swatches of double-coated pressure sensitive tape placed so that four 3- by 5-inch (75 by 125 mm.) cards can be positioned in a 5- by 12-inch area. The cards must be presorted before copying according to the number of copies to be made. The cards are then copied and the image transferred to a paper offset master from which the desired number of copies can be made on 5- by 12-inch pre-drilled card stock.

Card reproduction can also be done in relatively small amounts on the Xerox 914 Copier. To handle card stock as thick as 0.10 inches, adjustments must be made to the paper-feeding mechanism. Also, images on card stock will not fuse satisfactorily because of the thickness of the stock, unless the fusing temperature setting is raised. For 914 Copying, a special card stock, available from library supply houses, is used on which four cards can be copied at a time and which is perforated and pre-drilled (Figure 103). Four originals (of proof sheets, printed cards, typewritten cards) are then placed on the scanning glass of the 914, and

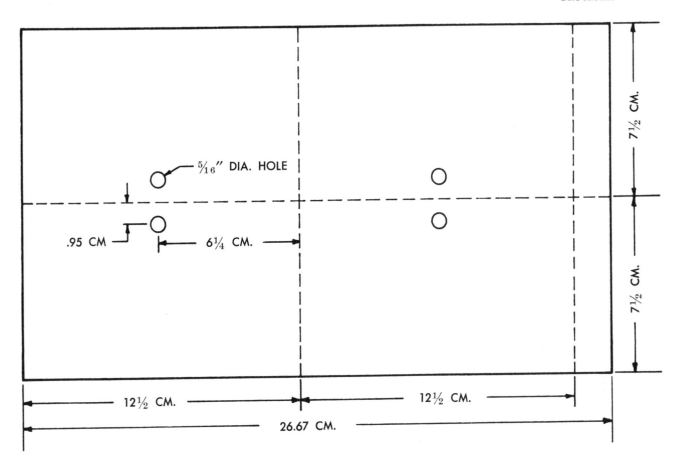

Fig. 103. Layout of perforated and pre-drilled stock for card reproduction on the Xerox 914 Copier.

the machine is set for the desired number of copies. The four-card sheets are then separated along the perforated lines. As is shown in Figure 103, perforations are at the edges and bottom of the cards leaving the top edge true.

Where a large volume of card copying is to be done—several hundred thousand or more per year —printing by Copyflo can be used to advantage. There are a number of special requirements for card reproduction by Copyflo. In the first place, the cards must be precisely positioned for microfilming. To eliminate shadow lines around the edges of the card and the hole, a plexiglass jig should be used with a subsurface illuminator. To take advantage of the speed of automatic electronic cutters, a cutting mark should be permanently fixed to the jig and filmed with each exposure. To eliminate black frame lines between frames which could trip the cutter, the frame

spacing on the camera should be adjusted so that there is a slight overlap between the frames and no clear space. The cards to be reproduced are pre-selected in accordance with the number of copies that must be made and an equivalent number of frames are exposed. For example, if seven cards are to be reproduced, seven successive exposures are made.

Since the cost of Copyflo printing is based on machine running time, it would be wasteful to run a single web of five-inch stock. Two laboratories using Copyflo for card reproduction have each solved this problem in a different way. One films two cards at a time side by side and prints on a 10-inch web of card stock. The other films on 16 mm. film and simultaneously prints two rolls of 16 mm. film on two parallel webs of five-inch paper. The former system requires a collating operation after cutting while the latter does not.

An additional fusing element must be added to the Copyflo printer to fuse images on card stock. While the card stock is still warm from fusing, it is immediately fed through the automatic cutter. This eliminates bow in the cards caused by their being in roll form and which would remain if the card stock was allowed to cool. Following this first cut to separate the cards, they are guillotined to an exact height of 75 mm. Cards printed side by side on 10-inch stock are than separated. The final step is the drilling of the tray rod hole.

Detailed descriptions of the two methods mentioned are given in items 63 and 84 in the Bibliography.

Manufacturer

Xerographic equipment is manufactured by:
Xerox Corporation
Rochester, New York 14603

Equipment

A number of types of xerographic equipment have been developed for different purposes. The original xerographic copying system, which is still widely used, particularly for making offset plates, consists of two different types of cameras, a processing unit, and two types of fusers.

Camera Number One—This camera is a fixed-focus optical copier employing a wide-angle lens operating at 100 percent of original size. The maximum image size is 8½ by 13 inches.

Camera Number Four—This unit is a small process-type camera which offers reduction or enlargement of image size over a range of from 50 percent to 150 percent.

Both Camera Number One and Camera Number Four employ a selenium plate mounted in a holder equipped with a dark slide. These holders are very similar in appearance and function to the film holders used for photography with sheets of silver sensitized film.

Processor D—The Model D Processor includes all equipment necessary for charging xerographic plates, developing the electrostatic image, and transferring it to ordinary paper, offset masters, or other supports.

Heat fuser—The heat fuser consists of an enclosure containing a heating element and a drawer-type tray on which processed paper copies or offset masters are placed for fusing the image.

Vapor fuser—The vapor fuser consists of a compartment which forms a vapor chamber and a drawer in which copies are placed for fusing. Vapor fusing is used when copies are being made on plastic, acetate, or other substances which cannot withstand heat fusing.

Tone tray—The tone tray is an accessory device used when continuous-tone subjects or subjects containing large solid areas are being copied.

With the foregoing equipment, all of the steps in the process—charging the plate, exposing, cascading powder particles over the plate to develop the latent image, positioning the paper or offset master for image transfer, and fusing—are carried out by hand. In all other types of xerographic equipment, a selenium-coated drum rather than a plate is used and all of the steps in the process are automated.

914 Copier—The 914 Copier is a completely automated optical device which is capable of making copies up to 9 by 14 inches at 100 percent of original size from either loose-sheet or bound materials at a maxium rate of seven copies per minute. It can also be used to make offset masters, translucencies for diazo printing, or copies on card stock, such as library catalog cards.

813 Copier—The 813 Copier is considerably smaller than the 914 Copier and is limited to the making of copies from loose-sheet originals. The maximum image area is 8½ by 13 inches and copies are reduced approximately 6 percent from original size. Copies are produced at a rate of approximately five per minute.

1824 Printer—The 1824 Printer is a completely automated printer producing hard copy from microtransparencies either in rolls or mounted in aperture cards. The unit was designed for the reproduction of 35 mm. microtransparencies of engineering drawings and operates at a fixed magnification ratio of 14.5:1. A variant model known as the *Universal Input Model* is also capable of reproducing from jacketed film or microfiches up to 5 by 8 inches in size. The 1824 Printer is not a *reader*-printer since the screen on which the projected image of a microtransparency appears is only about 4 by 4½ inches.

Copyflo 11 Continuous Printers—

(a) The Copyflo 11 Model 1 is a microfilm enlarger for 16 or 35 mm. film which produces a roll of enlarged prints from a roll of film at a speed of 20 feet per minute. The maximum paper width the machine will accept is 12 inches, but the maximum image width is 11 inches. From 35 mm. film, ten different magnifications are possible within a range of from 7X to 15X. With 16 mm. film, five additional magnifications—17X, 18X, 19X, 22X, and 24X—may be used. Copyflo prints can be made on a variety of paper stocks including bond papers of different weights, translucent stock, offset masters, card stock, and 100 percent rag stock.

(b) The *Copyflo 11 Model 2* is a copier—not an enlarger—which produces copies of original documents at a rate of 20 paper feet per minute. Originals as large as 24 inches wide can be copied. The maximum print width is 11 inches. The size of the image is controllable over a continuous range from 46 percent reduction to 200 percent enlargement.

(c) The *Copyflo 11 Model 3* is a combination unit which can be used either as a microfilm enlarger or a copier for originals.

(d) The *Copyflo 24 C Continuous Printer* is similar in operation to the Copyflo 11 Model 1, but was designed specifically for the making of 18- by 24-inch prints from microtransparencies of engineering drawings mounted in aperture cards.

(e) The *1860 Printer* is a copier capable of producing copies as large as 18 by 60 inches from originals as large as 36 by 120 inches. It operates at 100 percent of original size or at five fixed percentage reductions: 95, 75, 62, 50, and 45.

Equipment for reduced-cost multiple copies:
330 Copier—The 330 Copier is a modification of the 813 Copier. The former has a special metering device for recording the making of multiple copies from a single original. The purpose of the 330 Copier is to provide lower per-copy costs in applications where substantial numbers of multiple copies are being made. It operates at a maximum speed of 330 copies per hour.
420 Copier—This machine is a modification of the 914 Copier which, like the 330 Copier, provides for lower per-copy costs when substantial numbers of multiple copies are being made. It operates at a maximum speed of 420 copies per hour.

720 Copier—This copier is similar in type and purpose to the 420 Copier but operates at a maximum speed of 720 copies per hour.
2400 Copier—The 2400 Copier is similar to the 914 Copier in that either loose-sheet or bound originals can be reproduced. The maximum-size original that it will accept is 8⅞ by 14⁷⁄₁₆ inches. The maximum image size is 8½ by 13 inches. The 2400 Copier is capable of much greater speed (2,400 copies per hour) and at lower per-copy costs for multiple copies than any other Xerox copier.

THE ELECTROFAX PROCESS

While both the xerographic process and the Electrofax process are forms of electrostatic copying, they differ in one very important respect. In xerography, the image is formed on a metal plate or drum coated with a thin layer of selenium which is photoconductive, and then transferred by electrostatic attraction to a sheet of ordinary, uncoated paper or other suitable support. In the Electrofax process, the paper on which the image is formed is coated with zinc oxide which is photoconductive.

In the Electrofax process, the zinc oxide-coated paper is first exposed to a corona discharge unit in the dark which imparts to its surface an electrical charge. At this point, the paper is light sensitive since light falling on the charged sheet will dissipate the charge. When an image of a document formed by a lens is projected onto this light-sensitive surface, light reflected from the white background areas of the document dissipates the electrical charge while light falling on the black text areas is absorbed and hence causes no change. The electrical charge is thus retained in the text areas, forming an electrostatic latent image. This latent image can be made visible by two methods. In the first method, a magnetic brush holding finely divided powder particles having an opposite charge to that of the electrostatic latent image, is passed over the surface of the exposed sheet. This causes the powder particles to adhere to the image area by electrostatic attraction, thus making the image visible. In the second method, finely divided powder particles, also having an opposite charge to that of the electrostatic

TABLE 14
The Electrofax Process
(Principal Characteristics)

1. The process is:	Wet	X *
	Dry	X *
2. Copies can be made by the following methods:	Contact Copying	
	Contact-Reflex Copying	
	Optical Copying	X
	Microcopying	
	Projection Printing	X
3. The process is capable of producing copies that are:	Positive, from Positives	X
	Negative, from Positives	
	Positive, from Negatives	
	Negative, from Negatives	X *
4. The process is capable of producing intermediates or masters for subsequent edition printing by:	Diazo	X
	Offset	X
	Spirit Duplicating	
5. The permanence of copies is:	Archival	X *
	Limited	
	Unknown	
6. The quality of copies of continuous-tone originals is:	Excellent	
	Fair	X
	Poor	
7. The reproduction of fine details (e.g., small type faces, fine lines) is:	Excellent	X
	Fair	
	Poor	
8. The contrast of copies is:	High	X *
	Moderate	X *
	Low	

9. The ability of the process to reproduce colored lines is:	Broad	X
	Limited	
10. The paper stock used is:	Plain, Any Color	
	Specially Coated	X
	White	X
	Off-White	X *
11. The tendency of copies to curl is:	High	
	Noticeable	X
	Low	
12. The potential waste factor is:	Considerable	
	Moderate	
	Low	X
13. The approximate time required to make an 8½- by 11-inch copy is:	About 10 seconds and up.	
14. The materials cost per 8½- by 11-inch copy is:	About 2½¢ and up, depending on volume.	
15. Equipment for the process is priced at:	$395.00 and up.	

16. Other characteristics: Zinc oxide coatings tend to crack if strongly creased and mar from contact with metal objects such as paper clips.

*NOTES

1. Both completely dry developing systems and systems that use a liquid are in use.
3. Depending on the type of equipment and materials and the developing system used. Some machines produce fairly good copies of negatives, whereas, with others, the background may be mottled and lacking in density.
5. See "Permanence," page 160.
8. In general, dry development tends to yield copies having higher contrast than copies produced by liquid development.
10. Tinted stocks are also available.

latent image are suspended in a liquid hydrocarbon. The exposed sheet may then be passed through a tray of this liquid, or the liquid may be sprayed on the surface of the print. In either case, the same result occurs: the powder particles are attracted to the image area and adhere to it by electrostatic attraction.

Once the powder image has been formed, it is necessary to affix it to the paper support. Dry powder particles applied by magnetic brush are fused to the paper surface by the application of heat. Powder particles in liquid suspension are affixed to the paper surface by evaporation of the liquid, by the application of heat, or both.

Materials

A number of manufacturers supply materials coated for use with Electrofax process copiers. These coatings are on a relatively thin paper stock, but, because of the weight of the zinc oxide coating, these papers are approximately 25 to 35 percent heavier than 20-pound bond papers. Tinted stocks are also available for systems applications. Some manufacturers also supply a stock which can be used as a master for short-run offset duplicating and a translucent stock for diazo printing. For machines which employ the dry development systems, toner in the form of a dry powder is supplied. For machines employing liquid development, both a liquid developer containing the powder particles in suspension and a liquid replenisher, which contains a higher concentration of powder particles, are supplied.

Contrast

Copies made with liquid development systems tend to be relatively low in contrast. The darkest tone is a shade of gray which is well below the density of a full black. Solid areas are usually darker at their edges and lighter in the center, and may also be mottled. Copies made with dry development systems have greater contrast and greater density and tend to hold a more even tone over solid areas. Neither method of development yields a tone scale which produces good-quality copies of continuous-tone originals. Copies produced by liquid development have a short tone range and often exhibit a poor rendering of solid areas.

Copies produced by dry development are relatively contrasty and show losses of detail in both highlight and shadow areas.

Resolving power

The reproduction of fine lines made by dry development is inferior to that of copies made by liquid development. While lines and spaces as small as five per millimeter can be resolved, the lines themselves are not distinct. This may be due in part to the size of the powder particles used in dry development. Fine lines reproduced by liquid development are more clearly defined, and small type faces having a fine line structure are clearer and more legible.

Exposure latitude

Exposure latitude with either dry or liquid development is fairly broad. With dry development, some breaking and filling of fine lines and spaces is apparent due, in part, to the higher contrast of dry development. With liquid development, legibility is only impaired if copies are substantially overexposed. Underexposed copies exhibit some background tone but legibility of the text is not impaired.

Speed

The speed of either dry or liquid development materials is high enough to permit very short exposures.

Color sensitivity

The color sensitivity of Electrofax coatings is broad. Light yellows and blues record somewhat faintly but all other colors record well. Background tone of tinted paper stocks can be eliminated by increasing exposure.

Keeping qualities

If stored in a cool, dry place in unopened packages, Electrofax materials have an indefinite shelf life.

Permanence

Since the zinc oxide coating itself and the image-forming substances are stable, Electrofax copies should have a high degree of permanence.

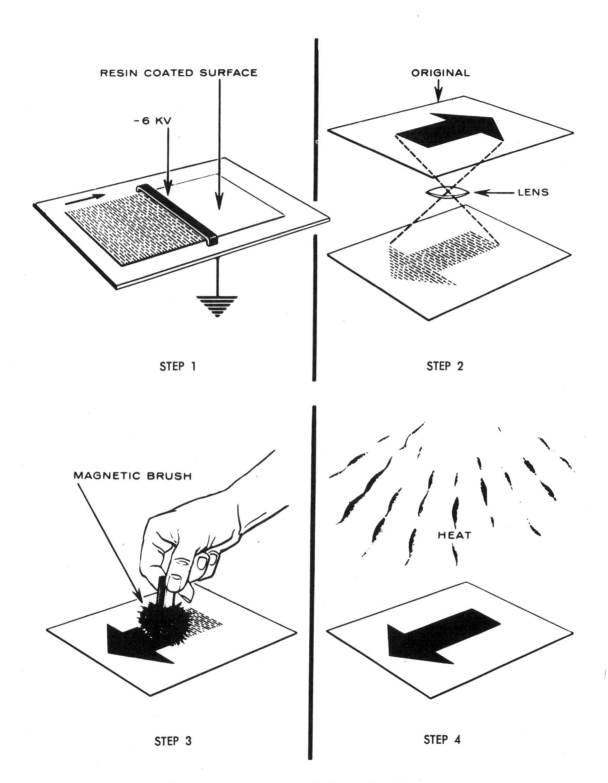

Fig. 104. Schematic representation of the basic Electrofax processing steps.

Other characteristics

The zinc oxide coating of Electrofax materials tends to crack if strongly creased and mars rather easily from contact with metal objects such as paper clips.

Suitability

(1) For bound volumes—generally suitable.

Since most Electrofax process equipment has been designed for the copying of office records, models which can be used for bound volume copying, with one exception, are limited to a maximum page size of 8½ by 14 inches. The Bruning Model 2100 is capable of copying originals up to 11 by 17 inches in size. Tightly bound volumes having narrow inner margins may be difficult or, in extreme cases, impossible to copy because of the foreshortening of the text at the inner margin and the depth of field limitations of the particular copier being used.

(2) For newspaper files—limited.

Only clippings or portions of newspaper pages up to the maximum print size of the copier used can be reproduced.

(3) For typescripts—suitable.

Since emphasis in the commercial development of the Electrofax process and equipment has been placed on its utility for copying office records, most of which are typewritten, the process is well suited for the reproduction of typescript materials.

(4) For manuscripts—generally suitable.

Certain combinations of colored ink on colored paper stock may not record well. Pencil lines which are faint may require a degree of underexposure which may produce considerable background tone.

(5) For continuous-tone originals—limited.

Copies of continuous-tone illustrations produced by dry development are contrasty and show some loss of highlight and shadow detail. Copies made by liquid development may be mottled and lack density in solid areas.

(6) For maps—limited.

The copying of maps is limited to the maximum-size copy the equipment is capable of producing, and the copying of colored maps is limited by the color sensitivity of the process.

(7) For card files—limited.

No Electrofax coatings on card stock are currently available. The process can, however, be used for the making of short-run offset masters which could serve as intermediates for card reproduction where small editions are required.

(8) For copies made by other processes—generally suitable.

Most positive copies made by other processes can be reproduced satisfactorily but the uneven background tone of solid areas which frequently occurs with liquid development makes copies of negatives unsightly and in some cases illegible.

(9) For microforms:

(a) Camera recording—unsuitable.

No Electrofax materials have thus far been developed for microrecording.

(b) Duplicating—unsuitable.

There are no Electrofax coatings suitable for microform duplication.

(c) Eye-legible copies from microforms—suitable.

Several reader-printers have been marketed which employ the Electrofax process for making hard copy from microtransparencies.

Manufacturers and distributors

The following list is not comprehensive. No endorsement of these firms or their equipment is implied. Before making selection of equipment, the prospective purchaser should consult local equipment directories or buying guides.

American Photocopy Equipment Company APECO
2100 West Dempster Street
Evanston, Illinois 60202

Anken Chemical & Film Corporation
10 Patterson Avenue
Newton, New Jersey 07860

Charles Bruning Company
1800 W. Central Road
Mt. Prospect, Illinois 60056

Copease Corporation
10401 Decatur Road
Philadelphia, Pennsylvania 19154

Copia Manufacturing Corporation
1055 Stewart Avenue
Garden City, New York 11533

Copystatics Manufacturing Corp.
One Penn Place
Pelham Manor, New York 10803

Dennison Manufacturing Company
300 Howard Street
Framingham, Massachusetts 01701

A. B. Dick Company
5700 West Touhy Avenue
Chicago, Illinois 60648

Ditto, Inc.
6900 McCormick Road
Chicago, Illinois 60645

Ferrania
Via Appia Nuova, 803
Rome, Italy

Fotoclark
Friedrich Grün KG
Bonn, West Germany

Frantz Industries, Inc.
Vestal Parkway East
Vestal, New York 13850

Minolta Corporation
200 Park Avenue South
New York, New York 10003

Old Town Corporation
750 Pacific Street
Brooklyn, New York 11238

Polyclair
52 Rue de Ponthieu
Paris VII, France

Savin Business Machines Corporation
161 Sixth Avenue
New York, New York 10003

SCM Corporation
410 Park Avenue
New York, New York 10022

THE DIAZO PROCESS

The diazo process is based on the behavior of a class of compounds known as diazonium salts, so called because the compounds in this family possess a pair (di-) of nitrogen (azo, from the French word for nitrogen, "azote") atoms in their structure. These compounds are capable of combining chemically, through the action of other substances known as *couplers,* with phenols or amines to produce substances which are strongly colored. What makes diazonium salts suitable for use in a reproduction process is that, in addition to the foregoing characteristics, they also possess a particular kind of photosensitivity.

In silver halide processes, the action of light brings about a change which, on development, causes those areas which have been struck by light to darken, thus forming a negative image. In the diazo process, the action of light does just the opposite. It destroys the ability of the diazonium compounds to react with a coupler to form a visible dye image.

If a sheet of diazo-coated material is processed without exposure to light, the sheet will be darkened by the formation of dyestuffs over its entire surface. If, however, a sheet of diazo-coated material is placed in contact with a document sufficiently translucent to permit light to pass through it, the characters of the text will prevent light from reaching the photosensitive diazo coating. Where light is freely transmitted through the non-text areas, the diazonium salts will be rendered inert. When processed, the diazonium salts in the text areas which were unaffected by the action of light react with the coupler to form a visible image. The process thus forms a direct-positive image rather than a negative one.

The diazo process is also called the diazotype process, or diazotypy, and is often referred to as "whiteprinting" (in apposition to "blueprinting").

There are three major variants of the diazo process and several minor ones. The difference between the major variants turns largely on the way the latent image is developed, and are referred to as *vapor, moist,* or *thermal.*

(1) The vapor diazo process: In this process, both the diazonium salts and the coupler are incorporated in the coating, together with an

TABLE 15
THE DIAZO PROCESS
(Principal Characteristics)

1. The process is:	Wet	X *
	Dry	X *
2. Copies can be made by the following methods:	Contact Copying	X
	Contact-Reflex Copying	X
	Optical Copying	
	Microcopying	
	Projection Printing	X
3. The process is capable of producing copies that are:	Positive, from Positives	X
	Negative, from Positives	X *
	Positive, from Negatives	X *
	Negative, from Negatives	X
4. The process is capable of producing intermediates or masters for subsequent edition printing by:	Diazo	X
	Offset	X
	Spirit Duplicating	
5. The permanence of copies is:	Archival	
	Limited	X
	Unknown	
6. The quality of copies of continuous-tone originals is:	Excellent	X *
	Fair	X *
	Poor	
7. The reproduction of fine details (e.g., small type faces, fine lines) is:	Excellent	X *
	Fair	
	Poor	
8. The contrast of copies is:	High	X *
	Moderate	X *
	Low	

9. The ability of the process to reproduce colored lines is:	Broad	
	Limited	X
10. The paper stock used is:	Plain, Any Color	
	Specially Coated	X
	White	X *
	Off-White	
11. The tendency of copies to curl is:	High	
	Noticeable	X *
	Low	
12. The potential waste factor is:	Considerable	
	Moderate	
	Low	X
13. The approximate time required to make an 8½- by 11-inch copy is:	See "Notes."	
Per linear foot (18 inches and up in width) is:	0.5 seconds and up.	
14. The materials cost per 8½- by 11-inch copy is:	About 1¢ and up.	
Per linear foot (18 inches in width) is:	1.9¢ and up.	
15. Equipment for the process ranges in price from:	$300.00 to $12,000.00.	

*NOTES

1. The three forms of the process include one that employs a solution to develop the latent image, one that employs a vapor, and one using heat only.

3. Special materials are available for negative-to-positive and positive-to-negative copying which are relatively expensive compared to ordinary diazo materials.

6. The diazo materials normally used for document reproduction give only fair-quality reproductions from continuous-tone transparencies, but special materials for continuous-tone copying (e.g., General Aniline and Film Corporation's "Dryphoto") are available.

7. The process is capable of very high resolving power, but the sharpness of the copies will be affected by the thickness and translucency of the support the originals are on and the method by which the copies are produced.

8. Depending on the type of materials used.

10. Several colored stocks are also available.

11. Bond-weight or heavier stock has little tendency to curl but, with coatings on thin stocks, curl is more noticeable.

13. The time required to make copies varies with the type of machine used, the intensity of the printing lamp, the type of diazo material used, and the degree of transparency of the original. Small, inexpensive machines operate at speeds of about five feet per minute or sometimes even less. Large machines for volume production operate at speeds as high as 125 feet per minute.

organic acid to prevent a premature reaction between salts and coupler. An exposed sheet of this material is processed by passing it through a device having an enclosure containing ammonia vapor. The strongly alkaline ammonia neutralizes the acid present in the coating, allowing the coupler and the diazonium salts in the unexposed image areas to combine to form a visible image. A variation on this method, which has recently been introduced, is the use of anhydrous ammonia gas instead of liquid ammonia. The introduction of a small quantity of water in the developing chamber provides the moisture needed for development to take place.

(2) The moist diazo process: In this process, the coating contains only the diazonium salts. An exposed sheet of this material is processed by passing it through a device which moistens the coating with a alkaline solution which contains the coupler.

(3) The thermal diazo process: In an effort to eliminate both the use of a solution in the moist process and the ammonia fumes which accompany dry processing, processes which apply only heat to produce the necessary reaction to make the latent image visible have been recently introduced. In the thermal diazo process, all of the components required to form the final image are contained in the coating.

(4) Other variations on the process: The principal variant from the processes described above is a diazo reversal material. While reversal material can be processed in conventional diazo machines, the coating is such that, unlike any other diazo material, a positive image is produced from a translucent negative and vice versa. After development, reversal materials must be washed to preserve the image.

Other variants, in which the light-sensitivity of diazo materials is employed to aid in the forming of a latent image which is not a dye image, include the Kalvar process (which is described separately), a metal diazonium process which ultimately yields a silver image, and a method for the production of lithographic plates.

One principal disadvantage of the diazo proc-ess is the very low degree of sensitivity to light of diazonium salts. The process is limited almost exclusively to the reproduction of one-sided translucent originals by the contact method and very high-intensity light sources must be employed. This disadvantage is offset to some degree by the fact that diazo coatings are among the least expensive available for document reproduction. The materials' cost of letter-size copies is approximately 1 cent or less. The cost of coatings on films or other special supports are higher but not excessive.

Materials

The most common and most widely used diazo material for document reproduction purposes is a coating on a white, light-weight or bond-weight paper support which, on development, yields a black or blue line image. In addition, there are coatings on paper stocks of many different colors, on medium- to heavy-weight papers, on card stock, gum-backed stock, plastic-coated stock; on transparent and on double-coated stock; on films and cloths of various types, thicknesses, and colors; and on an offset-master stock. Since the image is dye-formed, many of the stocks available also provide a wide choice of image color. While most of the materials are used for the reproduction of line originals and hence have a contrast range from moderate to relatively high, there are also continuous-tone films and papers which yield copies having a relatively long tone scale. Still another class of diazo materials includes those which, because of the high resolution of diazo coatings, are widely used for the duplication of micro-images in roll and sheet form. Where circumstances require it, a coating is also available which is erasable.

Contrast

The contrast of diazo materials ranges from moderate to high, depending on the type of coating and the purpose for which it is intended.

Resolving power

Unlike silver halide coatings which have a granular structure, each grain being made up of a number of molecules, the structure of diazo coatings is molecular. Habib and Hodgkins[8] state that the size of a silver grain in a high-resolution silver halide coating measures about 3,000 angstrom units (one angstrom unit equals one-millionth of a millimeter) whereas the size of a typical azo dye molecule is about 15 angstroms, or about 1/200th the size of the silver grain. The inherent resolving power of diazo coatings is thus extremely high. In contact printing a transparency of the NBS Micro-copy Test Chart, lines and spaces as fine as 10 per millimeter (2500 per inch) can be reproduced with great clarity. A limiting factor, however, is introduced by the method ordinarily employed in diazo copying. To make a diazo copy of a one-sided translucent original, the original is placed face up on a sheet of diazo-coated paper. The image on the original is thus separated from the diazo coating by the thickness of the paper support of the original. This lack of contact between the image and the coating will cause some loss of sharpness which will be proportional to the thickness of the paper support of the original. With very light-weight papers, this loss is negligible. Where maximum sharpness is important and/or a number of copies are to be made from a single original, the original can be placed face down on a sheet of translucent diazo stock to produce a reverse-reading copy which can then be used as a printing master for subsequent copies. Where typewritten copy is being prepared for diazo reproduction, it is advantageous to place a sheet of carbon paper behind each sheet being typed, to form an image on the back of the sheet, which will not only provide an image in intimate contact with the diazo coating but will increase printing density as well. Red carbon is preferable since it acts as an ultraviolet filter.

Exposure latitude

Exposure in diazo copying machines is controlled by the rate at which the original and the sensitized material pass a high-intensity tubular light source. Slowing the rate of advance results

in overexposure which yields a copy which will be faint and bleached in appearance. Increasing the rate of advance results in underexposed copies which will have a background tone. In general, exposure latitude is affected more by the characteristics of the process itself. In copying originals which are on a highly transparent support such as film, exposure latitude is fairly broad, but, if the support is low in translucency, exposure settings become quite critical. While copies of originals of the latter type may cause a certain amount of waste, the wastage is more in the form of time rather than materials since the materials costs of ordinary diazo coatings are quite low.

Copies made from a film transparency of the NBS test chart shown in Figure 18 have a resolution of 10 lines per millimeter (2,500 lines per inch) at speeds ranging from 10 to 13 feet per minute on a relatively slow diazo coating. At four feet per minute, which is a considerable overexposure, line patterns as small as 4.5 lines per millimeter (115 lines per inch), which is close to the limit discernible to the unaided eye, record quite clearly. At 20 feet per minute, which is a considerable underexposure, strong background tone is present, but resolution is on the order of 7.9 lines per millimeter (200 lines per inch).

Speed

The speed of diazo materials is very low which limits the process largely to reproduction by contact printing. While much work has been done in efforts to increase the speed of diazo materials, thus far the results have not been significant.

In general, the larger and more costly diazo machines designed for large-volume production have much stronger-intensity light sources than smaller machines and can thus operate at much higher speeds in terms of feet per minute.

In recent years, two pieces of equipment have been developed by which it is possible to make projection prints on diazo materials. These are the Keuffel and Esser *Helios* enlarger and the Caps-Jeffree Ultra Violet enlarger. Both of these enlargers rely on the use of a highly efficient light source operating at an intensity which provides enough

[8] D. P. Habib and G. R. Hodgkins, "The Diazotype Process," in *Symposium on Unconventional Photographic Systems* (New York: Society of Photographic Scientists and Engineers, 1964).

illumination in the ultraviolet and near ultraviolet regions to keep exposures short enough to be practical.

Color sensitivity

Diazo compounds are sensitive only to light in the blue end of the visible spectrum and to ultraviolet in the nonvisible spectrum. Diazo coatings are consequently limited in their ability to reproduce blue lines. Colored lines which act as filters for blue light, such as yellow, orange, and red, record strongly. It must be remembered, however, that in the direct-contact printing method, opacity, quite apart from color, is also a factor. If, for example, a white crayon is used to make a line on a white sheet of paper, the waxy crayon substance which is relatively opaque will record as a dark line on a diazo copy.

Despite the fact that diazo materials are color blind, the process is nonetheless very useful in many applications where color in the copy is an asset because dyes of many different colors can be employed in the coatings. Color proofing can be done, for example, by making diazo transparencies on foils that yield cyan, magenta, and yellow images.

Keeping qualities

Most manufacturers of diazo materials offer a shelf life guarantee of from 3 to 6 months, but, under good storage conditions, in which the relative humidity does not vary much from 50 percent and the temperature from 70° F, acceptable copies can be produced on materials which have been stored for considerably longer periods than the warranty period.

Permanence

No firm statement can be made about the permanence of diazo copies. Since, in general, dyes are susceptible to fading from the action of light, storage conditions are an important factor. The useful life expectancy of diazo copies stored in files where they are protected from the action of light, and under conditions which do not vary greatly from a temperature of 70° F. and a relative humidity of 50 percent has been variously estimated as being between 50 and 100 years.

Intermediates for diazo copying

The diazo process can only be thought of as a copying process if the original document to be copied meets the particular requirements of the process. Failing this, an intermediate copy which is one-sided and translucent must be made by some other process. The added cost of the intermediate, however, is seldom justified if only a single copy is to be made from it. The usual role of the intermediate is to provide a means whereby a number of low-cost diazo copies can be made. The process thus becomes highly useful for small-edition duplicating rather than just copying.

Intermediates suitable for diazo reproduction can be made by a number of processes, as shown in Table 16.

The quality of intermediates made by other processes is a variable which depends on a number of process characteristic factors and is not directly proportional to cost, but, in general, the best-quality intermediates are those employing more expensive materials. In addition to the processes listed, the diazo process itself can be used to produce intermediates which are superior in their printing characteristics to many translucent originals. For example, a finely detailed original on a semi-translucent but somewhat thick paper stock might only be printable at a very slow speed setting and might exhibit a significant loss in sharpness because of the thickness of the paper base. If such an original is copied with the text in contact with a diazo coating on a film base, a sharp, reverse-reading transparent intermediate can be produced which can then be used to make additional copies at a much higher machine setting and without noticeable loss of sharpness.

The processes listed are, for the most part, contact or contact-reflex processes. Other optical methods can also be used to make translucent or transparent intermediates for diazo printing. Material can be copied on film using a camera and the resulting negative used to make positive transparencies on film or paper by contact printing or enlarging. This method has the advantage of introducing control over the size of the intermediate. Enlargements on translucent paper or transparent film to any desired size can also be made from microtransparencies.

The extremely low cost of diazo copies has resulted in the development of a number of systems applications in which original documents are produced to meet the requirements of diazo copying. For many years, numerous European firms have used translucent paper stocks for office records of various kinds. A disadvantage of this practice lies in the fact that paper stocks which are inexpensive but still translucent enough for efficient diazo printing are usually quite thin and difficult to file and are often insufficiently opaque for easy reading. Improvements in this method have recently been made in this country with the introduction of special bond papers which have relatively high opacity to the eye but have a high degree of ultraviolet light transmission. The cost of these paper stocks is approximately the same as the cost of ordinary bond papers.

TABLE 16
Processes Which Can Be Used to Make Diazo Intermediates

Process	Type of Intermediate
Silver halide	Translucent paper
"	Transparent film
Stabilization	Translucent paper
Autopositive	Translucent paper
"	Transparent film
Verifax	Translucent paper
Ektalith	Translucent paper
Diffusion-transfer-reversal	Translucent paper
" " "	Translucent film
" " "	Transparent film
Diaversal	Translucent paper
"	Transparent film
Eichner	Translucent paper
"	Transparent film
Ektafax	Translucent paper
"	Translucent film
Dual Spectrum	Transparent film
Xerography	Translucent paper
"	Transparent film
Electrofax	Translucent paper

The use of translucent paper for printed materials has also resulted in useful applications and noteworthy economies. Both the British and Dutch patent offices, which formerly kept on hand large inventories of copies of patents, now retain only a single copy on translucent paper from which diazo copies are made whenever a request for a copy is received.

Other possible applications of the diazo process to problems encountered in the reproduction of research materials include the use of translucent paper for theses and dissertations and for journal articles. Both of these applications have been repeatedly proposed but have not been used to any great extent. Since the demand for copies of theses and dissertations is not predictable, the existence of a copy on translucent paper would make it possible to produce single copies on demand quite inexpensively. The principal problem here would occur in the illustrations, especially photographic illustrations, which would have to be specially prepared for diazo reproduction. With journal articles also, the demand for reprints is not predictable, and once the supply is exhausted, copies must be made by relatively expensive photocopying processes. An extra copy on one-sided translucent stock would make it possible to keep such materials permanently in print, so to speak, since additional copies could be made on demand. While here, again, the illustrations may present a problem, it must be remembered that most photocopy processes yield rather poor reproductions of continuous-tone illustrations.

While large numbers of theses and dissertations and journals have been preserved on microfilm, the production of hard copy from microfilm currently entails processes which are considerably more expensive than diazo.

In recent years, the use of diazo materials for reproducing microtransparencies has become increasingly widespread. A number of companies market continuous printers for roll-to-roll film duplication and, with the growing use of microfiches, sheet-to-sheet printers for both low-volume and high-volume work. While diazo films do not have the archival permanence possible with silver halide emulsions, the high resolution of diazo materials and the simplicity of the processing step, as compared with silver halide materials, make it highly useful for the production of distribution copies from a silver master negative. Individual microfiches, for example, can be duplicated under ordinary room-light conditions by means of small and relatively inexpensive equipment in approximately one minute and at a materials cost of a few cents.

Suitability

(1) For bound volumes—unsuitable.

The diazo process is limited to contact copying by the direct method from one-sided originals or to reflex copying from loose-sheet originals.

(2) For newspaper files—unsuitable.

While reflex copies of clippings can be made, the method is slow and relatively costly as compared with other processes.

(3) For typescripts—limited.

If a typewritten text of sufficient opacity is on a paper of sufficient translucency, diazo copies can be made. Good results can be produced if typewritten copy has been specially prepared for diazo reproduction. The paper used should be recommended by or supplied by a manufacturer of diazo materials to meet the requirement of a high degree of translucency to ultraviolet light. The ribbon used in the typewriter must have high opacity and/or high ultraviolet absorbing properties. The use of carbon backing (see "Resolving power," page 167) is also helpful.

(4) For manuscripts—limited.

Relatively few manuscripts meet all the requirements for diazo copying which include high line opacity, translucency of the paper stock, and text on one side of the sheet only.

(5) For continuous-tone-originals—limited.

While fairly good-quality continuous-tone copies can be made on diazo materials, an intermediate usually must be made which will meet the requirements of the diazo process.

(6) For maps—limited.

As with continuous-tone originals, an intermediate usually must be made unless the map is already on a thin, translucent stock. With a good intermediate, however, good-quality copies of very large maps can be produced at relatively low materials costs.

(7) For card files—limited.

The opacity of card stock makes direct copying on diazo materials impossible. If, however, a translucent intermediate is made by DTR, xerography, or some other process, duplication can be done on diazo-coated card stock.

(8) For copies made by other processes—limited.

The copies usually produced by other copying processes are too opaque for diazo reproduction. A number of processes, however, are capable of producing copies on translucent or transparent stocks. Such copies can be excellent intermediates for diazo reproduction and are often made for this purpose to take advantage of the low cost of diazo copying when a number of copies from a single original are required.

(9) For microforms:

(a) Camera recording—unsuitable.

Because of the slow speed of diazo materials, neither equipment nor materials are available for camera recording.

(b) Microform duplicating—suitable.

Diazo coatings on film are capable of producing excellent duplicates of microtransparencies in roll or sheet form from either positives or negatives.

(c) Eye-legible copies from microforms —limited.

Equipment

Two pieces of equipment are available for projection printing onto diazo materials—the Keuffel and Esser *Helios* enlarger and the Caps-Jeffree Ultra Violet Enlarger.

Manufacturers and distributors

The following list is not comprehensive. No endorsement of these firms or their equipment is implied. Before making selection of equipment, the prospective purchaser should consult local equipment directories or buying guides.

Atlantic Microfilm Corporation
700 South Main Street
Spring Valley, New York 10977

Charles Bruning Company
1800 W. Central Road
Mt. Prospect, Illinois 60056

Caps Equipment Ltd.
7 Westmoreland Road
London N.W. 9, England

CBS Laboratories
227 High Ridge Road
Stamford, Connecticut 06905

Copia Manufacturing Corporation
155 Stewart Avenue
Garden City, New York 11533

Copymation, Inc.
1800 Greenleaf Avenue
Elk Grove Village, Illinois 60007

Diazit Company, Inc.
Monmouth Junction, New Jersey 08852

Ditto, Inc.
6800 McCormick Road
Chicago, Illinois 60645

General Aniline and Film Corporation
140 W. 51st Street
New York, New York 10020

Grico Inc.
234 Portage Trail
Cuyahoga Falls, Ohio 44221

International Business Machines Corp.
Information Records Division
Post Office Box 10
Princeton, New Jersey 08540

3M Company
2501 Hudson Road
St. Paul, Minnesota 55101

Océ Manufacturing Company
American distributor:
B. K. Elliott Company
536 Penn Avenue
Pittsburgh, Pennsylvania 15222

Frederick Post Company
3650 Avondale Avenue
Chicago, Illinois 60618

Reeves Industries, Inc.
302 E. 44th Street
New York, New York 10017

Remington Office Systems
122 East 42nd Street
New York, New York 10017

Reproduction Engineering Corporation
75 Plains Road
Essex, Connecticut 06426

Rotolite Sales Corporation
328 Essex Street
Stirling, New Jersey 07980

Tecnifax Corporation
195 Appleton Street
Holyoke, Massachusetts 01040

THE KALVAR PROCESS

Although based on the use of diazonium compounds, the Kalvar process is not only quite unlike other diazo processes but is also markedly different from all other copying processes as well. In the Kalvar process, a very thin layer (approximately 0.0005 inches) is coated on a polyester film base. When a sheet of this material is placed in contact with a translucent original and exposed to ultraviolet light in a range of from 3500 A° (Angstrom units) to around 4150 A°, the diazonium compound decomposes and liberates nitrogen in the form of tiny bubbles. Development of the image is accomplished by heat which causes the gaseous nitrogen to expand and form tiny vesicles in the plastic coating. These vesicles, which range in size from 0.5 to 2 microns in diameter, act as light-scattering centers since their ability to transmit light is different from that of the unexposed areas surrounding them (Figure 105). Heat development is accomplished by the use of either a heated roller or a platen. Since, as is the case with silver halide films, light-sensitive compounds are still present in unexposed areas, development must be followed by a "fixing" step. This is accomplished by exposing the entire film to ultraviolet light for a time interval approximately four times as great as that required for image formation. This completely decomposes the residual light-sensitive compounds. When viewed by reflected light, the exposed areas made up of these light-scattering centers are whitish in appearance, and the unexposed areas appear dark. When the Kalvar image is viewed by transmitted light (e.g., in a microfilm reader), light is transmitted by the unexposed areas but is dispersed by the light-scattering centers in the exposed areas so that these areas appear dark. The high light intensity required to expose Kalvar materials limits the process largely to contact copying from translucent originals but its high resolution, along with other characteristics, make it a very useful process for duplicating microtransparencies.

Materials

Kalvar materials include a number of types of film and one type of paper. The films are available in both roll and sheet form for the duplication of roll microforms and microfiches. Most of the films are negative-working—i.e., produce a positive image from a negative transparency and vice versa. One film, known as Type 50, is capable of producing either a negative or a positive by changes in the way in which exposure and development are carried out. Kalvar paper consists of a Kalvar emulsion coated on a black paper base.

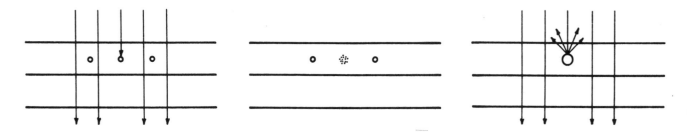

Fig. 105. Schematic diagram of the Kalvar process. Left: light strikes the diazonium compounds which (center) release nitrogen. The application of heat causes the nitrogen gas to expand and form tiny vesicles (right) which act as light-scattering centers.

Since the exposed areas, when developed, appear white when viewed by reflected light, a white-on-black print is formed.

Contrast

Kalvar films are available in both medium- and high-contrast grades. Medium-contrast Kalvar films are useful for reproducing microtransparencies of material which include half-tone illustrations. High-contrast materials are useful in reproducing microtransparencies of originals which are low in contrast. One Kalvar film, known as Type 80, is developed by light instead of by heat and offers control over contrast by varying the amount of light used for development. The light source used for development is an ultraviolet, gas discharge lamp.

Resolving power

The resolving power of Kalvar films used to duplicate microtransparencies is stated by the manufacturer to be in a range of from 144 to 250 lines per millimeter depending upon the type of film used. Some Kalvar emulsions are claimed to have resolving power of more than 500 lines per millimeter. Highest resolving power is attained if the light source used is within a range of 3600 to 4000 A°. Resolution is also affected by the time and temperature of development. In general, short exposure and development times produce greater sharpness. These factors are controlled by the manufacturer in the design of Kalvar exposing and developing units.

Exposure latitude

While optimum results will be obtained from Kalvar material if an optimum exposure is used for printing, the resolution and contrast characteristics are such as to permit a reasonable degree of latitude in exposure without serious degradation of the image.

Speed

Currently available Kalvar materials are quite slow and hence require high-intensity, ultraviolet light sources. This limits the process almost exclusively to copying by the contact method.

Color sensitivity

As has been stated, sensitivity of Kalvar materials is strongest in the ultraviolet region. This, however, is not a limiting factor in applications such as microform duplication since such originals are in the form of black-and-white transparencies.

Keeping qualities

The shelf life of unexposed Kalvar film is claimed to be virtually unlimited.

Permanence

Properly exposed, developed, and fixed Kalvar images are claimed to have a high degree of stability, but the permanence of the image appears to be related to factors in processing which may not always be as controllable under actual working conditions as they are under laboratory conditions. It is possible, for example, for Kalvar images to retain some degree of sensitivity to light and heat after they are processed. Until more evidence is obtained, Kalvar images cannot be rated as archivally permanent.

Suitability

The Kalvar process, at its present stage of development, is not suitable for the making of eye-legible copies directly from originals such as bound volumes, newspapers, typescripts, manuscripts, continuous-tone originals, maps, card files or eye-legible copies made from other processes (Classes 1 through 8). Its principal use is in the making of contact duplicates from film negatives or positives from microtransparencies.

(9) For microforms:

(a) Camera recording—limited.

A single piece of equipment has been developed with which it is possible to make microtransparencies on Kalvar film with a camera. This camera was designed by William A. Pfaff, and the rights to its manufacture have been turned over to the Kalvar Corporation. Because of the very slow speed and limited response to light of Kalvar film, a powerful light source is used which requires that air be blown over the document surface during exposure to prevent it from burning. The exposed frame is then processed by heat within the camera

TABLE 17
THE KALVAR PROCESS
(Principal Characteristics)

1. The process is:	Wet	
	Dry	X
2. Copies can be made by the following methods:	Contact Copying	X
	Contact-Reflex Copying	
	Optical Copying	
	Microcopying	X *
	Projection Printing	
3. The process is capable of producing copies that are:	Positive, from Positives	X
	Negative, from Positives	X
	Positive, from Negatives	X
	Negative, from Negatives	X
4. The process is capable of producing intermediates or masters for subsequent edition printing by:	Diazo	X *
	Offset	
	Spirit Duplicating	
5. The permanence of copies is:	Archival	
	Limited	
	Unknown	X *
6. The quality of copies of continuous-tone originals is:	Excellent	X *
	Fair	X *
	Poor	
7. The reproduction of fine details (e.g., small type faces, fine lines) is:	Excellent	X
	Fair	
	Poor	
8. The contrast of copies is:	High	X *
	Moderate	X *
	Low	

9. The ability of the process to reproduce colored lines is:	Broad	
	Limited	X
10. The paper stock used is:	Plain, Any Color	
	Specially Coated	
	White	
	Off-White	
11. The tendency of copies to curl is:	High	
	Noticeable	X
	Low	
12. The potential waste factor is:	Considerable	
	Moderate	
	Low	X
13. The approximate time required to make a copy (single sheets, e.g., microfiches) is:	30 seconds and up.	
Per linear foot (35 mm. in width) is:	.3 to 3 seconds.	
14. The materials cost per 4- by 6-inch copy is:	10¢ to 12¢.	
Per linear foot (35 mm. in width) is:	4.1¢ to 4.8¢	
15. Equipment for the process ranges in price from:	$570.00 to $4,950.00.	

*NOTES

2. Limited. See "Suitability," pages 173 and 176.
4. Contact diazo copies can be made from Kalvar microtransparencies.

5. See "Permanence," page 173.
6. and 8. Films of different degrees of contrast are available.

in the space of one second. The camera uses 16 mm. roll film and is limited to the recording of documents no larger than 8½ by 11 inches at a fixed reduction ratio of 1:20. Within the limits imposed, it is presumably possible to microfilm various types of research material on Kalvar film by means of the Pfaff camera, provided due allowance is made for the hazards to the original which the heat of the light source creates.

(b) Microform duplicating—suitable.

The Kalvar process is eminently suitable for the duplication of microtransparencies in both roll and sheet form. Both the Kalvar Corporation and other companies as well manufacture and market equipment for roll-to-roll duplicating and for duplicating microfiches. The high resolution of the material, its contrast characteristics, the fact that the process is completely dry and the speed with which duplicating can be done under conditions of ordinary room light are all advantageous.

(c) Eye-legible copies from microforms —unsuitable.

No Kalvar material or equipment has been developed which is suitable for making hard copy from microforms.

Manufacturers and distributors

The following list is not comprehensive. No endorsement of these firms or their equipment is implied. Before making selection of equipment, the prospective purchaser should consult local equipment directories or buying guides.

Canon U. S. A., Inc.
554 Fifth Avenue
New York, New York 10036

Caps Equipment Company
7 Westmoreland Road
London N. W. 9, England

Colight Corporation
123 North Third Street
Minneapolis, Minnesota 55401

Copia Manufacturing Corporation
1055 Stewart Avenue
Garden City, New York 11533

B. K. Elliott Company
536 Penn Avenue
Pittsburgh, Pennsylvania 15222

Kalvar Corporation
909 South Broad Street
New Orleans, Louisiana 70125

THE DUAL SPECTRUM PROCESS

The Dual Spectrum process receives its name from the fact that radiant energy in the form of visible light from one band of the electromagnetic spectrum is used to form a latent image, and invisible radiant energy in the infrared region of the spectrum is used to make the latent image visible on the copy paper. The process is thus completely dry.

Two materials are used for making copies—an intermediate sheet which has a light-sensitive coating on one side and a receptor sheet. The steps in making a copy are as follows:

(1) An intermediate sheet is placed with its coated side against the surface of the document to be copied.

(2) The two sheets are placed on an exposing surface with the document on top.

(3) The two sheets are covered to hold them in firm contact and the exposure made (about 15 to 20 seconds).

(4) The intermediate sheet is then removed and placed in contact with a receptor sheet.

(5) The two sheets are placed in contact with a heated platen or drum where the action of heat forms an image on the receptor sheet (about 5 to 20 seconds).

(6) The intermediate sheet is then removed and discarded.

With most Dual Spectrum machines, the foregoing steps are performed manually. With one machine—the Model 209—most of the steps are automated.

Materials

Three types of light-sensitive intermediate materials have been introduced for Dual Spectrum copying. The first of these is an extremely thin, pink sheet similar in its physical characteristics to onionskin paper; it is called Type 655. A second type, called Type 606, is in the form of a thin, transparent, pink film. These two types of intermediate materials are supplied in sheet form in several standard sizes. A third type, which is called Type 657, is quite similar to Type 655 but is supplied in roll form for use in one machine only —the Model 209. Types 655 and 606 intermediate materials are notched in one corner to indicate which side of the sheet carries the light-sensitive coating.

These intermediate sheets respond to light in a manner which is the reverse of the familiar pattern exhibited by ordinary silver halide materials. In silver halide photocopying, an area that has been struck by light is darkened in development, thus producing a negative image. With Dual Spectrum materials, areas that have *not* been affected by light become darkened (and hence visible) through development. If an unexposed sheet of Dual Spectrum intermediate material is developed in contact with the receptor sheet, the receptor sheet will develop out totally black. In the Dual Spectrum process, the action of light thus desensitizes the material in such a way that the subsequent action of heat in the developing stage produces no visible change in the appearance of the white receptor sheet. When a document is being copied, the light reflected from the white background desensitizes the intermediate sheet, but the light striking the black letters of the text is absorbed with very little light being reflected back to the intermediate sheet. When the intermediate sheet is then heat-developed in contact with a receptor sheet, the text areas which have not been desensitized by the action of light develop out on the receptor sheet as a black, visible image against a clear, white, completely desensitized background. The Dual Spectrum process is, therefore, a direct-positive process.

Two types of receptor sheets are available for Dual Spectrum copying—Type 658 copy paper, which is used in conjunction with Type 657 intermediate materials in the Model 209 Copier, and Type 607 copy paper, which is used with either Type 655 or Type 606 intermediate materials in all other Dual Spectrum copiers. The receptor sheets are similar in appearance to ordinary, white, bond-weight paper stocks but are specially coated and are slightly sensitive to light. A small, light blue flame emblem is imprinted on the back of each sheet to distinguish the coated from the uncoated side. The receptor sheets tend to curl from the heat of development but readily flatten out. They can be marked on with a fountain pen, ballpoint pen, pencil, or typewriter. The light sensitivity of the receptor sheets is so low that no special precautions need be taken in the course of copying, but, if the boxes in which they are contained are left open for any extended period of time, one or more sheets will show some discoloration when processed.

A transparent receptor sheet (Type 627) on a film base is available for making transparent positives for use with overhead projectors.

Offset plates can be made on 3M "Z" offset plates by using a special intermediate known as Type 632, provided a Thermo-Fax copier as well as a Dual Spectrum copier is available. The original is first exposed in contact with a Type 632 intermediate sheet on a Dual Spectrum copier and then processed in contact with a "Z" plate by passing the sheets through a Thermo-Fax copier.

Contrast

Types 655 and 657 intermediate materials are moderate in contrast and exhibit fairly good tonal gradation. Copies of continuous-tone originals such as photographic illustrations are not perfectly faithful to the tone scale of the originals but are nonetheless of fairly good quality. Type 606 intermediate material has greater contrast than either Types 655 or 657 and hence shows a somewhat greater loss of highlight and shadow detail.

Resolving power

The resolving power of Types 655 and 657 intermediate materials is approximately 5.0 lines per millimeter. The resolving power of Type 606 intermediate material, on the other hand, is remarkable. At optimum exposures, line patterns as fine as ten lines per millimeter, or more than 2,500 lines per inch, can be distinguished with the aid of a magnifying glass.

Exposure latitude

Exposure latitude for small texts of designs which are difficult to reproduce is approximately

TABLE 18
THE DUAL SPECTRUM PROCESS
(Principal Characteristics)

1. The process is:	Wet	
	Dry	X
2. Copies can be made by the following methods:	Contact Copying	
	Contact-Reflex Copying	X
	Optical Copying	
	Microcopying	
	Projection Printing	
3. The process is capable of producing copies that are:	Positive, from Positives	X
	Negative, from Positives	
	Positive, from Negatives	
	Negative, from Negatives	X
4. The process is capable of producing intermediates or masters for subsequent edition printing by:	Diazo	X
	Offset	X
	Spirit Duplicating	
5. The permanence of copies is:	Archival	
	Limited	X
	Unknown	
6. The quality of copies of continuous-tone originals is:	Excellent	
	Fair	X
	Poor	
7. The reproduction of fine details (e.g., small type faces, fine lines) is:	Excellent	X *
	Fair	X *
	Poor	
8. The contrast of copies is:	High	X *
	Moderate	X *
	Low	

9. The ability of the process to reproduce colored lines is:	Broad	X
	Limited	
10. The paper stock used is:	Plain, Any Color	
	Specially Coated	X
	White	X
	Off-White	
11. The tendency of copies to curl is:	High	
	Noticeable	X
	Low	
12. The potential waste factor is:	Considerable	
	Moderate	X
	Low	
13. The approximate time required to make an 8½- by 11-inch copy is:	20 to 40 seconds.	
14. The materials cost per 8½- by 11-inch copy is:	4.4¢ to 8.1¢.	
15. Equipment for the process ranges in price from:	$150.00 to $1,495.00.	

16. Other characteristics: Some types of pressure-sensitive transparent tape will cause the background to discolor.

*NOTES

7. Reproduction of fine details is excellent when Type 606 intermediate materials are used, and is fair when Type 655 and Type 657 intermediate materials are used.

8. Contrast is high when Type 606 intermediate materials are used, and is fair when Type 655 and Type 657 intermediate materials are used.

± 15 percent of the optimum exposure time. Exposure latitude for bolder texts of more easily reproduced designs is much greater, ranging from approximately minus 30 percent of the optimum exposure time to plus 50 percent.

Speed

The sensitivity to light of the various intermediate materials is very low. Consequently, they can be handled quite freely under very bright room light conditions. However, the boxes in which they are stored should be kept closed since prolonged exposure to ambient light will desensitize them. Their low light sensitivity requires an illumination source of fairly high intensity if exposures are to be kept reasonably short. For example, twenty-four 30-volt, 39-watt lamps are used in the exposing section of the Model 76 Dual Spectrum copier. Type 655 materials are slightly faster than Type 606 when exposed on a Model 76 Dual Spectrum copier.

Color sensitivity

With either Types 655 or 657 intermediate materials, pink, blue, green, goldenrod, salmon, and orange stocks reproduce with a noticeable background tone. This background tone can be eliminated by increasing the exposure by approximately 20 percent. With Type 606 intermediate material, which yields copies having higher contrast, the background tone of colored stocks containing portions or red—pink, goldenrod, salmon, and orange—are quite dark and can only be lightened by substantial increases in exposure.

With the exception of light yellow shades, lines of different colors reproduce satisfactorily on all types of intermediate materials. Light yellow lines can be reproduced by reducing the exposure to the point where background tone is noticeable.

Keeping qualities

The shelf life of Dual Spectrum process intermediate materials is estimated at approximately six months. While they may keep longer than this, better results can be expected from fresh materials.

Dual Spectrum receptor sheets are subject to deterioration from age, especially after the box seal has been broken. If properly stored, they will keep for many months, but, as with the intermediate materials, only enough stock should be kept on hand to meet immediate and short-term needs rather than long-term future needs.

The receptor sheets exhibit some sensitivity to light both before and after heat processing. Receptor sheets which have been partially exposed to light before processing will, when processed, show a brownish discoloration in the exposed area. The slight sensitivity of processed receptor sheets can be advantageous in improving the appearance of copies which are slightly over- or underexposed. A weak image caused by overexposure can be strengthened by again passing the copy through the developing section of the machine. Conversely, the background tone of an underexposed copy can be reduced by giving it a second exposure. To what extent this sensitivity to light and heat may affect the permanence of copies is not known.

Permanence

According to the manufacturer, if Dual Spectrum copies are made at correct exposure times and developed at the correct development temperature and stored under normal office conditions, it is estimated that copies will remain legible for at least 25 years. Additional laboratory testing of the permanency of Dual Spectrum copies is now being conducted.

Other characteristics

Certain types of originals are difficult to copy satisfactorily. Originals which have a surface sheen, such as Thermo-Fax copies or glossy photographs, may reproduce with uneven and blotchy backgrounds. Blotchy backgrounds also may appear on copies made from originals on certain types of erasable bond papers. The appearance of the background of copies from such originals can sometimes be improved by using a special carrier which the manufacturer supplies.

Another characteristic of Type 606 intermediate material is its ability to take on a static charge. Sliding the material over the surface of the original causes it to cling to the original. This can be very helpful in copying from bound volumes where the problem of achieving good contact can often be quite difficult.

It has been noted also that some types of pressure-sensitive transparent tape have a marked effect on the receptor sheets. If such tapes are applied to the coated surface of finished copies to mend a tear or to affix the copy to some other support, a marked yellow-brownish discoloration of the background occurs after a few weeks. However, 3M Brand Magic Mending Tape showed no discoloration over extended time periods.

Suitability

(1) For bound volumes—limited.

Certain machines employing the Dual Spectrum process can be used for copying from bound volumes by the contact-reflex method. The maximum-size page which can be copied is 8½ by 14 inches. Although the Model 71 and Model 114 Transparency Makers are capable of making copies of 11- by 17- and 18- by 24-inch originals, respectively, these devices were not designed for book-copying applications. While the problem of contact is somewhat alleviated by the fact that Type 606 intermediate materials readily take on a static charge which causes them to adhere to the page being copied, many problems with contact and coverage as outlined in Part 4, "Methods and Techniques," will be encountered. *Rare books should not be copied on Dual Spectrum equipment because of the intensity of the light source used and the heat this generates, and because of the danger of accidental damage when copying volumes in an upside-down position by the contact-reflex method.*

(2) For newspaper files—unsuitable.

The size limitation of 8½ by 14 inches for most equipment currently available limits the copying of newspaper pages to sections of unbound originals.

(3) For typescripts—generally suitable.

Difficulties may be encountered in reproducing markedly uneven typing because of the contrast of the sensitized material, but average- to good-quality typescripts reproduce satisfactorily. One particular problem not encountered with any other process derives from the surface characteristics of the paper on which the image is typed, rather than from the image itself. Certain "erasable" bonds or papers with a sheen may reproduce with very blotchy backgrounds. This sometimes can be eliminated by using a special silk screen carrier, but this tends to cause the image to be grayish and lacking in contrast. Type 657 intermediate materials perform better with such originals than Types 606 and 655.

(4) For manuscripts—limited.

Manuscripts exhibiting unevenness in line density may not record well at normal exposures. Underexposure may be required to strengthen fine or faint lines, which in turn may result in considerable background tone. A more serious limitation is imposed by the intensity of the light source and the consequent temperature rise of the exposure surface. *Manuscripts which are fragile, faded, or subject to fading should not be copied on Dual Spectrum process equipment.*

(5) For continuous-tone originals—limited.

The Dual Spectrum process has a rather limited tone scale which causes some loss of both highlight and shadow details. This is more marked when Type 606 intermediate materials are used. Glossy originals often record with blotchy backgrounds as well.

(6) For maps—limited.

Within the size limitations of the equipment, black-and-white maps or sections thereof can be copied. Colored maps may or may not be reproducible depending upon the colors used. For finely detailed maps, the use of Type 606 intermediate materials is preferable because of their unusually high resolving power.

(7) For card files—limited.

The Dual Spectrum process can be used to copy from originals on card stock but no card-weight receptor materials are available for card-to-card duplication.

(8) For copies made by other process—Limited.

Copies made by other processes can generally be reproduced legibly with Type 657 intermediate materials. Slightly poorer results are obtained with Type 655 intermediate materials. With Type 606 intermediate materials, the heightened contrast may cause unsatisfactory copies if the material being copied is itself quite contrasty. With both Type 655 and Type 606 intermediate materials, copies made by other processes which exhibit any surface sheen such as Thermo-Fax copies, Dry-Silver copies and certain diffusion-transfer-reversal copies may record with blotchy backgrounds.

(9) For microforms—unsuitable.

The Dual Spectrum process is limited to the making of eye-legible copies from original documents.

Manufacturer

Dual Spectrum process equipment is manufactured by

3M Company
2501 Hudson Road
St. Paul, Minnesota 55119

and distributed through 3M Business Products Sales, Inc., with offices in principal cities.

Equipment

3M "209" Automatic Copier
3M "107" Copier
3M "107" Copier, Portable
3M "70" Dry Copier
3M "71" Dry Copier
3M "114" Dry Copier

THE ELECTROLYTIC PROCESS

The electrolytic process is a negative-working process which yields positive prints from negative microtransparencies or negative prints from positive microtransparencies. It was introduced by the 3M Company in 1958 as a means for producing hard copy from microfilm in their Filmac line of reader-printers.

In the electrolytic process, the sensitized material consists of three layers: a paper base, a thin layer of a metallic substance which acts as a conductor, and, on top of this, a coating of zinc oxide in a resin binder. This zinc oxide coating provides a photoconductive layer which in the dark acts as an insulator, i.e., has high electrical resistance. The action of light during exposure lowers the resistance in those areas where light strikes the surface. Thus, a latent image is formed in terms of differences in electrical resistance, the image areas having now become electrically conductive through the action of light. If the exposed sheet is then placed very briefly in contact with a suitable electroplating solution and if a direct current electric potential is applied, current can flow between the solution and the conductive layer. This causes metal ions in the solution to deposit or "plate out" on the zinc oxide surface in the image areas to form a visible metallic image. This processing step in which electrolytic formation of the image occurs is accomplished with great simplicity and rapidity, requiring, as it does, nothing more than drawing the zinc oxide surface over an ordinary cellulose sponge soaked with the solution. The processing of an 8½- by 11-inch print requires no more than about 4½ seconds, and, since the surface of the print is only barely moistened during processing, the print can be considered, for all practical purposes, as dry.

Materials

Two types of materials are available for the electrolytic process which are quite similar in their characteristics but differ in the type of material used for the conductive layer. Type 761, which was the first material introduced, uses a layer of metallic foil for the conductive layer. The disadvantages of this material are that (a) it is relatively thick and heavy, and (b) the foil layer makes prints hazardous to use around electrical circuits. Type 764 uses a different type of conductive layer which makes it much lighter in weight and eliminates the electrical hazard present in Type 761.

Both types of paper have a marked tendency to curl and, like other zinc oxide coatings, their surfaces can be marred by contact with metal objects such as paper clips. The zinc oxide coating also tends to crack if prints are folded.

The materials are supplied in rolls of various standard paper widths and in lengths ranging from 237 feet to 300 feet, depending upon the particular type of reader-printer in which they are to be used.

The electrolytic solution, which the manufacturer calls an activator, is supplied in one-pint dispensing bottles.

Contrast

Prints made by the electrolytic process are relatively low in contrast and the deepest tone is never a solid black. The contrast of prints will vary, of course, with the contrast of the originals but, since the originals used for this process are microtransparencies of relatively high contrast, the low contrast of the process is often advantageous. Low contrast also favors microtransparency images of continuous-tone illustrations. The best-quality prints are produced from microtransparencies which are quite contrasty and which have a high background density.

Resolving power

The resolving power of the zinc oxide coating is high. The sharpness of electrolytic process images will depend on the sharpness of the micro-image itself, the resolving power of the lenses supplied, and on the accuracy of focus.

Exposure latitude

The strength or line density of prints produced from negative microtransparencies can be controlled both through variations in the exposure time and through variations in processing. Exposure control is simply a matter of changing the timer setting to increase or decrease the length of time that light falls on the sensitized material. Processing control is affected by means of a rheostat which regulates the intensity of the electric current which passes between the electrolyte and the conductive layer. The higher the intensity of this current, the greater is the deposit of image-forming components on the zinc oxide surface. Although considerable subtlety of control over image density is possible, the electrolytic process possesses remarkable latitude. With most microtransparencies, satisfactory prints can be made over a wide range of exposure and processing settings. While image density will range from light to dark, clarity of the image is not affected.

Speed

Electrolytic process materials exhibit ample speed for the rapid production of hard copy from microtransparencies. Exposures from normal density negatives are of only a few seconds' duration and exposures from fairly dense negatives are not excessive.

Color sensitivity

The color sensitivity of electrolytic process materials has no functional relevance because the process is only used at present for the making of hard copy from black and white microtransparencies.

Keeping qualities

Electrolytic process materials are quite stable and have an indefinite shelf life if stored in a cool, dry place.

Permanence

No comprehensive study of the permanence of electrolytically produced images has thus far been reported in the literature. Nelson, referring to testing work conducted by a private laboratory, makes the following statement:
"Electrochemical [i.e., electrolytically produced] prints have been subjected to fading and aging tests, and . . . have proved to be stable." [9]

Other characteristics

Type 764 materials are approximately the same weight as twenty-pound bond paper, but Type 761 materials are approximately 34 percent heavier.

Suitability

The electrolytic process is suitable only for the making of hard copy from negative and positive roll-form and sheet-form microtransparencies. With the exception of the Filmac 300, print sizes are fixed and the magnification is controlled by changing lenses. This, of course, limits the range of available magnifications. Satisfactory hard copy can be made only if the image size and reduction ratio used in filming are compatible with the size of the film aperture and the magnification ratio of the particular lens (or lenses) being used.

Although the maximum size of prints which can be made with the Filmac 200 and 200R reader-printers measures 18 by 24 inches, the area

---

[9] Carl E. Nelson, *Microfilm Technology—Engineering and Related Fields* (New York: McGraw-Hill, 1965), p. 168.

TABLE 19
THE ELECTROLYTIC PROCESS
(Principal Characteristics)

1. The process is:	Wet	
	Dry	X *
2. Copies can be made by the following methods:	Contact Copying	
	Contact-Reflex Copying	
	Optical Copying	
	Microcopying	
	Projection Printing	X
3. The process is capable of producing copies that are:	Positive, from Positives	
	Negative, from Positives	X
	Positive, from Negatives	X
	Negative, from Negatives	
4. The process is capable of producing intermediates or masters for subsequent edition printing by:	Diazo	
	Offset	
	Spirit Duplicating	
5. The permanence of copies is:	Archival	X *
	Limited	
	Unknown	
6. The quality of copies of continuous-tone originals is:	Excellent	
	Fair	X
	Poor	
7. The reproduction of fine details (e.g., small type faces, fine lines) is:	Excellent	X
	Fair	
	Poor	
8. The contrast of copies is:	High	
	Moderate	
	Low	X

9. The ability of the process to reproduce colored lines is:	Broad	
	Limited	X
10. The paper stock used is:	Plain, Any Color	
	Specially Coated	X
	White	X
	Off-White	
11. The tendency of copies to curl is:	High	X
	Noticeable	
	Low	
12. The potential waste factor is:	Considerable	
	Moderate	
	Low	X
13. The approximate time required to make an 8½- by 11-inch copy is:	10 seconds.	
14. The materials cost per 8½- by 11-inch copy is:	9¢.	
15. Equipment for the process ranges in price from:	$729.00 to $3,600.00.	

*NOTES

1. Although an electrolyte in solution is used, it is only momentarily applied to the zinc oxide coated surface. A slight amount of moisture on the print surface is apparent when the print emerges from the machine, but this evaporates very quickly.

5. See "Permanence," page 183.

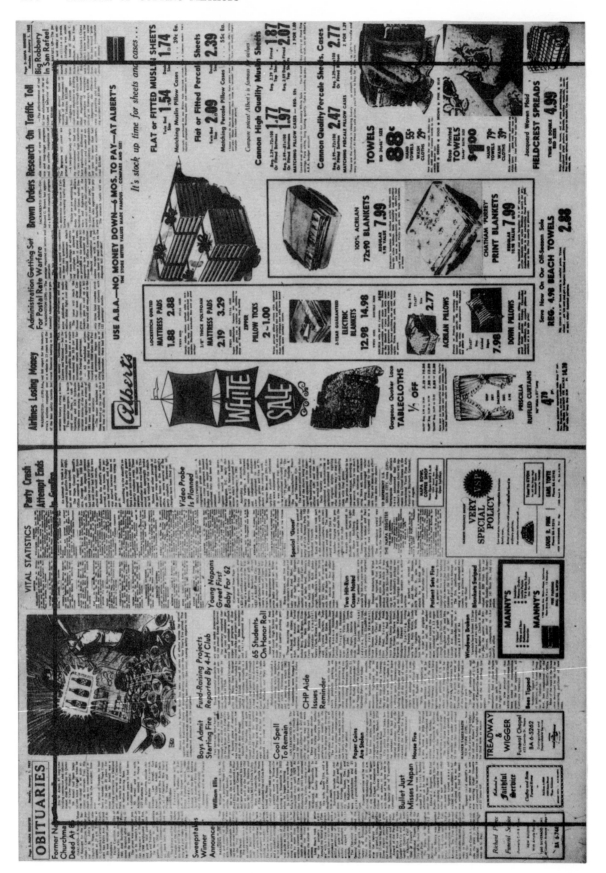

Fig. 106. Coverage of a newspaper filmed in position 2-B. The inscribed lines show the maximum area that can be reproduced on a print made on a Filmac 200R reader-printer.

reproduced in the print is not as large as the standard full frame used for the microfilming of newspapers (Figure 106).

Microtransparencies of newspapers can be reproduced if their frame size is within the limits imposed by the reader-printers.

Further information on the preparation of microfilms for hard copy production on Filmac equipment is given in "Eye-Legible Copies from Microforms," pages 287–94.

Manufacturer

Electrolytic process equipment is manufactured by:
3M Company
2501 Hudson Road
St. Paul, Minnesota 55101

and distributed by 3M Business Products Sales, Inc., with offices in principal cities.

Equipment

There are two basic and three variant models of Filmac reader-printers available from the 3M Company. The basic models are designated as:
Filmac 200
Filmac 400
The Filmac 200 is designed for the production of hard copy up to 18 by 24 inches in size from single frames of 35 mm. microfilms of engineering drawings mounted in aperture cards.

The Filmac 200R is identical with the Model 200 but is equipped with spindles for reading and for printing from 35 mm. microfilm in roll form.

The Filmac 400B (basic model) is equipped for handling 16 or 35 mm. roll film, or, by means of accessories, jacketed film or microfiches up to 5 by 8 inches in size. The Filmac 400B has a manual film advance.

The Filmac 400M handles 16 or 35 mm. roll film and has a motorized film advance. The Filmac 400M can also be equipped to handle jacketed film or microfiches up to 5 by 8 inches in size by means of accessories.

The Filmac 400C is designed for 16 mm. film in cartridges and has a motorized film advance.

All three models of the Filmac 400 series produce prints which are 8½ by 12 inches in size with a maximum image area of 8 by 10¾ inches,

and can operate at ten different magnifications by means of interchangeable lenses.

PROCESSES UNDER DEVELOPMENT

In the continuing search for new image-forming systems, new methods have been devised and new materials having radically different patterns of behavior have been investigated. In the following section, a brief description of a number of processes employing new methods and materials is given. At the present time these processes are in various stages of research and development and, although some have been publicly demonstrated, they are not yet in wide or active use.

THE IMAGIC PROCESS

The Imagic process[10] is essentially thermographic in nature but employs methods and materials which are radically different from those used in conventional thermographic copying devices.

The steps entailed in making a copy by this process are as follows:

(1) The document to be copied is first coated with a very thin film of light oil.

(2) A sheet of ordinary paper used as a receptor sheet for the copy image is then placed in contact with the oil-treated surface of the document.

(3) Exposure to a source of infrared radiation causes the ink in the image area to heat up which, in turn, causes the oil in the image areas to vaporize and to condense on the surface of the receptor sheet.

(4) At this point, the receptor sheet carries a latent image of condensed oil. This image is called a "disprint."

(5) To render the disprint image legible, the receptor sheet is dusted with a resin-containing powdered ink which adheres to the oil image.

(6) This ink is made permanent by fusing it to the receptor sheet by the application of heat.

Copies made in this fashion are positive, but, according to a recent patent (Brit. 934, 402), negative copies can be produced by coating the receptor sheet instead of the original document with a thin film of oil. The application of infrared

[10] The Imagic process is a development of Imagic Processes Ltd., London, England.

TABLE 20

Suitability of Copying Processes
(For Reproducing the Principal Classes of Research Materials)

Key:
S . . . Suitable
GS . . Generally Suitable
L . . . Limited
U . . . Unsuitable

	Silver Halide	Stabilization	Autopositive	Verifax	Ektalith	DTR	Diaversal	Polaroid	Dry Silver	Thermo-Fax	Eichner	Ektafax	Xerography	Electrofax	Diazo	Kalvar	Dual Spectrum	Electrolytic
1. For bound volumes	S	S	L	L	L	L	S	U	U	U	U	U	GS	GS	U	U	L	GS
2. For newspaper files	S	L	L	U	L	L	S	U	U	U	U	L	L	L	U	U	U	U
3. For typescripts	S	GS	L	GS	L	GS	GS	U	U	GS	L	GS	S	S	L	U	GS	U
4. For manuscripts	S	GS	L	GS	L	GS	L	U	U	L	L	L	GS	GS	L	U	L	U
5. For continuous-tone originals	S	S	L	U	U	L	U	S	U	U	U	U	L	L	L	U	L	U
6. For maps	S	L	L	L	L	L	L	U	U	L	L	L	L	L	L	U	L	U
7. For card files	L	L	U	L	S	L	U	U	U	L	L	GS	S	L	L	U	L	U
8. For copies made by other processes	S	GS	L	L	L	L	L	U	U	L	L	L	GS	GS	L	U	L	U
9. For microforms a. Production	S	U	U	U	U	U	U	U	U	U	U	U	L	U	U	L	U	U
b. Duplication	S	U	U	U	U	U	U	U	U	U	U	U	U	U	S	S	U	U
c. Hard copy	S	S	S	U	U	L	L	U	GS	U	U	U	S	S	L	U	U	S

radiation then causes the printed areas to heat to a point where the oil in the corresponding areas of the receptor sheet is evaporated. This yields a negative disprint which, when dusted with powdered ink, produces a negative image.

Another variant method which has been suggested requires the use of an intermediate, oil-coated sheet which is placed face up over the document being copied and covered with a receptor sheet. Heat from the images distills oil from the intermediate sheet to form the disprint. This method would eliminate the need to coat the original with a film of oil.

Since transference of the oil image is made from the face of the original document to the surface of the receptor sheet in contact with the document, the copies, whether negative or positive, are reverse reading—i.e., they are mirror images of the original. To secure a first copy which is readable, a translucent receptor sheet must be

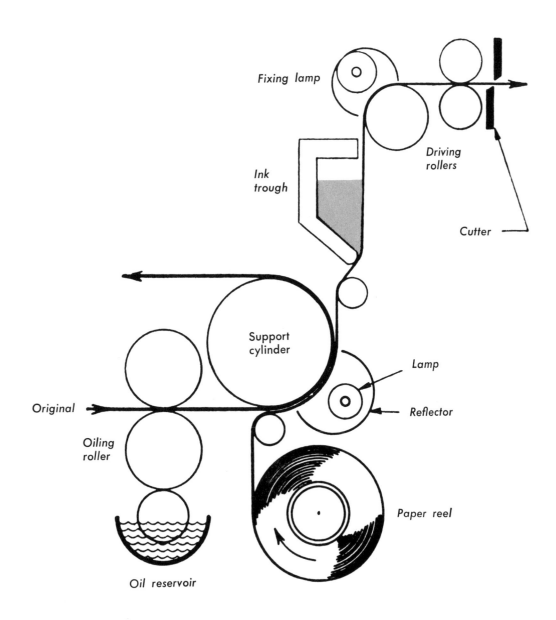

Fig. 107. Schematic diagram of Imagic process copying. (Copyright 1961 by the McGraw-Hill Publishing Company. Reprinted from *Product Engineering*, July 3, 1961.)

TABLE 21
THE IMAGIC PROCESS
(Principal Characteristics)

1. The process is:	Wet	
	Dry	X
2. Copies can be made by the following methods:	Contact Copying	X
	Contact-Reflex Copying	X
	Optical Copying	
	Microcopying	
	Projection Printing	
3. The process is capable of producing copies that are:	Positive, from Positives	X
	Negative, from Positives	X
	Positive, from Negatives	
	Negative, from Negatives	
4. The process is capable of producing intermediates or masters for subsequent edition printing by:	Diazo	X
	Offset	X
	Spirit Duplicating	
5. The permanence of copies is:	Archival	X *
	Limited	
	Unknown	
6. The quality of copies of continuous-tone originals is:	Excellent	
	Fair	
	Poor	X
7. The reproduction of fine details (e.g., small type faces, fine lines) is:	Excellent	
	Fair	X
	Poor	
8. The contrast of copies is:	High	X
	Moderate	
	Low	

9. The ability of the process to reproduce colored lines is:	Broad	
	Limited	X
10. The paper stock used is:	Plain, Any Color	X
	Specially Coated	
	White	
	Off-White	
11. The tendency of copies to curl is:	High	
	Noticeable	
	Low	X
12. The potential waste factor— If measured in area, is: If measured in cost, is:	Moderate	
	Low	
13. The approximate time required to make an 8½- by 11-inch copy is:	8 seconds.	
Per linear foot (8½ inches in width) is:	4 seconds.	
14. The materials cost per 8½- by 11-inch copy is:	See "Notes."	
15. Equipment for the process is priced at:	See "Notes."	

*NOTES

5. Copies are permanent if transferred to permanent supports.

14. While the actual cost of the materials is quite low, no cost-per-copy figures have been established.

15. The equipment is not yet commercially available.

used so that it can be read through the back. The alternative to this is to make a second copy from the first, thus re-reversing the image.

As with other thermographic processes, copies can be made only from originals printed with inks that are capable of absorbing infrared radiation. Most colored inks used in printing contain aniline dyes, which do not absorb heat and hence cannot be reproduced by the Imagic process. Other dye-formed images produced by such processes as diazo, Ektafax, spirit duplicating, etc., also cannot be copied. The process, moreover, is limited to contact and contact-reflex copying methods. An optical copying method, which would eliminate contact problems and provide for control over the size of the image, is not possible.

Despite these limitations, the Imagic process exhibits a number of characteristics of considerable interest and potential utility in the document-copying field. In the first place, the cost of the materials entailed (the oil and the powder used to form the image) is very low and, since the images are formed on ordinary paper stock, the cost per copy can be very low indeed. Secondly, copying can be done at quite a high rate of speed. Prototype equipment is reported to operate at 75 feet per minute. Thirdly, archival permanence of the copies can be achieved by transferring the images to high quality 100 percent rag stock or other suitable paper stocks.

At the present time, the Imagic process is not commercially available. Advanced research and developmental work on the process is now being done by the Unibeam Division of Unilever Ltd., in London, who have a licensing agreement with Imagic Processes Ltd., the parent company, covering certain European territories but not the United States. The prototype machines, which were demonstrated at an International Symposium on Document Copying held in London in 1962, were rotary-type machines for copying from loose-sheet documents, but a flat-bed model for copying pages from bound volumes has also been designed. It appears likely that a production-model office copier using the Imagic process would be both small and relatively inexpensive. Since resin-containing powdered inks are used to form the image, such a machine could also be used for the production of

very inexpensive paper masters for offset printing. From what is known about the process at this time, it would appear to have potential utility as a rapid, low-cost, card-reproduction process.

PHOTOCHROMIC PROCESSES

Photochromic substances may be defined as substances which can exist in two states—a colorless state and a colored state, and which can be changed from one state to the other by the action of light of appropriate wave length. With some photochromic substances, the change to a colored state results in a fairly stable image whereas, with other substances, the change is readily reversible. With these latter substances, images produced by light of a certain wave length can be "erased" by exposing the image to light of another wave length. Since image formation is accomplished entirely by the action of light, no development step is necessary and the process is, of course, completely dry.

Photo-Chromic Micro-Images

Extensive research on photochromism has been carried out by the National Cash Register Company[11] and has led to the development of a microreproduction system for documents which they call PCMI (Photo-Chromic Micro-Images). In the PCMI system, original documents are first converted to micro-images on 35 mm. perforated microfilm at a relatively low reduction ratio—e.g., 1:10. This film is then used as the input for a "camera-recorder." In the camera-recorder, an optical system is used to project images at a further reduction in size from the input microfilm to glass plates coated with a photochromic layer where they are recorded in a series of rows. The final reduction ratio can be controlled at this stage and may be as great as 1:220—a reduction in area of almost 50,000 times. The product of the camera-recorder is thus a high-reduction microfiche containing a very large number of images. A widely publicized example of the capabilities of PCMI is the recording of the complete text of a copy of the *Holy Bible* having 1,245 pages on a sheet of film only two inches square. In another application,

---

[11] National Cash Register Company, Industrial Products Division, Main at K Streets, Dayton, Ohio 45409.

2,520 pages were recorded on a 3- by 5-inch sheet of film.

Since images are formed immediately on the photochromic layer by the action of light alone, they can be inspected as they are recorded. This is done in the camera-recorder by means of a microscope. When a row of images has been recorded, the operator examines the images starting with the last image in the row and ending with the first. If all images are satisfactory, the photochromic plate is then advanced to a position for recording a second row of images. If any defective images are encountered, they are erased by exposure to light, and a new image is immediately recorded by repositioning the input microfilm to the needed page and making a second exposure.

Photochromic substances of the types used in PCMI are relatively stable at low temperatures, but not at the temperatures that would normally prevail in the making of duplicates from a photochromic master. Consequently, an intermediate copy is made on a high-resolution, silver halide emulsion to produce a photographic micro-image (PMI) master which is used in turn to produce copies for distribution. Despite the fact that distribution copies are of the third generation, the extremely high-resolution characteristics of the photochromic coating and the silver halide coatings employed make possible a resolution in the distribution copies of 650 to 750 lines per millimeter. Because of the extreme reduction in size of photochromic images, the surface of distribution copies must be protected from the possibility of scratching. This is accomplished by laminating the film between two thin sheets of a special plastic material.

For reading Photo-Chromic Micro-Images, the National Cash Register Company has devised a special reader which is capable of enlarging the extremely small images to original size.

The PCMI system[12] is not a copying system but a system for producing an intermediate (PMI) master from which distribution copies can be made. Its utility is therefore in the field of micro-

publishing, where a sizable edition is needed to defray the relatively high costs of producing the PMI master.

The Copy-Chrome process

The Copy-Chrome process is a photochromic process developed by Copymation, Inc.,[13] in which sheets of paper coated with photochromic substances are used to produce copies from translucent originals by direct-contact printing. The photochromic substances used are sensitive to ultraviolet light in a range of from 3,400 to 3,500 Angstroms and produce a blue image. They are relatively slow in speed—too slow for projection printing—but can be exposed in conventional contact printers, such as those used for diazo printing, provided the light source emits radiation of the wave length indicated.

Unlike the photochromic substances used for the production of Photo-Chromic Micro-Images, the substances used in the Copy-Chrome process are not easily reversible. The unexposed portions of Copy-Chrome copies retain their sensitivity to ultraviolet light. In certain copying applications, this can be an advantage since additional data can be added to a copy. It is also, however, a disadvantage since ultraviolet light—e.g., sunlight—can cause copies to darken.

XEROGRAPHIC FROST IMAGING

Frost imaging is a term applied to a special form of xerographic recording in which an electrostatic latent image is formed on a thin layer of plastic material.[14] Heat is then applied to the plastic layer to soften it. This causes the charged areas to wrinkle, or "frost," to a degree which is roughly proportional to the amount of exposure. When a frost image is projected through a lens, light, instead of being absorbed (as is the case with metallic silver or dye-formed images), is scattered by the frost pattern. This light-scattering effect is also roughly proportional to the degree of frosting. The frost pattern thus controls the amount of light

[12] A more detailed description of the PCMI system is given in: Wilbur C. Meyers, *PCMI Technology and Potential Applications* (Hawthorne, California: The National Cash Register Company, 1964).

[13] Copymation, Inc., 1800 Greenleaf Avenue, Elk Grove Village, Illinois 60007.
[14] Frost imaging is a development of the Xerox Corporation, Midtown Tower, Rochester, New York 14604.

TABLE 22
Photo-Chromic Micro-Images
(Principal Characteristics)

1. The process is:	Wet	
	Dry	X
2. Copies can be made by the following methods:	Contact Copying	
	Contact-Reflex Copying	
	Optical Copying	
	Microcopying	X
	Projection Printing	
3. The process is capable of producing copies that are:	Positive, from Positives	
	Negative, from Positives	
	Positive, from Negatives	X
	Negative, from Negatives	
4. The process is capable of producing intermediates or masters for subsequent edition printing by:	Diazo	
	Offset	
	Spirit Duplicating	
5. The permanence of copies is:	Archival	X *
	Limited	
	Unknown	
6. The quality of copies of continuous-tone originals is:	Excellent	X *
	Fair	
	Poor	
7. The reproduction of fine details (e.g., small type faces, fine lines) is:	Excellent	X
	Fair	
	Poor	
8. The contrast of copies is:	High	
	Moderate	X
	Low	

9. The ability of the process to reproduce colored lines is:	Broad	X *
	Limited	
10. The paper stock used is:	Plain, Any Color	
	Specially Coated	
	White	
	Off-White	
11. The tendency of copies to curl is:	High	
	Noticeable	
	Low	
12. The potential waste factor is:	Considerable	
	Moderate	
	Low	X
13. The approximate time required to make an 8½- by 11-inch copy is:	See the description of the process in the text.	
14. The materials cost per 8½- by 11-inch copy is:	See the description of the process in the text.	
15. Equipment for the process is priced at:	See "Notes."	

TABLE 23
The Copy-Chrome Process
(Principal Characteristics)

1. The process is:	Wet	
	Dry	X
2. Copies can be made by the following methods:	Contact Copying	X
	Contact-Reflex Copying	
	Optical Copying	
	Microcopying	
	Projection Printing	
3. The process is capable of producing copies that are:	Positive, from Positives	
	Negative, from Positives	X
	Positive, from Negatives	X
	Negative, from Negatives	
4. The process is capable of producing intermediates or masters for subsequent edition printing by:	Diazo	
	Offset	
	Spirit Duplicating	
5. The permanence of copies is:	Archival	
	Limited	
	Unknown	X
6. The quality of copies of continuous-tone originals is:	Excellent	
	Fair	X
	Poor	
7. The reproduction of fine details (e.g., small type faces, fine lines) is:	Excellent	X
	Fair	
	Poor	
8. The contrast of copies is:	High	
	Moderate	X
	Low	

9. The ability of the process to reproduce colored lines is:	Broad	
	Limited	X
10. The paper stock used is:	Plain, Any Color	
	Specially Coated	X
	White	X
	Off-White	
11. The tendency of copies to curl is:	High	
	Noticeable	X
	Low	
12. The potential waste factor is:	Considerable	
	Moderate	X
	Low	
13. The approximate time required to make an 8½- by 11-inch copy is:	A few seconds and up, depending on exposing equipment used.	
14. The materials cost per 8½- by 11-inch copy is:	About 5¢.	
15. Equipment for the process is priced at:	See "Notes."	

*NOTES

15. Copy-Chrome materials can be exposed in a number of contact copiers currently used for diazo copying.

reaching the projection surface, just as differences in density do in light-absorbing materials. When suitable transparent materials are used, a frost image is analogous in its function to transparencies produced by other processes, such as silver halide or diazo.

At the present time, frost imaging is still in a developmental stage, and no equipment is available. The characteristics of the frost-imaging technique appear to have considerable promise not only for document reproduction but also for other kinds of photography. The minimum frost grain size is stated to be about one micron (1/1000 of a millimeter), and a resolving power in excess of 100 lines per millimeter is routinely obtainable. This is comparable to the resolution obtained with silver halide films used for microphotography. Also, the fact that the degree of frosting (and hence of light-scattering) varies with the amount of exposure received indicates that frost imaging may be useful for recording continuous-tone subjects. Experimentally produced, continuous-tone frost images, while inferior to good silver halide images, are nonetheless greatly superior in quality to continuous-tone images produced by conventional xerographic methods.

THERMOPLASTIC RECORDING

Thermoplastic recording is a method of recording images which was developed by the General Electric Company[15] and is analogous in certain respects to frost imaging. A thermoplastic coating is laminated on a surface which is electrically conductive. Image formation is accomplished by depositing a pattern of electrons on the surface of the thermoplastic material in a manner similar to the way an image is formed on a television screen. In television, the electron pattern falls on a fluorescent screen, causing it to light up. In thermoplastic recording, heating the thermoplastic layer causes it to soften to a point where the electrons on the thermoplastic surface are attracted by the opposite charge of the electrically conductive layer. As in frost imaging, this causes a deformation of the plastic coating which is "fixed" by

cooling. The deformed areas have different light-transmitting properties from the undeformed areas and hence form a visible image when viewed through an optical system of appropriate design.

EDITION PROCESSES

Copying and *duplicating* have traditionally been regarded as completely different methods of reproducing documents, as indeed they were. The equipment, methods, and techniques used for producing single copies were quite different from the equipment, methods, and techniques used for producing an edition of, say, one hundred copies. In recent years, improvements in technology have brought, and continue to bring, copying and duplicating into a closer and closer interrelationship. Not only is it possible with a number of the newer copying processes to produce masters for spirit duplication or for offset printing, but, with one process—xerography—the cost of making copies in an edition directly from an original document is now competitive with the cost of short-run duplicating, thus bringing into being a "masterless" duplicating method. This advance is having a marked effect in business, industry, and government where short-run duplicating is extensively used and may presently have effects on the reproduction of research materials in those applications where multiple copies are needed.

Edition processes which have been in widespread use for many years include *mimeography, spirit duplicating*, and *offset duplicating*.[16]

Mimeography

Mimeography,[17] which is also known as stencil duplication, entails the use of a stencil made of strong, fibrous, coated tissue which is impervious to ink. The preparation of a stencil for printing is

---

[15] Thermoplastic recording is a development of the General Electric Company, Research Services and Research Laboratory, 1 River Road, Schenectady, New York 12306.

[16] An excellent guide for preparing masters for duplication processes is: *Instructions for Preparing Materials to be Printed or Duplicated* (Available for 35¢ from the Superintendent of Documents, U.S. Government Printing Office, Washington, D.C.).

[17] "Mimeography" comes from "Mimeograph" which originally was a trademark of the A. B. Dick Company. But, like "Photostat," the term has come to be generally used to refer to copies made by a *process* instead of copies made with a particular make of equipment.

most commonly done with a typewriter but can also be done by other means which are described later. When the type characters strike the surface of the stencil, they cut the surface so that ink can then pass through to form an image.

Stencils are printed on rotary-type machines usually consisting of a metal drum which contains ink and which has fine holes in its surface, an impression roller, a mechanism for feeding successive sheets of paper between the drum and impression roller, and a receiving tray for the finished copies. One type of machine employs a "dual-cylinder" method in which the ink is transferred from oscillating rollers through a silk screen to the stencil. Machines may be either of a hand-operated type equipped with a handle for rotating

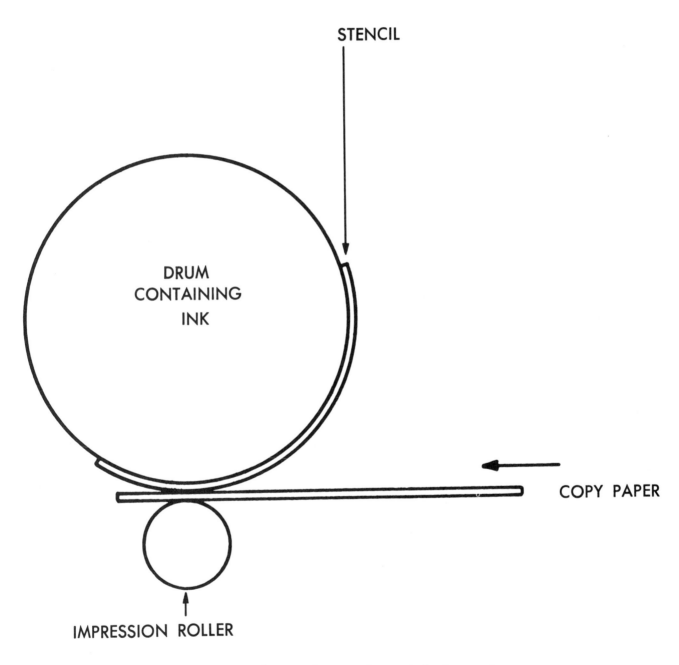

Fig. 108. Schematic diagram of a typical mimeograph duplicator.

the drum or may be electrically driven. With the stencil affixed to the drum, a sheet of copy paper is fed between the impression roller and the drum where ink is transferred by pressure through the image portions of the stencil to the copy paper (Figure 108).

There are three other methods that can be used for the preparation of stencils. Since physical cutting of the stencil surface is required to produce a printable image, drawings can be produced by mimeography by drawing directly on the stencil surface with special styli. A method that can be used to transfer the image of an existing original to a stencil is called *electronic scanning*. In a typical electronic scanner, the original to be copied and the stencil are wrapped side by side around a drum. As the drum rotates, the surface of the original is scanned by a tiny light beam. Differences in reflectance in the image are read by a photo-cell, converted into electrical impulses, and fed to a small electrical probe passing synchronously over the surface of the stencil. The electrical impulses cut the surface of the stencil in proportion to their strength. Electronic scanning produces stencils from which good-quality line copies and recognizable continuous-tone illustrations can be made. Since the original must be wrapped around a drum, electronic scanning is limited to the copying of materials in loose-sheet form.

Another method for the production of stencils from existing originals is a photographic technique which entails the use of a special photosensitive stencil. This method produces positive copies from

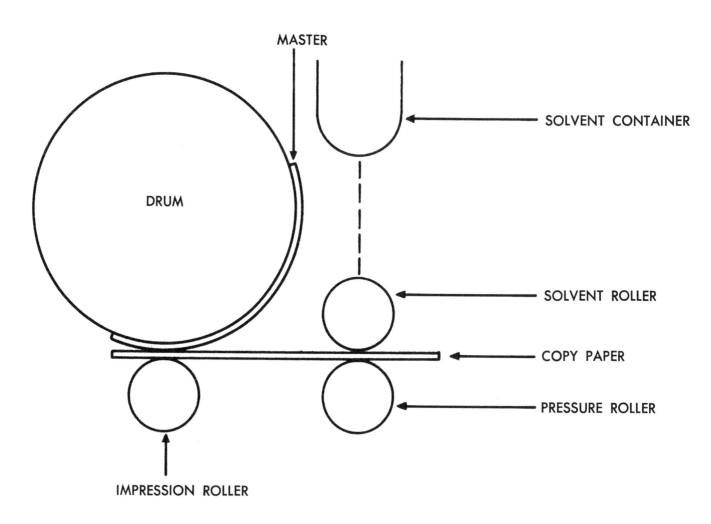

Fig. 109. Schematic diagram of spirit duplicating.

positive originals either by contact printing from translucent originals or projection printing. Exposed photosensitive stencils must be wet-processed and dried before they are used, which makes this method rather slow.

Depending upon the kind and quality of stencil used and the method of preparation, runs of from a few hundred up to several thousand are possible from mimeography.

Spirit duplicating

In spirit duplicating (also known as the hectograph process), a master, which is a specially prepared sheet of glazed paper, and a carbon backing sheet are employed. When an image is typed or drawn on a master, a carbon image is transferred to the back of the master sheet. The master is then printed on a small press which consists, typically, of a paper feeding mechanism, a pair of rollers (one of which is moistened with a solvent), a drum on which the master is placed, an impression roller, and a receiving tray for finished copies. When a sheet of copy paper is fed through the machine, its surface is moistened with solvent from the moistening roller and then passed between the drum holding the master and the impression roller. The solvent on the surface of the paper causes a thin layer of the carbon image on the master to adhere to the paper as it is pressed in contact with the master by the impression roller (Figure 109). Since a certain amount of the carbon is removed from the master with the making of each successive copy, spirit duplicating is limited to relatively short runs of up to a maximum of about 500 copies.

Spirit masters can also be prepared from existing originals by photographic and thermographic means using DTR or the Eichner process. Two methods are reported for making spirit masters by DTR. In one, developed by Agfa, a special dye-coated positive transfers dye to the unexposed (image) portions of the negative when the two sheets are processed together in a DTR processor. The negative, when dry, becomes the spirit master. In the second method, developed by Gevaert, a soft dye image is formed on the positive receiving sheet. This sheet is then pressed in contact with an ordinary spirit master to transfer the dye

image to the master. In the Eichner process, a thermocarbon and spirit master are placed in contact with the original to be copied and exposed in a thermographic exposing unit. Heat from the letters or lines making up the text softens the carbon so that it transfers to the spirit master. The use of Eichner process materials for making spirit masters is limited, of course, to the copying of texts which have a carbon or metallic content that will absorb and dissipate heat.

Offset duplicating

Offset duplicating gets its name from the fact that the right-reading image on an offset master must be transferred or "offset" to an intermediate roller to form a reverse-reading image which, in turn, is transferred to the copy paper to form a right-reading image. The printing principle of offset duplicating is one which has been used for centuries in lithography, i.e., that water and oil do not mix. Images on masters used for offset duplicating must be receptive to the somewhat oily inks used, while the background areas must be water-receptive.

Offset duplicators are somewhat more complex than stencil or spirit duplicators; they are generally more expensive and require greater operator skills. The offset process, however, is capable of much higher quality and much longer runs than mimeography or spirit duplicating. The essential elements of an offset duplicating machine, in addition to paper feeding and receiving components, are a series of rollers. These include a large roller which holds the offset master, rollers which ink the image, rollers which apply water to the background area, an intermediate rubber-covered roller called a blanket roller to which the image from the plate is transferred, and an impression roller which presses the copy paper in contact with the blanket roller (Figure 110).

Masters for offset duplicating are of many sizes and types, ranging from inexpensive paper masters for short-run duplicating to metal masters where very long runs must be made. Offset masters can be prepared by typing or drawing and by means of a number of photographic and thermographic processes, including Verifax, Ektalith, DTR, Thermo-Fax, Ektafax, xerography, Electro-

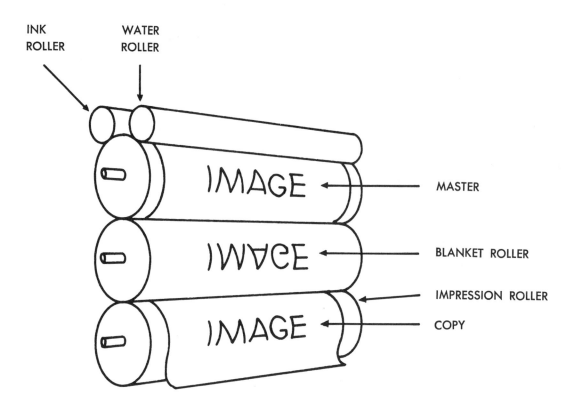

INK ROLLER

WATER ROLLER

IMAGE — MASTER

IWAGE — BLANKET ROLLER

— IMPRESSION ROLLER

IMAGE — COPY

Fig. 110. Schematic diagram of offset duplicating.

fax, Dual Spectrum (in conjunction with Thermo-Fax) and one autopositive process.

Adherography

Adherography is a duplicating process developed by the 3M Company which is similar in its working to the Imagic process, in that images in both of these processes are formed by the adherence of powder to a tacky latent image. For adherography, masters of two types are offered —direct image and facsimile. With direct-image masters, material is typed or drawn on the master. With facsimile masters, images from existing originals can be copied on to the master by using a Dual Spectrum intermediate and a Dual Spectrum copier.

Duplication from masters is done with a unit

called the "Speed Copier." In the Speed Copier, the master is wrapped around a drum. As the drum is rotated, sheets of a plain copy paper are fed into contact with the master and both sheets are exposed to infrared radiation. Heat from the image portions of the master causes substances on the surface of the master to soften and to adhere to the copy paper. The copy paper passes through a tray of black powder (toner) which covers the entire surface of the paper. The paper then moves to a vibrator, which dislodges loose powder from the background areas leaving a powder image clinging to the tacky image portions. The surface of the copy is then vacuumed to remove the loose powder and subjected to heat which fuses the powder image to the paper.

Copies are produced at a rate of forty per

minute and runs of approximately 200 to 250 copies can be made from a single master.

Xerographic duplicating

The Xerox Corporation now offers four machines for the making of low-cost multiple copies. (See the section on "Xerographic process.") Three of these are adaptations of the Xerox Model 813 and the Model 914 office copiers. Although the unit costs per copy are higher than equivalent costs of copies made by duplicating processes, the fact that the cost of preparing a master is eliminated makes duplicating by direct xerographic copying competitive for short runs. These machines operate at speeds ranging from 330 to 720 copies per hour. A fourth machine—the Xerox Model 2400—was designed for longer runs at lower per copy costs and at a speed of 2,400 copies per hour.

TABLE 24
Principal Characteristics of Reproduction Processes

		Silver Halide	Stabilization	Autopositive	Verifax	Ektalith	DTR
1. The process is:	Wet	X	X	X	X	X	X
	Dry						
2. Copies can be made by the following methods:	Contact copying	X	X	X	X		X
	Contact-reflex copying	X	X	X	X		X
	Optical copying	X	X	X		X	X
	Microcopying	X					
	Projection printing	X	X⁻	X			X
3. The process is capable of producing copies which are:	Positive, from positives	X	X*	X	X	X	X
	Negative, from positives	X	X	X*		X	X*
	Positive, from negatives	X	X	X*			X*
	Negative, from negatives	X	X*	X			X
4. The process is capable of producing intermediates or masters for subsequent edition printing by:	Diazo	X	X	X	X	X	X
	Offset	X*		X	X	X	X
	Spirit duplicating						X
5. The permanence of copies is:	Archival	X*		X*			
	Limited		X		X*	X*	X
	Unknown						
6. The quality of copies of continuous-tone originals is:	Excellent	X	X*				
	Fair		X*	X*			
	Poor				X	X	X
7. The reproduction of fine details (e.g., small type faces, fine lines) is:	Excellent	X	X*	X		X	X
	Fair				X		
	Poor						
8. The contrast of copies is:	High	X*	X*	X	X	X	X
	Moderate	X*	X*				
	Low	X*	X*				
9. The ability of the process to reproduce colored lines is:	Broad	X	X		X	X	X
	Limited			X			
10. The paper stock used is:	Plain, any color				X*	X*	
	Specially coated	X	X	X			X
	White	X	X	X			X
	Off-white	X*					X*
11. The tendency of copies to curl is:	High						
	Noticeable	X	X	X	X		X
	Low					X	
12. The potential waste factor is:	Considerable						
	Moderate	X	X	X	X		X
	Low					X	
13. The approximate time required to make an 8½- by 11-inch copy is:		X*	20 sec. up	15 sec. up	30 sec. or less	1 min. or less	30 sec. up
14. The materials cost per 8½- by 11-inch copy is:		4¢ up	5¢ up	6¢ up	12¢ to 2½¢	17¢ to 2½¢	6¢ up
15. Equipment for the process ranges in price from:		X*	$175 up	$225 up	$188 up	$565 up	$49 up

X* For explanatory data, refer to the full description of the process in Part 3, "Processes."

Diaversal	Polaroid	Dry Silver	Thermo-Fax	Eichner	Ektafax	Xerography	Electrofax	Diazo	Kalvar	Dual Spectrum	Electrolytic	Imagic	PCMI	Copy-Chrome
X							X*	X*						
	X*	X	X	X	X	X	X*	X*	X	X	X*	X	X	X
X*				X				X	X			X		X
			X	X	X			X		X		X		
X	X					X	X							
						X			X*				X	
X		X		X		X	X	X			X			
X	X		X		X	X	X	X	X	X		X		
		X						X*	X			X	X	X
		X				X		X*	X			X	X	X
X	X		X		X		X*	X	X	X				
X				X	X	X	X	X	X*	X		X		
			X	X	X	X	X	X		X		X		
			X	X										
	X*				X*	X*	X*				X*	X*	X*	
			X					X		X				
X		X*		X*										X
	X							X*	X*				X*	
		X					X	X*	X*	X	X			X
X			X	X	X	X						X		
X	X	X				X	X	X	X	X*	X		X	X
					X					X*	X			
			X	X										
X	X*	X	X*	X	X	X	X*	X*	X*	X*		X		
	X*		X*				X*	X*	X*	X*			X	X
											X			
X	X	X*				X	X				X		X*	
			X	X	X			X	X		X	X		X
				X*	X*	X						X		
X	X	X	X				X	X		X	X			X
X	X						X	X		X	X			X
		X	X*				X*							
											X			
X	X	X	X				X	X		X				X
				X	X	X	X	X	X			X		
X	X		X*	X						X		X*		X
		X				X			X		X	X*	X	
X*	2 min. up	5 to 10 sec.	4 sec.	15 sec.	25 sec. or less	1½ sec. up	10 sec. up	X*	30 sec. up	20 sec. up	10 sec.	8 sec.	X*	X*
10¢ up	X*	2¢	4¢ up	2.4¢ up	2¼¢±	1¢ up	2½¢ up	1¢ up	X*	4.4¢ up	9¢	X*	X*	5¢ up
X*	$60 up	$1795 up	$379 up	$240 up	$158 up	X*	$395 up	$300 up	$570 up	$150 up	$729 up	X*	X*	X*

4. METHODS AND TECHNIQUES

EYE-LEGIBLE COPIES FROM ORIGINALS

Eye-legible copies from original documents can be made by *contact copying* (either by the *direct method* or the *reflex method*) or by *optical-copying* methods in which a camera is employed. Copies made by contact methods are identical in size to that of the originals from which they were made, but optically produced copies, within the legibility limitations imposed by the unaided human eye, may be substantially smaller in size. Conversely, the legibility of a text printed in a small type face may be considerably enhanced if an optically produced copy is larger than the original document.

CONTACT COPYING: DIRECT METHOD

In contact copying by the direct method, the subject being copied is placed against a sheet of sensitized material and held in contact with it while light is passed *through the subject* to form a latent image (Figure 111). Subjects to be copied by the direct method must be:

(a) Sufficiently translucent to permit light to pass through them to the light-sensitive coating.

(b) Printed on one side only (See Figure 112).

Depending on the characteristics of the original, the process employed and the copying procedure used, four different types of copies can be obtained by the direct method:

(1) Right reading, negative
(2) Reverse reading, negative
(3) Right reading, positive
(4) Reverse reading, positive

If a positive original, such as a typewritten sheet, is placed face up on a sheet of negative-working sensitized material, the copy will be a right-reading negative (Figure 113). If it is placed face down, the copy will be a reverse-reading negative (Figure 114). If this reverse-reading negative is then placed face down on a sheet of negative-working material, the resulting copy will be a right-reading positive (Figure 115). A right-reading positive can also be obtained by copying a positive original in a face-up position on direct-positive material (Figure 116) and, by placing the original face down, a reverse-reading positive is obtained (Figure 117). Reverse-reading positives can be used in turn to make right-reading negatives or positives, according to the process employed.

A primary requirement for clarity in the copies to be obtained is uniform contact between the original and the sensitized material. When an original, such as a typewritten sheet, is copied in a face-up position to obtain a right-reading copy, the text is not in contact with the sensitized surface but is separated from it by the thickness of the paper used. This causes some lessening in the sharpness of the image formed and is proportional to the thickness of the paper. Typewritten texts of good quality are usually bold enough to withstand this loss without appreciable impairment of legibility, but printed texts with much smaller characters and a finer line structure may not be reproducible because of the loss of sharpness introduced by the thickness of the paper support on which they are printed (Figure 118). Such texts can be successfully reproduced by making a first contact copy with the text in a face-down position to obtain a reverse-reading copy and then making a second copy from the reverse-reading copy to obtain a right-reading copy (Figure 119). If a reverse-reading negative is made, it becomes an intermediate from which one or many positive copies can be made. Reverse-reading positives perform the same function in direct-positive processes.

CONTACT COPYING: REFLEX METHOD

In contact copying by the reflex method with light-sensitive materials, the subject being copied is held in face-to-face contact with a sheet of sensitized material while light is passed *through the sensitized material,* where it is absorbed by the black characters of the text but is reflected back to the surface of the sensitized material by the white background areas. Although light passes through the entire light-sensitive coating to reach the surface of the original, the characteristics of reflex-copying materials are such that, at normal exposures, only the combined effect of transmitted and reflected light in the white background areas is sufficient to form a latent image (Figure 120). Reflex copies, for the most part, are both reversed in values and reverse-reading. Depending on the process used, negative or positive copies which are

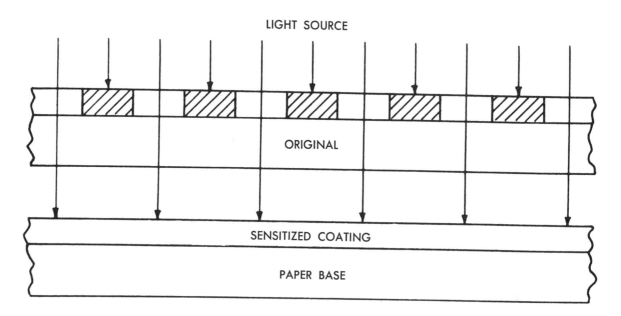

Fig. 111. Copying a document by the direct-contact method. The document is placed face up over a sheet of photosensitive material with the sensitized coating also face up. Light passes through the background areas of the document to the light-sensitive emulsion layer, but it is absorbed by the black characters of the text. There is always a slight loss of clarity in copies made by the direct-contact method, because the printed surface of the original and the emulsion surface of the photosensitive paper are not in contact. The extent of this loss will vary with the thickness of the paper base of the original document. The resulting copies are negatives which are right-reading.

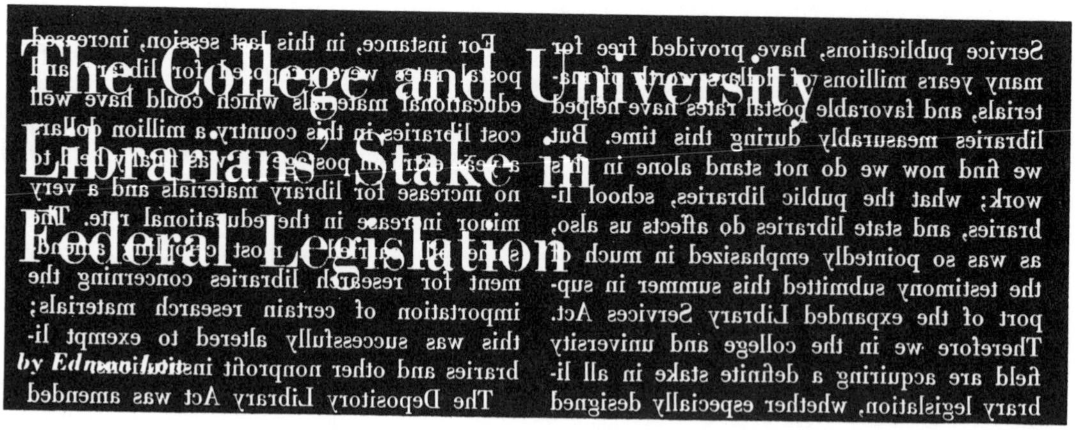

Fig. 112. Two-sided originals cannot be copied by the direct method because the text on both sides of the original would record on the sensitized material.

```
a b c d e f

g h i j k l

m n o p q r

s t u v w x

y z 1 2 3 4
```

Fig. 113. Left: original. Right: right-reading, direct-contact negative copy made with the original face up.

```
a b c d e f

g h i j k l

m n o p q r

s t u v w x

y z 1 2 3 4
```

Fig. 114. Left: original. Right: reverse-reading, direct-contact negative copy made with the original face down.

```
a b c d e f

g h i j k l

m n o p q r

s t u v w x

y z 1 2 3 4
```

Fig. 115. Left: reverse-reading negative. Right: right-reading, direct-contact positive copy.

a b c d e f   a b c d e f

g h i j k l   g h i j k l

m n o p q r   m n o p q r

s t u v w x   s t u v w x

y z 1 2 3 4   y z 1 2 3 4

Fig. 116. Left: original. Right: right-reading, direct-contact positive copy made with original face up.

a b c d e f   ʇ ǝ b ɔ d ɐ

g h i j k l   l ʞ ſ ı ɥ ƃ

m n o p q r   ɹ b d o u ɯ

s t u v w x   x w ʌ n ʇ s

y z 1 2 3 4   ⅎ Ɛ ᄅ l z ʎ

Fig. 117. Left: original. Right: reverse-reading, direct-contact positive copy made with original face down.

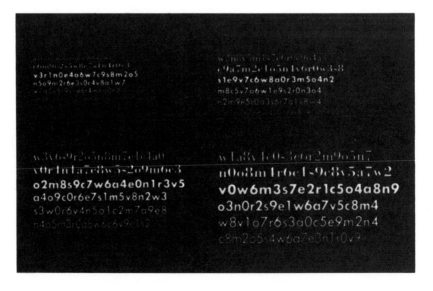

Fig. 118. Loss of sharpness resulting from direct-contact printing of an original printed on a thick paper base.

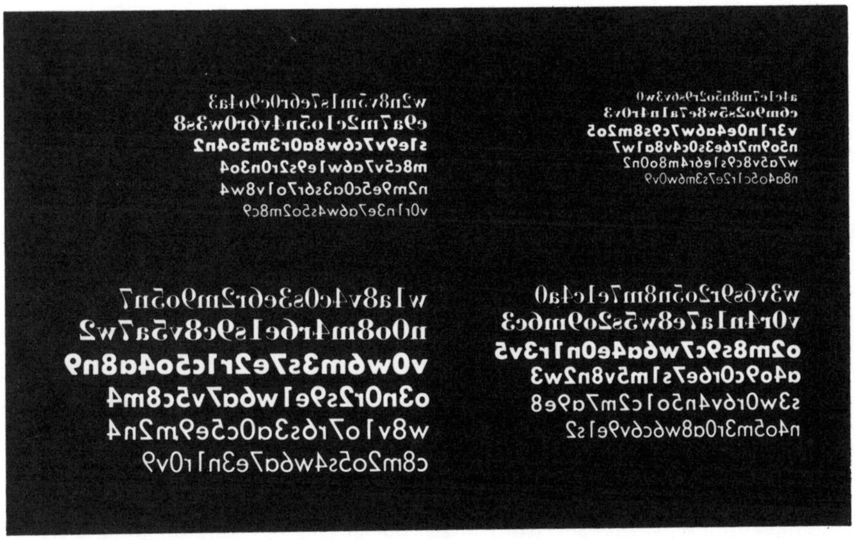

a4c1e7m8n5o2r9s6v3w0
c6m9o2s5w8e7a1n4r0v3
v3r1n0e4a6w7c9s8m2o5
n5o9m2r6e3s0c4v8a1w7
w7a5v8c9s1e6r4m8o0n2
n8a4o5c1r2e7s3m6w0v9

w2n8v5m1s7e6r0c9o4a3
e9a7m2c1o5n4v6r0w3s8
s1e9v7c6w8a0r3m5o4n2
m8c5v7a6w1e9s2r0n3o4
n2m9e5c0a3s6r7o1v8w4
v0r1n3e7a6w4s5o2m8c9

w3v6s9r2o5n8m7e1c4a0
v0r4n1a7e8w5s2o9m6c3
o2m8s9c7w6a4e0n1r3v5
a4o9c0r6e7s1m5v8n2w3
s3w0r6v4n5o1c2m7a9e8
n4o5m3r0a8w6c6v9e1s2

w1a8v4c0s3e6r2m9o5n7
n0o8m4r6e1s9c8v5a7w2
v0w6m3s7e2r1c5o4a8n9
o3n0r2s9e1w6a7v5c8m4
w8v1o7r6s3a0c5e9m2n4
c8m2o5s4w6a7e3n1r0v9

Fig. 119. Above: reverse-reading negative made by placing an original printed on a thick paper base face down on the sensitized material. Below: right-reading positive obtained by direct-contact printing from reverse-reading negative.

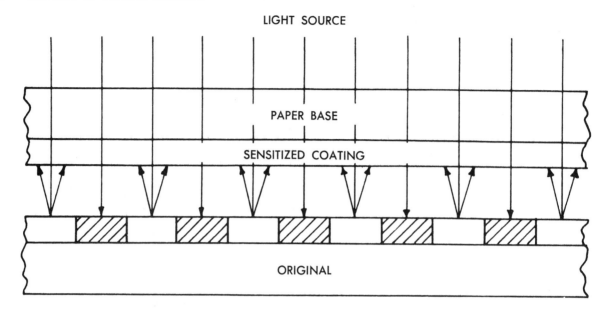

Fig. 120. Copying a document by the contact-reflex method. The document is placed face up and covered with a sheet of photosensitive paper with the sensitized coating face down. Light is passed through the paper base and sensitized coating to the surface of the document where it is absorbed by the black characters of the text but is reflected back to the light-sensitive surface by the white background areas. Although light passes through the entire sensitized surface to reach the surface of the original, only the additional exposure that the sensitized coating receives by the light reflected back from the white areas of the original affects the coating to the point where a visible image can subsequently be produced by development. The copy, which is both negative and reverse reading, can be used as a master for printing right-reading positives by the direct-contact method (see Figure 121).

right-reading can be made from the reflex copy by contact printing by the direct method (Figure 121). An important advantage of the reflex method is that it can be used to copy originals printed on both sides of the paper. In direct-contact copying, the maximum resolution which can be obtained is of a very high order, but in contact-reflex copying some loss occurs due to light-scattering effects (Figure 122).

In copying with heat-sensitive materials, heat is passed through the sensitized material to the surface of the subject being copied where it is absorbed by the characters of the text and radiated back to the heat-sensitive material to darken it. An essential requirement for subjects to be copied by thermal processes is that the text have a carbon or metallic component which will absorb and dissipate heat. Reflex copies made by thermal methods have the same tonal relationship as the original and are right-reading.

CONTACT COPYING: EQUIPMENT FOR CONTACT AND CONTACT-REFLEX COPYING

Equipment for contact copying ranges from the extremely simple and inexpensive to large, expensive, high-volume, automated equipment. One of the simplest devices, which has been used since the earliest days of photography, is the printing frame. The printing frame consists of a wooden frame and a sheet of glass, similar in design to a simple picture frame, and a platen equipped with springs to hold the sensitized material and the document in firm contact (Figure 123). Contact-reflex exposures of pages from bound volumes can be made with nothing more than a light source and a sheet of glass to hold the sensitized material in contact with the page to be copied, provided the page is flat enough for good contact (Figure 124).

Equipment for document reproduction by con-

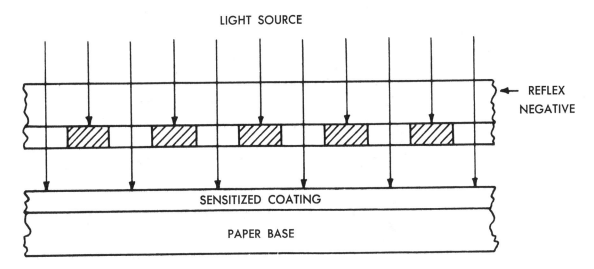

Fig. 121. Making a positive copy from a reflex negative. The reflex negative is placed face down over a sheet of photosensitive paper with the sensitized coating face up. Because the reflex image is in contact with the photosensitive coating, the resulting copies are quite sharp.

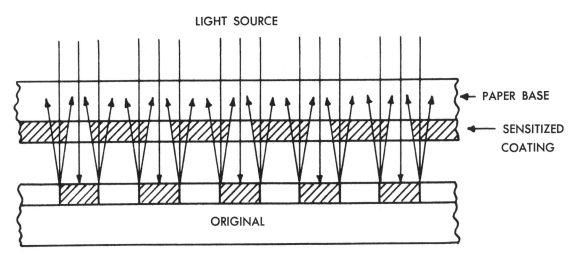

Fig. 122. Light-scattering effects. In contact-reflex copying, when light is reflected from the surface of the original document back to the surface of the sensitized material, it does not return in a direct line but scatters to each side of the point on which it falls. This causes a gradation of density at the edges of the lines which reduces sharpness.

tact methods is of two types—*rotary printers* and *flatbed printers*. Rotary printers (Figure 125) consist of a light source, usually tubular, and a set of belts and rollers which transport the original to be copied in contact with a sheet of sensitized material past the light source. Exposure is regulated by varying the amount of light falling on the material being copied or by varying the speed at which the material passes the light source. Rotary printers are limited to the copying of loose-sheet material.

Flatbed printers consist of an enclosure, usually in the form of a box deep enough to contain the light source, which is covered with a sheet of glass or translucent plastic, and a cover plate. The subject to be copied and the sensitized material are placed in contact on the glass (called the *exposure surface*) and held in firm contact by

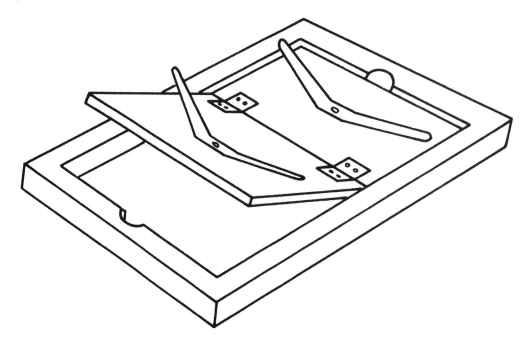

Fig. 123. Contact printing frame.

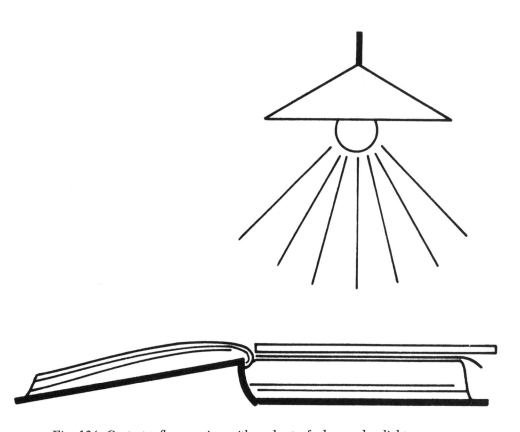

Fig. 124. Contact-reflex copying with a sheet of glass and a light source.

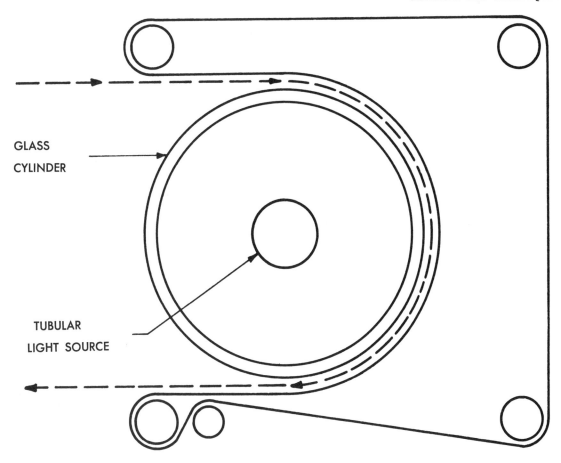

GLASS
CYLINDER

TUBULAR
LIGHT SOURCE

Fig. 125. Schematic diagram of a rotary printer.

means of the cover (Figure 126). Flatbed print-ers can be used to copy either loose-sheet material or material in bound form.

Variations in the design of flatbed printers can have considerable influence on their utility and efficiency as devices for making contact reflex copies of pages from bound volumes. Of particular importance is the *book-position angle*. Flatbed printers in the form of a rectangular box usually have a book position angle of 90° (Figure 126). Combination machines, such as those commonly used with the diffusion-transfer-reversal process which have a developing unit in front of the exposure surface, often have a book-position angle much greater than 90° (Figure 127). Others show evidence of having been designed with a clearer idea of the problems entailed in bound-volume copying and have book-position angles of less than 90° (Figure 128). As the illustrations show, the smaller the book-position angle, the easier it is to

position the volume in contact with the exposing surface, while, at the same time, the possibility of damage to the spine of the volume from the

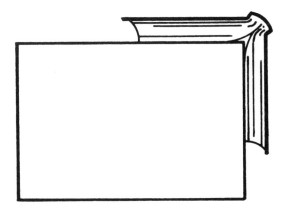

Fig. 126. Schematic diagram of flatbed printer consisting of a box containing a light source surmounted by a sheet of glass on which the sensitized material and the subject to be copied are placed.

application of pressure to achieve contact and coverage is greatly reduced.

A second design feature of importance in bound-volume copying has to do with the manner in which the glass exposure surface is mounted. In some flatbed printers, the glass is supported at the edge where the inner margin of the volume is placed with a strip of wood or metal which is fairly wide (Figure 129). Such a design may make

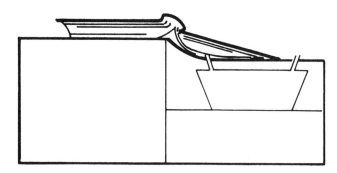

Fig. 127. Schematic diagram of a combination exposing and processing device showing the effect that the location of the processing section has on the book position angle.

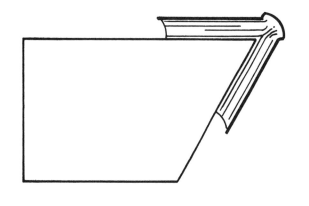

Fig. 128. Book position angles of less than 90°.

it impossible to copy pages from volumes having narrow inner margins since the support will obscure part of the text. Pages having narrow inner margins are much more easily copied on printers having a very narrow support or none at all along the edge where the inner margin of the page will be placed.

Equipment for making eye-legible copies by the direct-contact or contact-reflex methods, and in some cases both, is available for use with the following processes (q.v.):

(1) Silver Halide
(2) Stabilization
(3) Autopositive
(4) Gelatin-dye-transfer (Verifax, Ready-print)
(5) Diffusion-transfer-reversal
(6) Diaversal
(7) Thermo-Fax
(8) Eichner
(9) Ektafax
(10) Diazo
(11) Dual Spectrum
(12) Imagic
(13) Copy-Chrome

CONTACT COPYING: TECHNIQUES

Exposure

The principal problem with most processes used for contact and contact-reflex copying is the predetermination of the proper exposure interval. This is most easily done by running a series of test copies typical of the originals to be copied and listing the exposure settings for the best copies obtained from each original. If copies are to be made from originals on paper stocks of various colors, tests should be run to determine what percentage of increase over the base exposure will be required. Similar tests should be run for paper stocks having different reflectances, such as newsprint or coated stocks having a high sheen.

For making copies by the direct method, tests should be run on originals having different degrees of translucence. For making direct-contact copies from reflex negatives, exposure tests should be run on negatives of different densities.

With some types of materials, there may be some variation in the exposure settings required

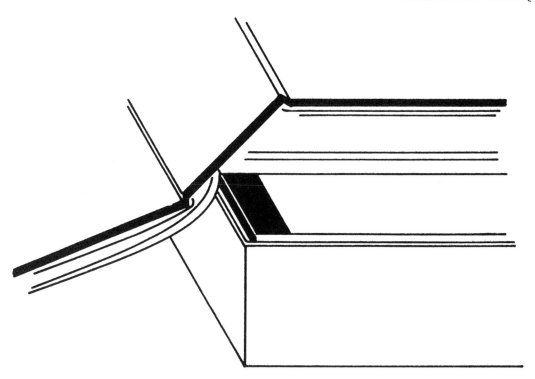

Fig. 129. A metal strip supporting the edge of the glass exposing surface prevents the copying of text close to the inner margin.

because of variations in speed between one manufacturing run and another. Each manufacturing run is usually identified by a serial number printed on the container. If more than one package or box of materials is being ordered, the order should specify that all boxes carry the same number. When materials bearing a different number are received, a test exposure should be made to determine whether there is a difference in speed and the percentage of difference. This percentage difference can then be applied to the list of former settings, increasing or decreasing each by the same percentage.

Another factor affecting exposure is encountered in processes such as DTR or Verifax that use a solution containing developing agents. As the solution is used or becomes oxidized from exposure to air, it becomes progressively weaker. Changes in exposure may be required to compensate for this loss of developer strength.

Some processes are more susceptible to fluctuations in line voltage than others. In cases where this is a problem, the equipment should be installed on a line that does not carry other equip-

ment, such as electric heaters, which draw a great deal of current. If this is not possible, it may be necessary to install a voltage-regulating device to stabilize the electrical input to the equipment.

Processing

The processing of sensitized materials is best accomplished if it is done in accordance with the manufacturer's recommendations for the particular material used. With ordinary silver halide materials, processing follows the usual steps of developing, rinsing, fixing, washing, and drying. Some variations in development time can be tolerated to compensate for overexposure, but underexposures can seldom be salvaged by prolonging development. In estimating exposures, allowance should be made for this factor. If copies are to be permanent, care should be used in the fixing and washing steps. In the first place, fixing must be complete. All of the unexposed silver halides must be removed from the emulsion. At the same time, fixation must not be unduly prolonged. If prints are allowed to remain in the fixing bath too long, the materials in the fixing bath are taken up into the fibrous structure of the paper base and become very difficult to remove, even by very extended washing.

Following fixation, all of the residual chemicals remaining in the emulsion and paper base must be washed out. The washing step can be speeded up considerably if, after a first brief rinse, the prints are soaked in a hypo-clearing solution.

Processed films should be hung in a dust-free enclosure until they are dry, or they can be dried with a warm-air blower equipped with a filter to remove dust particles. If a belt-type dryer is used for print drying, *all* the prints must be thoroughly fixed and washed before drying, whether permanence is a requirement or not. Improperly washed prints will leave a residue of chemicals on the belt which can contaminate other prints dried at a later time.

With most of the processes currently used for document reproduction by contact methods, processing is done in small, compact machines, and no control over image quality in the processing step is possible. Here, again, the materials recommended by or supplied by the manufacturer should be used with due attention being paid to such factors as temperature and solution life. One variation from the machine-processed result is possible with the stabilization process. Following development and stabilization, prints can be made permanent by treating them in a fixing bath and washing them.

Loose-sheet originals

In copying loose-sheet originals, such as manuscript or typescript pages, card files, maps, or second-generation copies of originals by either the direct contact or contact-reflex method, little in the way of techniques is required, but certain precautions should be noted.

Originals or copies of originals which are high in contrast should, where possible, be copied on low- or moderate-contrast materials.

Rare, valuable, fragile, or brittle documents should only be copied on flat-bed printers that have relatively low-intensity light sources and generate no appreciable amount of heat. Under no circumstances should they be copied on rotary printers.

Card files

Cards can be reproduced by contact-reflex copying, either singly or in groups, by a number of processes and in several different ways.

(1) With processes such as conventional silver halide or DTR, copies can be made photographically on a card-weight stock.

(2) With Verifax and Ektalith, small editions can be produced by transferring the matrix image to a special card-weight stock that has sufficient absorbency to hold the dye image.

(3) With Ektafax and xerography, images can be transferred directly to standard library card stocks. With Ektafax, small editions can be produced from a single master.

(4) Card-weight diazo copies can be printed from transparent or translucent intermediates produced by the processes listed in Table 16.

(5) As is shown in Table 24, many processes are capable of producing intermediates for offset duplicating and some for spirit duplicating.

If single cards are copied directly, registration is a relatively minor problem. If, however, multiple copies are being made of cards in groups (e.g., four at a time on an 8½- by 11-inch sheet) by processes such as DTR or Verifax, great care must be taken at each step to maintain registration. Sets which are in proper registration can be cut in groups, whereas sets which are not in registration must be cut individually. If cards having a marked difference in reflectance are being copied, each group of four cards should be made up of cards having approximately the same reflectance.

Bound originals

In making contact-reflex copies from bound volumes, considerably more in the way of techniques is required. The problems which must be solved are:

(1) Handling the volume during copying in ways which will prevent damage to the volume.

(2) Positioning the volume on the copier so that the entire text area is on the exposure surface where light can reach it. This is referred to as *coverage.*

(3) Achieving uniform contact over the entire text area. This requires a certain amount of pres-

sure, applied either mechanically or by hand.

(4) Predetermining the correct exposure interval.

Volume handling. Since the design of most flatbed printers necessitates handling and placing the volume in an upside-down position, techniques for volume handling are of considerable importance. The variety of sizes, shapes, weights, and other conditions in bound volumes precludes the possibility of laying down specific rules for handling that will apply in all cases. An operator must experiment to find hand positions and hand motions that will be effective. There are, however, several general rules which have proved to be helpful:

(1) First of all, examine the volume carefully to determine what its characteristics are. Note in particular any points of fragility, such as weakness of the binding or brittleness of the paper.

(2) In lifting and placing the volume, use both hands, and move slowly and carefully.

(3) Before lowering the volume onto the exposure surface, examine it at both ends to make sure the page to be copied is flat and straight.

(4) To secure complete coverage at the inner margin, *pull* the page forward onto the exposure surface as shown in Figure 130. Do not push the volume as shown in Figure 131.

(5) If, because of size, weight, or tightness of the binding, it is apparent that difficulties may be

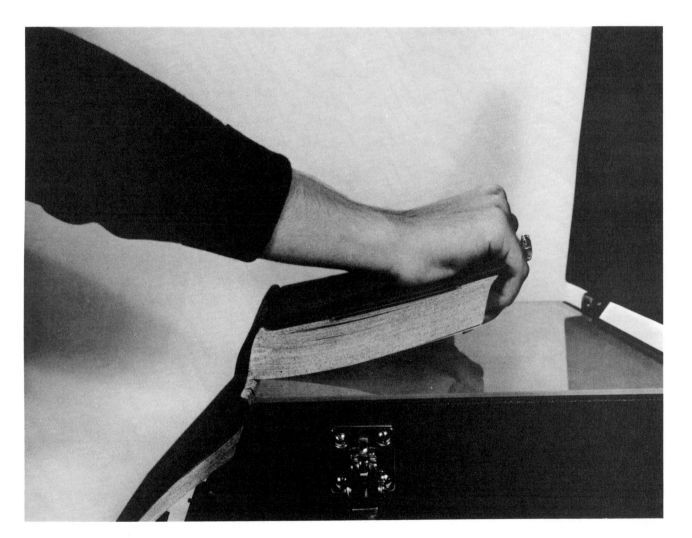

Fig. 130. Pulling a book onto the exposure surface to secure full coverage at the inner margin.

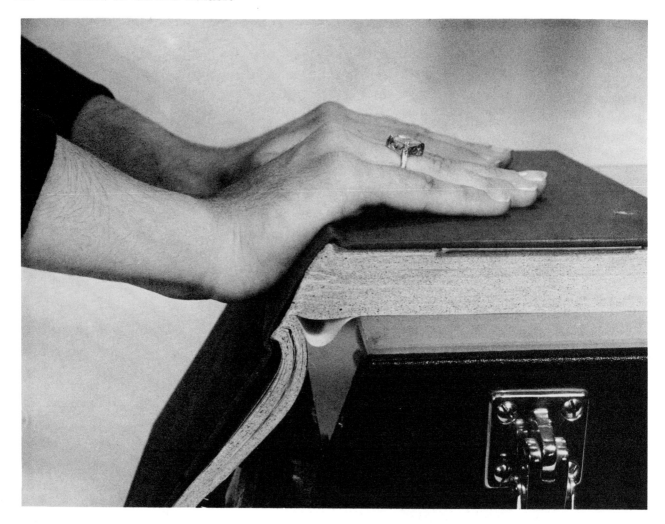

Fig. 131. Potential damage to a book page caused by pushing the book onto the copier.

encountered in positioning the volume for copying, make a trial run, using a sheet of ordinary paper in lieu of the sensitized paper, to determine what procedure will be best.

(6) After the exposure has been made, do not leave the volume on the copier unless it is certain that there is no possibility that it might fall off.

(7) In removing the volume from the copier, remove it slowly and with care. If it is necessary to remove the volume immediately after exposure, remove it together with the sensitized material, closing the volume as you do to protect the negative from exposure to ambient light (Figure 132).

(8) If the flatbed printer being used has a processing section at the front, be sure that over-

hanging pages do not come into contact with chemically contaminated surfaces. With most flatbed printers of this type, a cardboard shield can be easily installed which will prevent this from occurring.

Coverage. In copying book pages with any copier that employs the contact-reflex method, the two primary problems which must be solved are coverage and contact. For the most part, coverage is a matter of machine design, although certain techniques can be helpful.

Problems in coverage occur when (a) the inner margin of the page is narrow, (b) when the binding is tight, or (c) when both of these conditions exist. The solution to the problem of coverage is simply a matter of applying force by one means or another. How much force can be applied without damaging the binding is largely a matter of judgment and experience.

APPLYING PRESSURE. A volume that is tightly bound tends to force itself away from the edge of the exposing surface. The greater the angle to which the volume must be opened, the more marked this effect becomes. To overcome this, once the volume has been positioned on the copier, pressure must be applied against the spine of the volume to hold it in position in addition to the pressure needed for contact (Figure 133). In

copying large volumes by hand-pressure methods, an operator may occasionally require an assistant who can apply pressure to the spine for coverage while the operator applies pressure on the volume for contact.

As is shown in Figure 134, the problem of coverage is greatly simplified if the book position angle is substantially smaller than 90°.

Contact. The problem of contact can be solved in a variety of ways. Contact, as has been stated, requires a certain amount of pressure—at times a very great amount of pressure. Pressure alone,

Fig. 132. Removing a volume from a copier. With the sensitized material held in place, the volume is lifted and allowed to close of its own weight to protect the sensitized material from ambient light.

however, is not the only answer to the problem. Two other methods which simplify the problem of contact are in common use. The first is the use of some sort of firm backing material that can be placed behind a page to provide a surface against which the page can be flattened under pressure. The second is to provide a *soft* rather than a hard surface, which will permit the sensitized paper to conform under pressure to any unevenness of the surface of the page being copied. The methods and materials used to achieve contact in these different ways may be classed respectively as *non-conformable* or *conformable*. Each has its advantages.

The Contoura, which gets its name from its use of the principle of conformability, has, over its

light source, a translucent plastic envelope which is partially filled with air. A similar plastic envelope known as the "Book Printing Pillow," sold as an accessory by the Nord Photocopy and Business Equipment Corp., can be used as an accessory backing material with other machines.

THE USE OF BACKING MATERIALS. An ideal non-conformable backing material would be one that is thin enough to reach deeply into the inner margin of a book, flexible enough to follow the curvature of a tight binding, and rigid enough to provide a firm, flat surface against which a page can be flattened.

Of the various conformable and non-conformable backing materials that can be used—cardboard, plastic, metal, Masonite, the Book Printing

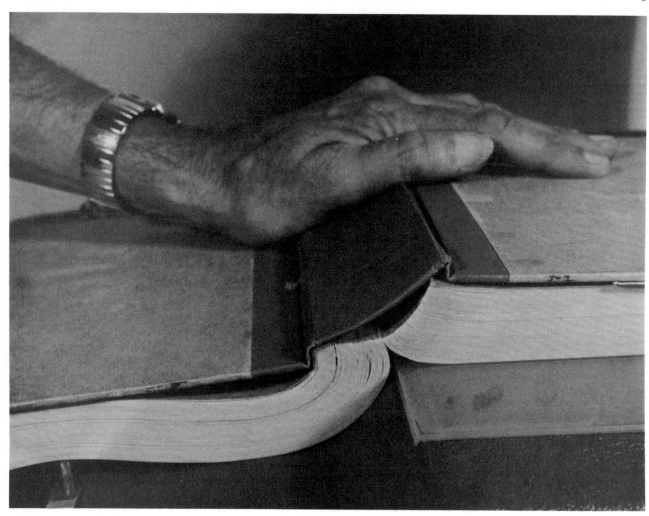

Fig. 133. Applying hand pressure to the spine to improve coverage and contact at the inner margin.

Fig. 134. Improved coverage at inner margin with copier having a book position angle of less than 90°.

Pillow—none possesses the properties or combination of properties that would make it universally useful. The choice of a backing material, therefore, must be based on the particular conditions encountered in the volume being copied. Here again, no specific rules can be laid down. Experience alone can show which material will work best with each subject. In general, however, it has been found that, in copying pages which are considerably wrinkled, creased, or warped, conformable backing materials often yielded superior results with less effort on the operator's part. Non-conformable backing materi-

als could be used with such subjects only if a very great amount of pressure could be brought to bear to flatten such pages into contact with the sensitized material.

A non-conformable plastic backing sheet is thin and provides a very smooth surface. However, its very toughness, its springiness, and the sharpness of its edges may make it hazardous to use when copying pages that are dry and brittle and inclined to crack easily. With subjects such as these, thin cardboard, which is much softer, may be the preferred material. As is shown in Figure 135, a rigid backing material tends to force the book page to bend sharply around the edge of the backing sheet. Even fairly good-quality papers may become weakened by such treatment.

In the interests of protecting the volume from accidental damage, while at the same time providing a suitable backing surface for proper contact, the backing material should not be placed directly behind the page to be copied. Three or four or more additional pages should be allowed to inter-

material from slipping away from the inner margin area is to fold it at the edge so that it overlaps well into the inner margin area. (Figure 136). This technique is also sometimes helpful in improving contact at the inner margin. With unusually large or heavy volumes, the sensitized material can be pre-positioned on the copier and held in place with tape (Figure 137). When this technique is used, room lights must be dimmed or the material

Fig. 135. Sharp bending of a book page caused by using too rigid a backing sheet.

vene wherever possible. The additional thickness of a few pages adds strength, which reduces the chances of accidental damage to the page being copied.

With the introduction of a backing material as a necessary aid for contact, techniques must be devised for the accurate positioning of three components—the page to be copied, the backing sheet, and the sensitized material. Frequently, one or more of these may get out of position or become skewed. One method of preventing the sensitized

shielded from the light until the book has been placed over it.

The backing material should be cut to a size only slightly larger than the height of the page being copied. If it extends too far out at either side, it becomes difficult to examine and correct the positioning of the page and the sensitized material.

If the backing sheet extends only from the inner margin to slightly beyond the outer margin of the book, it may tend to slip away from the inner margin or to become skewed. If a glass-topped copier is being used, the backing sheet should be cut to fit against the back edge of the copier and should extend forward to reach exactly to the front edge of the glass. As the book is positioned on the copier, the backing sheet will then remain firmly in place and will extend all the way into the inner margin as far as the binding will permit.

Copies of thin or translucent originals, such as folding plates printed on one side, are improved if such originals are backed with a white material. Copies of two-sided materials which are thin are often improved if the original is backed with a dark-colored material. This reduces the propensity of the text on the one side of the page to partially record and thereby obscure the text on the other side. However, if the field of illumination of the copier is at all uneven, dark backing materials tend to accentuate this condi-

tion, causing considerable local under- or overexposure.

If the volume is removed from the copier (as shown in Figure 132) with both the exposed negative and the backing sheet still in their place, the backing sheet will serve as a place marker if additional pages are to be copied.

The efficiency of any given backing material will be affected by the number and condition of the pages *behind* the backing sheet. If, for example, there are several folded plates between the backing sheet and the cover, pressure, regardless of the amount applied, will be uneven unless a very rigid backing material can be used.

The presence of book-charge-card envelopes, tipped-in plates, or even place-marker slips may also cause pressure to be uneven resulting in loss of contact. This effect may also occur if the cover of the volume is warped. Contact can be improved in all such cases by interposing a second backing

Fig. 136. Folding the sensitized material to fit into the margin.

Fig. 137. Holding the sensitized material in place with tape.

sheet of a very rigid material (such as Masonite) at another point in the volume where it can function to even out the pressure applied.

Once an operator has become experienced in the uses of different types of backing materials, the kind of backing material to be selected for any given book-copying problem can usually be determined from an examination of the page to be copied and the volume in which it is found. Any unevenness of the surface of the page can be discovered by running one's fingers across it. An examination of the pages beneath will reveal the presence of folding plates or other conditions which may interfere with the evenness of contact pressure. The quality of the paper, the extent of the inner margin, the tightness of the binding, and other conditions will all affect the choice of the backing material to be used and how it will be used. The important thing, if failures, waste, and possible damage to the book are to be avoided, is that the operator first study his subject to learn just what problems he has to deal with before he attempts to make a copy.

APPLYING PRESSURE. If a copier has no mechanical pressuring system, hand pressure must be applied to achieve proper contact. Just how much hand pressure an operator must apply is a matter of experience and judgment. If the text is bold, a slight loss of contact may not impair legibility. If, on the other hand, the characters are small, perfect contact must be maintained. More pressure will be required if the surface of the page is warped, creased, or wrinkled. Because the amount of pressure required for any given subject cannot be determined in advance, waste copies from poor contact can be avoided only if more than enough pressure is always applied. If hand pressure must be used, the copier should be placed on a low table so that the operator's weight, not just the strength he can exert with his hands, can be used.

The use of a sheet of rigid material, such as Masonite, placed at some point between the cover of the volume and the page being copied is often very useful in evening out the pressure applied to the volume and should be used wherever possible. As was pointed out earlier, the amount of operator effort in applying hand pressure can be materially reduced if the copier is equipped with an exposure-interval timer sensitive enough to permit the use of fast papers at very short exposures.

OPTICAL COPYING

The basic principles of optical copying are outlined in the following sections. More detailed techniques for the optical copying of research materials are presented in the section on "Microtransparencies," page 240 ff., since, for research materials, microfilming is the most widely used form of optical copying. Detailed techniques for the copying of unusual originals can be found in the Kodak Advanced Data Book, *Copying*, available at 75¢ from Eastman Kodak dealers.

Fundamentals

In optical copying, an image is formed within a camera on a plane where a sheet of light-sensitive material can be placed and acted upon by light rays passing through a lens.

One of the most important advantages of optical copying lies in the degree of control in a continuous range over the size of the image

offered by this method. Depending upon the equipment employed, copying can be done at 100 percent of the size of the original (one-to-one copying), at more than 100 percent of the size of the original (greater than one-to-one copying), or at less than 100 percent of the size of the original (less than one-to-one copying). See Figures 138, 139, and 140.

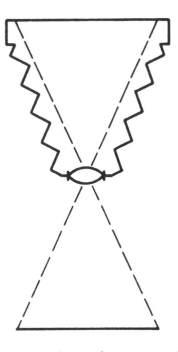

Fig. 138. Schematic of optical copying at 100 percent (1:1)

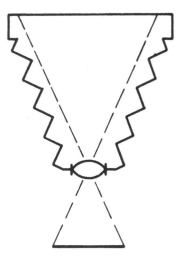

Fig. 139. Schematic of optical copying at 200 percent (2:1)

There are two basic optical methods for making eye-legible copies of documents:

(1) The indirect method, which requires the formation of an intermediate image from which the final copy is made.

(2) The direct method, in which the image is formed directly on the surface of the sensitized material which, when processed, becomes the copy.

Ordinary silver halide photography, which requires the making of an intermediate film negative from which the final copy is made by contact or projection printing, is the best known exemplar of the indirect method. Xerography also employs the

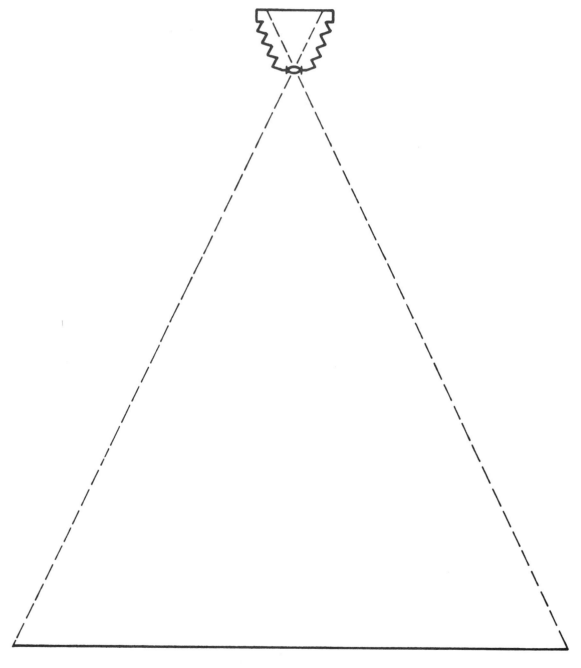

Fig. 140. Schematic of optical copying at 10 percent (1:10).

indirect method, since the image is first formed on an intermediate selenium plate or drum and then transferred to a suitable support which becomes the final copy.

Examples of the direct method include photostating, in which optical copying is done through a prism which forms a right-reading image directly on a sheet of silver halide sensitized material, and the Electrofax process, in which an image is similarly formed on a sheet of zinc oxide coated paper that has been rendered photoconductive.

In copying with silver halide materials by the indirect method, the intermediate negative is usually smaller and, in microphotography, very much smaller than the original. Eye-legible copies from such negatives are subsequently made by projection printing. With the exception of a recently developed form of recording known as microxerography, images formed in xerographic copying and in equipment employing the direct method are at or near the size of the original document.

Equipment

Many types of cameras and lenses can be used for the production of eye-legible copies via intermediate silver halide film negatives. These range from small hand cameras using 35 mm. film (such as are widely used in amateur photography) on up to the press and view cameras used by professional photographers and the large process cameras used by photoengravers. The essential requirements of a camera to be used for copying a variety of documents of diverse types and sizes are as follows:

(1) It must accept film large enough for the particular original being copied.

(2) It must be equipped with a lens which is adequately sharp over the entire film area for the recording of the finest details of the original.

(3) It should be equipped with a focusing mechanism that will provide for easy control of focus at all camera-to-subject distances down to the smallest size subjects that will be copied. While close-up copying of small subjects can be accomplished with extension tubes to bring about the needed increase in lens-to-film distance, or with supplementary close-up lenses, these methods are less efficient when copying subjects which

vary considerably in over-all size.

(4) It should be equipped with an iris diaphragm for control of depth of field.

(5) It should be equipped with a shutter which is accurate and consistent.

Techniques

The copying set-up. In copying with a camera, the fundamental requirements of rectilinearity, rigidity, and evenness of illumination must first be met.

RECTILINEARITY. If the image is to be free of rectilinear distortion, the lens, the film, and the subject must be in precisely parallel planes.

With good-quality cameras which have no film-plane or lens-plane adjustments, parallel alignment of these two planes is taken care of in the manufacturing process. To align these planes with the plane on which the subject is to be placed, a small spirit level is used to adjust the subject plane and the camera to a true horizontal (or vertical).

With some types of view cameras equipped with "swings," which allow for adustments of both the film plane and the lens plane, it may be necessary to check the level of both the lens and film planes to ensure that they are parallel to each other. If any one of the planes is not parallel with the other two, distortion will occur (Figure 141).

Although the three planes must be parallel, it is not necessary that the relationship between subject, lens, and film be symmetrical. The use of a camera which provides for some vertical (or horizontal) movement of the lens board can be helpful in some situations. For example, if the subject being copied must be flattened by overlaying it with a sheet of glass, shiny metal surfaces on the camera may be reflected by the glass surface and record as "hot spots" on the negative. Such reflections can sometimes be eliminated quite easily by shifting the position of the lens board in relation to the film plane as shown in Figure 142.

RIGIDITY. A second essential in optical copying is rigidity. In using either a horizontal or a vertical position for copying, the easel on which the copy is placed and the stand that supports the camera must be free from any possibility of vibration or movement.

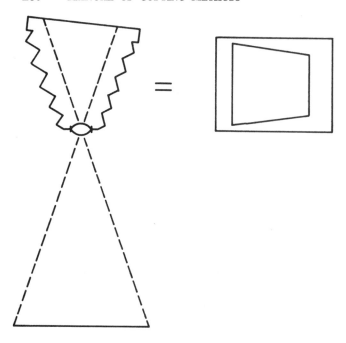

Fig. 141. Rectilinear distortion resulting from improper leveling of camera with respect to subject plane.

EVENNESS OF ILLUMINATION. There is a widely held misconception that the making of high-quality copies requires perfect evenness of illumination of the copyboard. What is really required is evenness of the intensity of light falling on the surface of the sensitized material. As is shown in Figure 143, light reflected from the outer edges of the copyboard follows a longer path. This, together with other optical phenomena, causes the light reaching the outer edges of the sensitized material to be weaker in intensity. This, in turn, causes the density of the image to be lower at the outer edges than at the center. It will thus be seen that, if uniform exposure of the sensitized material is to be achieved, the amount of light reflected from the edges and corners of the copyboard must

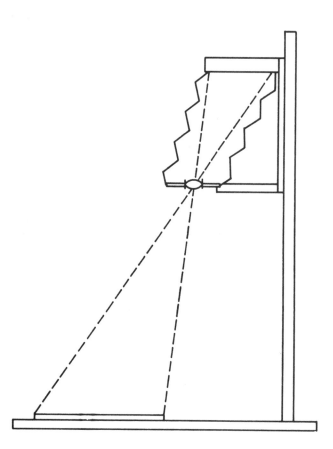

Fig. 142. Shifting the position of the lens board to eliminate reflections from glass overlay sheet.

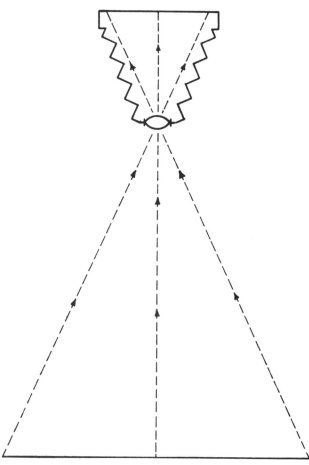

Fig. 143. Light reflected from the outer edges of the copyboard follow a longer path than light from the center. The lighting of the outer edges must therefore be higher in intensity if even density is to be obtained.

be greater than the amount of light reflected from the center.

While the copying of small subjects can be successfully done with two lamps of equal intensity on each side and equidistant from the subject (Figure 144), better control of illumination is possible if four lamps are used (Figure 145). The usual lamp arrangement for copying is to place the lamps at an angle of approximately 30 to 40° to the subject plane (50 to 60° to the optical axis) and to set them at a distance which will provide for adequate control of intensity over the copyboard area. If only two lamps are used, a somewhat lower angle is helpful in reducing the intensity of the light reflected from the center.

There are two rules of thumb which are useful in positioning the lamps for evenness of illumination. The first is to position each lamp at an angle pointing a little past the center of the copyboard. The second is to make final adjustments of the lamp positions so that the intensity of light reflected from the copyboard is in a ratio of from 5–5–4–5–5 to 4–4–3–4–4, i.e., approximately 25 to 35 percent brighter at the corners than at the center. This is most easily done by using an exposure meter of the cadmium sulfide type with a narrow-angle view (3°) at the camera position. There is only one certain way, however, of determining how even the illumination is. This is to cover the copyboard with a sheet of white paper, expose and develop a negative, and read the results on a densitometer. The results of such a test will indicate what changes need to be made. It should be noted that, if low-contrast materials are being used, small differences in the intensity of the illumination falling on the sensitized material will not be evident, but the use of high-contrast materials tends to accentuate slight differences in intensity. Test negatives made for the purpose of checking evenness of illumination should therefore be made on high-contrast materials.

Once the copying set-up has been made and the illumination adjusted for evenness, precautions should be taken to ensure that the lamps are not accidentally jarred out of position by other persons working nearby or passing through the area.

Another factor that can affect evenness of

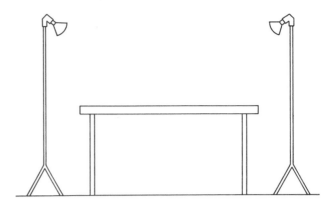

Fig. 144. Copyboard with typical two-lamp set-up.

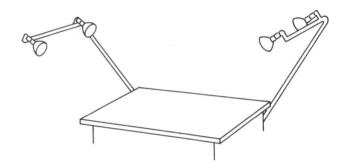

Fig. 145. Copyboard with typical 4-lamp set-up.

illumination is extraneous light. The copying set-up should be shielded from light coming from windows or skylights. Walls near the copying set-up should be dark in tone. When copying small originals on a large, white copyboard, black paper masks should be placed over the unused areas. Even light reflected from an operator's clothing, such as a white laboratory coat, can cause a noticeable unevenness in density, especially if the negative is developed to high contrast.

Another form of artificial light that is very useful for copying work is fluorescent light. Because of the tubular form of fluorescent lights, it is somewhat easier to illuminate large areas evenly with them than it is with bulbs. Fluorescent tubes are available in many lengths and may be used singly or in banks on each side of the copyboard, depending upon the amount of illumination required. A number of specialized copying cameras for both eye-legible copies and microcopies are equipped with fluorescent lights (Figure 146).

CONTROL OF REFLECTIONS. If book holders or sheets of glass are used to hold materials flat or if the subject is framed with glass, unwanted reflections must be eliminated. The angle at which the lamps are positioned must be adjusted so that the lamps themselves are not reflected, and a lens hood should always be used to protect the lens from stray light. Reflections from shiny metal parts of the camera must be eliminated by blackening them with a matte black paint, by covering them with black tape, or by interposing a sheet of matte black cardboard somewhat larger than the camera with a hole cut in it for the lens.

Another method of controlling reflections is through the use of polarized light filters. "Hot spots," which occur when light is reflected from a shiny surface, are called "specular" reflections (from the Latin word "speculum"—a mirror). The light rays emanating from specular reflections vibrate on a single plane and hence are described as "polarized." The function of polarized light filters is to filter out such rays so that the surface obscured by the specular reflection can be recorded. Such filters are of two types—one which

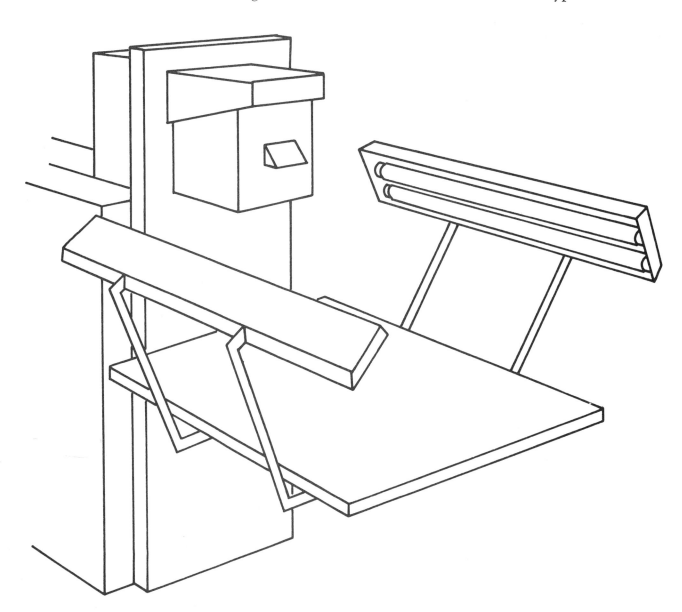

Fig. 146. Schematic of photostat camera with fluorescent lights.

can be placed over the camera lens and another which is placed directly over the light source. Maximum control of reflections can be achieved if both are used.

COPYING WITH AVAILABLE LIGHT. Available light is of three kinds—daylight, either outdoors or indoors through windows or skylights; existing artificial light, such as fluorescent ceiling fixtures in a reading room or work area; or a mixture of both artificial light and daylight. While available light may be quite satisfactory for reading, it may not be satisfactory for copying purposes. If, for example, a small hand camera is used on a stand for copying materials in a library, ceiling lights may cast a shadow from the camera onto the surface of the copyboard. Light from windows usually provides too much light on one side of the subject, thus causing the illumination to be uneven. This can sometimes be compensated for by placing a reflecting surface in the form of a large white card on the side of the copyboard farthest from the window. The best conditions for available light copying are those in which the light is the most diffuse. Skylights in high-ceilinged rooms often provide well-diffused light. The use of a cadmium sulfide exposure meter with a narrow (3°) angle of view is helpful in determining how even the available light at different locations in a room may be.

Choice of lens opening. There are three factors affecting the choice of the lens opening to be used when copying research materials:

(1) The optimum working aperture of the particular lens used

(2) Depth-of-field requirements

(3) The effective lens opening

THE OPTIMUM WORKING APERTURE. All lenses are not equally sharp at different aperture settings. In general, moderate aperture settings yield somewhat sharper images than either very large or very small settings. Some lenses, however, are sharpest at their very smallest aperture setting. A 35 mm. camera lens having a maximum aperture of, say, f3.5 and a minimum aperture of f22 may yield the sharpest images at settings around f8 to f11. The only way to determine what the optimum working aperture of any particular lens will be, short of having the lens tested in an optical laboratory, is to make a series of photographs of

resolution test charts, such as the National Bureau of Standards Microcopy Resolution Test Chart (Figure 18), under carefully controlled conditions to eliminate variables that would result in incorrect data. These variables include vibration or movement of the camera or subject, exposure errors, uneven illumination, or incorrect contrast resulting from improper development. The test charts should be placed in all four corners and in the center of the field to be copied. A careful reading of the results with a strong hand magnifier or low-power microscope will then reveal the resolution characteristics of the lens at each of the aperture settings.

DEPTH-OF-FIELD REQUIREMENTS. In copying loose-sheet originals or bound materials that can be opened flat, depth of field is not a problem, and the lens can be set at its optimum working aperture for maximum sharpness. In copying other types of bound materials that cannot be opened flat, depth-of-field requirements may necessitate the use of an aperture setting smaller than optimum if the entire text is to be clearly recorded. The most common instance in which this occurs is in copying tightly bound volumes having narrow inner margins (Figure 147).

Depth-of-field tables for different lens-to-subject distances are usually supplied with cameras as part of the instructional material or can be obtained by writing to the manufacturer. Practical depth-of-field limits for different apertures can also be determined by tests, such as using the National Bureau of Standards Microcopy Resolution Test Charts (Figure 18) arranged in a series of planes of varying height from the copying surface (Figure 148). If no tables are available and if it is known from previous tests that the sharpness of the image at a small aperture is adequate for the recording of the particular subject to be copied, satisfactory results can usually be obtained by using a small aperture and focusing according to the "one-third two-thirds" method. This method gets its name from the fact that depth of field is not equal on both sides of the plane focused on, but is approximately twice as great on the far side of the plane focused on as it is on the near side. If, for example, the subject being copied is 3 inches in thickness, the plane of focus for maximum depth of field would not be in the

Fig. 147. Depth-of-field problem presented by a tightly bound volume having a narrow inner margin.

center, i.e., 1½ inches from both near and far planes—but on a plane 1 inch from the near plane and 2 inches from the far plane.

THE EFFECTIVE LENS OPENING. The size of the opening in the lens through which light passes is controlled by an adjustable iris diaphragm patterned after the iris of the human eye. The various numerical settings used to denote openings of different diameters are an expression of the relationship between the diameter of the opening and the focal length of the lens. This relationship is called the "f" system. The focal length of the lens is the distance between the center of the lens and the film plane when the lens is focused at infinity.

A typical series of markings is as follows: f4, f5.6, f8, f11, f16.

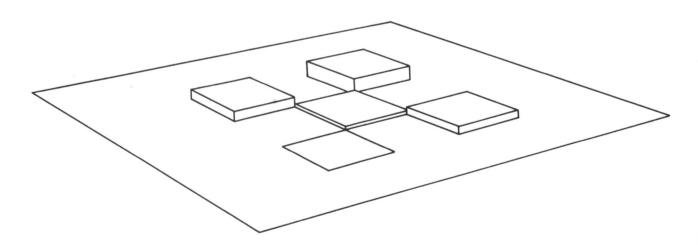

Fig. 148. Blocks of different heights on which resolution test charts can be placed for determining depth of field.

If a lens having a focal length of 2 inches is set at a lens opening of f4, the diameter of the opening would be ½ inch; i.e., the focal length of the lens would be greater than the diameter of the lens opening by a factor of 4. At the setting of f8, the focal length would be 8 times the diameter of the opening, which would be ¼ inch, and so on. If a lens having a 12-inch focal length were set at an opening of f8, the diameter of the opening would be one-eighth the focal length, or 1½ inches (Figure 149). Despite the fact that the f8 opening of the 12-inch lens is six times the diameter of the f8 opening of the 2-inch lens, the amount of light reaching the film plane would be identical be-cause of the differences in focal lengths.

As the diameter of the lens opening is made smaller, the exposure time required for a given subject must be increased. The extent of the required increase in exposure time can be seen by squaring the numbers used to denote the relative diameter of the lens opening:

	Normalized to:
$f4^2 = 16$	16
$f5.6^2 = 31.36$	32
$f8^2 = 64$	64
$f11^2 = 121$	128
$f16^2 = 256$	256

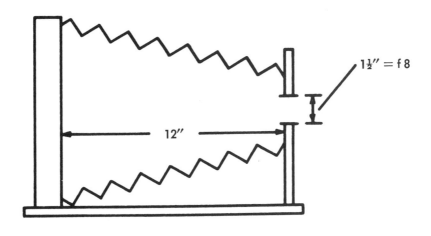

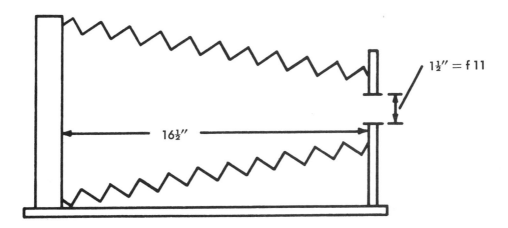

Fig. 149. If the lens-to-film distance of a lens having a focal length of 12 inches is increased to 16½ inches to copy a small subject, the effective lens opening at a marked setting of f8 becomes f11 and will require a 100 percent increase in exposure.

It will be seen from the relationship of these squares that the numbers used to mark lens openings are expressions of lens-opening diameter vs. focal length carried to one decimal place, which will require successive doublings of exposure time as the diameter is decreased, or successive halvings of exposure time as the diameter is increased. Transposing the figures in the above table into exposure times: if a given subject required an exposure of 16 seconds at f4, closing the lens opening to f5.6 would necessitate increasing the exposure to 32 seconds. Closing the opening still further to f8 would require an exposure of 64 seconds, and so on.

An understanding of the relationship of lens opening to focal length is important in copying because copying is done, not at infinity, but at close range.

To bring a subject at close range into focus on the film plane, the distance between the center of the lens and the film plane must be *increased,* and the closer the subject is to the camera, the greater the increase becomes. This, of course, alters the relationship between lens opening and focal length as given by the marked openings. If, in the example of the 12-inch lens having a 1½-inch lens-opening diameter at a marked setting of f8, the distance between the lens and film plane is increased to 16½ inches to bring a small subject at close range into focus, this distance will be 11 times the 1½-inch diameter lens opening (Figure 149). The *effective* lens opening under these conditions thus becomes f11 and, as the foregoing table shows, will require twice as long an exposure as would normally be called for at the marked setting of f8.

Because much copying work is done at close range where the exposure must be based on the effective lens opening rather than on the marked settings, tables should be made for each camera used for copying showing the effective lens opening and the percentage of increase in exposure at various camera-to-subject distances. A procedure for making up such tables is as follows:

(1) With the camera focused at infinity, place a scale below or at the side of the lens mount or any other part that moves with the lens during focusing. Use an inch or millimeter scale according to whether the focal length of the lens is given in inches or millimeters.

(2) Focus the camera on a subject at a distance of, say, 5 feet.

(3) Take a reading of the scale to determine how much the lens-to-film distance has been increased and add this to the focal length to determine the actual lens-to-film distance.

(4) Calculate the effective lens opening by the following formula:

$$\frac{\text{Marked Lens Opening} \times \text{Actual Lens-to-film Distance}}{\text{Focal Length}} = \frac{\text{Effective}}{\text{Lens Opening}}$$

(5) Repeat steps 3 and 4 with the camera focused at progressively shorter camera-to-subject distances.

Accurate calculations of effective lens openings are especially important in copying with color films because small errors in exposure can cause changes in color. A dial-type indicator that will eliminate some of the arithmetic entailed is available from the Eastman Kodak Company and its dealers as part of the *Kodak Master Photoguide.*

Focusing the image. Methods of ensuring sharp focus will vary with different types of cameras used for copying. Microfilm cameras are usually equipped with an "autofocus" mechanism which causes a helically mounted lens to rotate as the camera is moved up or down on its column. Provision may also be made for manual control, so that the plane of focus can be raised when filming bound volumes.

Prism-type cameras, such as photostat cameras, usually are scaled on a size-percentage basis which may range from 50 percent to 200 percent of original size. For flat material, the distances from the lens to the original and from the lens to the sensitized paper are set to the same scale marking. For bound volumes, deviations from the marked settings for the copy holder are made in accordance with the thickness of the volume.

Certain types of hand cameras have lenses in helical mounts and a scale indicating the lens-to-subject distance. When using cameras of this type, the lens-to-subject distance must be accurately measured and the lens set precisely if sharp focus is to be obtained. If "close-up" accessory lenses are used for shortening the lens-to-subject distance, a conversion table provided by the manufacturer is used to determine which of the marked settings is appropriate for a given lens-to-subject distance.

With two types of cameras, focusing is done visually on a ground-glass screen. The first type is the "view" or "press" camera in which the image appears on the ground glass upside-down. The second type is the "reflex" camera which may be either a "single-lens reflex" camera (SLR) or a "twin-lens reflex" camera (TLR). In SLR cameras, a mirror is interposed at an angle to reflect the image formed by the lens upward to a prism and thence to an eye-piece. When the camera shutter is released, the mirror moves out of the optical path to permit an image to be formed on the film plane (Figure 150). TLR cameras are equipped with both a "viewing lens" and a "taking lens" and employ a mirror interposed at an angle in the path of the viewing lens to reflect an image upward to a ground-glass screen (Figure 151). With SLR cameras, focusing is simply a matter of careful examination and adjustment to get the sharpest possible visual image through the reflex optical system. With view- or press-type cameras or TLR cameras, a small hand magnifier should be used if the camera is not already equipped with one.

With view- or press-type cameras, another method, called the "parallax method of focusing," is recommended by the Eastman Kodak Company.[1] In using this method, a clear spot must be produced on the ground glass by affixing a small piece of clear cellulose tape to the inner surface of the ground glass and a mark made on the tape with a grease pencil or with an ink that will adhere to the tape surface. A low-power (6–10X) magnifier is used to examine the area covered with the marked tape. In examining the image, the camera operator must move his head slightly either sideways or up and down. If the image of the subject moves behind the mark on the tape, the camera is not in focus. If the image of the subject and the mark move together, the camera is in focus.

Framing the image. With microfilm cameras, the proper framing of the subject to be copied is provided for either by means of a scaled copy holder, which shows the area covered by the lens at any given camera height, or by means of a "finder light," which projects a beam of light through the lens to the copy holder to show the area covered.

With prism-type cameras, the copy holder is scaled to show the area covered at various percentage settings. For precise positioning, an accessory ground-glass back is used.

With hand cameras which are not of the reflex type, a table is usually provided by the manufacturer that gives the length and width of the area covered at different lens-to-subject distances. With cameras of this type, both the camera and the copy board must be precisely aligned and the subject accurately centered.

With view- or press-type cameras and SLR cameras, framing can be accurately determined simply by examining the image on the ground-glass screen.

With TLR cameras, compensation must be made for the fact that the area "seen" by the viewing lens is slightly different from that of the taking lens. With some TLR cameras, compensation for this difference is provided for in the design of the camera. In others, compensation must be done manually by moving the position of the camera before the exposure is made to shift the axis of the taking lens to that of the viewing lens.

Exposure. Two methods are normally used for determining the exposure to be used for the optical copying of documents. Ordinarily, exposure determinations are made by using an exposure meter. Direct meter readings from the surface of a document often indicate exposures that are too long. One method of avoiding this is by placing a white card over the document and taking a reading of its surface. The indicated exposure should then be divided by 5. For example, if the indicated exposure is 5 seconds at f11, the correct exposure would be 1 second at f11. An alternative method is to cover the document with a neutral gray card and take a direct reading from this card instead of from the document. A card that is very useful for determining exposures in copying is the

---

[1] *Basic Photography for the Graphic Arts,* Kodak Publication Number Q-1 (Rochester, New York: Eastman Kodak Company, 1963), p. 10.

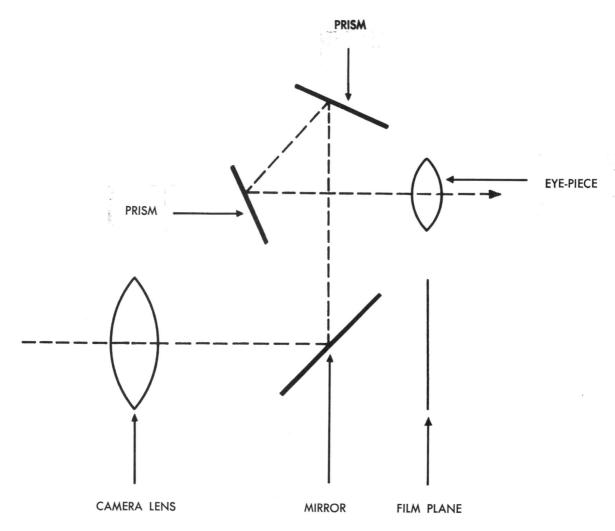

Fig. 150. Schematic diagram of the optical path of a single-lens reflex (SLR) camera.

Kodak Neutral Test Card, which has a white surface of 90 percent reflectance on one side and a gray surface of 18 percent reflectance on the other. This card can be used for either of the two methods indicated.

Where the optimum working aperture can be used, the duration of the exposure should be altered. Where depth of field is a problem, the aperture may have to be set at an opening smaller than optimum and the duration of the exposure increased accordingly. Allowance must also be made for the effective lens opening when close-up copying is done.

An exposure technique that is useful for reducing the contrast of high-contrast photocopy papers is the "flashing" technique, in which the paper is given a very slight over-all pre-exposure. If, for example, a large continuous-tone original is to be copied with a photostat-type camera on the relatively high-contrast paper normally used in such cameras, the copy board should be covered with a sheet of white paper and a brief exposure made. Some experimentation is necessary to determine the correct exposure at different camera settings that will reduce contrast without producing an over-all gray tone. The original is then copied at a slightly greater-than-normal exposure and developed slightly less than the normal time.

Processing. The processing of materials exposed in a camera will vary with the type of materials used and the type of copy needed. Except for the flashing technique, which is a function of exposure, little control over the contrast of silver halide coatings on paper is possible, but coatings on film are capable of yielding copies ranging from low to high contrast. This is accomplished by shortening or lengthening the development time. Extensive tables showing the contrast obtainable with a great number of different film and developer combinations are given in the *Photo-Lab Index*.

Negatives of continuous-tone illustrations are usually developed to a moderate degree of contrast to preserve the tonal relationships, but, in instances where the contrast of the original is low, it may be desirable to heighten the contrast of the copy by prolonging the development time. Line copy, unless the lines are markedly uneven in density, are usually developed to a high degree of contrast.

In other respects, the techniques for processing materials exposed in cameras are similar to those described earlier for processing materials exposed by contact methods.

Automated optical copying devices. In recent years, there has been an ever-increasing number of "office copiers" employing an optical system that can be used to copy pages from bound

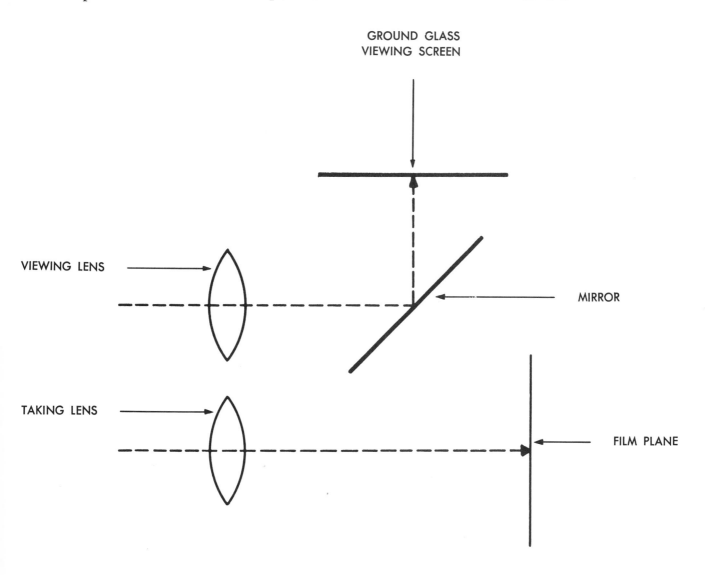

Fig. 151. Schematic diagram of the optical path of a twin-lens reflex (TLR) camera.

volumes. Typical of such copiers are the Xerox 914 copier, a number of Electrofax-process copiers, and coin-operated copiers employing the stabilization process. Most of these copiers operate at a fixed-size ratio of 1:1 or at a slight reduction from full size. Most work at a fixed-lens aperture, have a limited range of control over exposure or none at all, and have a fully automated processing section that delivers finished copies in a space of time which is usually well under one minute.

All of the copiers of this type that have appeared thus far are "upside-down" copiers, in which the lens is positioned to record documents placed upside-down on a horizontal glass exposing surface at the top of the unit. The upside-down arrangement works well enough with loose-sheet documents but has disadvantages in bound-volume copying since the handling of bulky, heavy, or fragile volumes in an upside-down position is awkward and may entail some risk to the material. Also, in copying large originals or portions of pages, the operator cannot always see how much of the material is within view of the lens. To use upside-down copiers to best advantage, certain techniques are helpful.

First, the techniques for handling volumes safely in an upside-down position, which were described on pages 219–20 should be observed. Secondly, it is important to ascertain what the depth-of-field limits of the copier are. This can be done by making a series of exposures of an original having a number of different size type faces at gradually increasing heights above the glass exposing surface. A series of increments of $\frac{1}{16}$ inch continued to a point where the largest typical type size becomes illegible will show how far text in type of a certain size can be out of contact with the glass exposing surface and still record legibly. When copying tightly bound originals, an operator will then know from the test data how close to the glass surface the text at the inner margin must be to record legibly. If the text at the inner margin cannot be brought within the needed limits, the operator will know in advance that a legible copy cannot be made, thus eliminating trial-and-error waste.

Another useful technique has to do with the position of the bound volume on the exposing surface. As is shown in Figures 152 and 153, a volume having a curving inner margin should be positioned with the inner margin as close to the center of the exposing surface as the size of the volume will allow. This reduces the foreshortening of the text along the curve and can often make the difference between a legible and an illegible copy.

MICROTRANSPARENCIES

Basic production methods and equipment schematics

Roll forms. To produce micro-images on a transparent support, the principal requirements are a camera equipped with a lens that will give the desired degree of reduction together with high resolving power and flatness of field, an efficient illumination system that is even, a method of controlling exposure, a film having characteristics appropriate for recording very fine details, and a method of development that will yield an image having characteristics that will be appropriate for the subsequent reading or printing of the content of the micro-image.

For the most part, the sensitized materials employed in microrecording are silver halide materials which yield a negative image. To produce a positive image, the negative must be printed onto a second film. Positive prints can be produced not only on silver halide materials, both transparent and opaque, but on diazo and Kalvar films as well. Positive images can also be formed directly on the original recording film by reversal processing, but this method is little used in the document-reproduction field. Two non-silver halide methods of recording micro-images, which are under development, are microxerography and Kalvar recording. In both, the processes used are completely dry, and the processing of the exposed material is done within the camera immediately after each exposure is made. Microxerography employs a specially designed camera with which it is possible to record successive images on sheet film (microfiche) by the xerographic process. An unusual feature of this method is its "add-on" capability. If only a portion of the available image-recording areas of a sheet is used, additional images can be added at a later time. Also, the process produces a positive instead of a negative transparency. In Kalvar recording, a special camera employing a

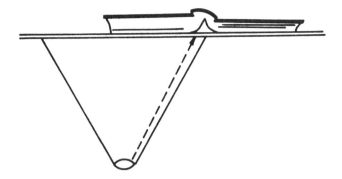
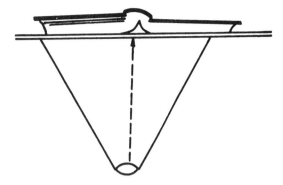

Shepard Line (General S.S. Corp.)_____Pier ;
Silver-Java Pacific Line (Burchard & Fisken) E. Waterway Doc;
States S.S. Co. _____Atlantic St. D..;
Westfal-Larsen Line (Gen. S.S. Corp.)—East Waterway Doc;
Weyerhaeuser SS Co. (Interocean SS Corp) Milwaukee Ocean D;
Westfal-Larsen Co. Line (General Steamship Corp.)____C;

TACOMA

Alaska Steamship Co. _____Portacoma Pier;
Alaska Transportation Co. _____McCormick S.S. Termin;
American-Hawaiian Steamship Co._____Baker Doc;
Arrow Line (Sudden & Christenson) _____Portacoma Pier;
Calmar Line (Swayne & Hoyt)_____Portacoma Pier;
Coastwise Line, Inc. _____Portacoma Pier;
California-Eastern Line _____Snaffer Term;
Coastwise Steamship Co._____Baker Doc;
Consolidated-Olympic Line _____Shaffer Termin;
Donaldson Line (Balfour, Guthrie & Co.)_____Portacoma Pier;
Blue Funnel Line (Dodwell & Co.)_____Portacoma Pier;
Blue Star Line _____Portacoma Pier;
Border Steamship Line (Dodwell & Co.)_____Shaffer Termin;
East Asiatic Line (European) _____Portacoma Pier;
E. K. Wood Lumber Co._____Baker Doc;
Fred Olsen Line (International Shipping Co.)_____Portacoma Pier;
French Line (General Steamship Corp.)_____Shaffer Termin;
Furness Line (Burchard & Fisken)_____Portacoma Pier;
Grace Line _____Portacoma Pier;
Gulf Pacific Line (Swayne & Hoyt)_____Shaffer Termin;
Hamburg-American Line (Sudden & Christenson) Portacoma Pier;
Hammond Shipping Co._____Baker Doc;
Holland-America Line (S. J. Maxwell)_____Portacoma Pier;
Interocean Line (Interocean S.S. Corp.)_____Portacoma Pier;
Isthmian Line (Norton, Lilly & Co.)_____Shaffer Termin;
Italian Line (General S.S. Corp.)_____Shaffer Termin;
Johnson Line (Grace Line)_____Portacoma Pier;
Kawasaki Kisen Kaisha _____Portacoma Pier;
Knutsen Line—U.K. Service(Inter'n S.S. Corp.) Portacoma Pier;
Luckenbach Steamship Co._____Portacoma Pier;
Matson Navigation Co. (Alexander & Baldwin)....Portacoma Pier;
McCormick Steamship Line._____McCormick Doc;
Mitsui Line _____Shaffer Termin;
Nippon Yusen Kaisha _____Portacoma Pier;
North German Lloyd._____Portacoma Pier;
O. & O. Nav. Co. (Alexander & Baldwin)_____Portacoma Pier;
Pacific Coast Direct Line _____Shaffer Termin;
Quaker Line _____Shaffer Term;
Royal Mail Lines, Ltd. (S. J. Maxwell)_____Portacoma Pier;
Shepard Steamship Co. (General S.S. Corp.)_____Shaffer Termin;
Silver-Java Pacific Line (Burchard & Fisken)___Portacoma Pier;
States S.S. Co. _____Shaffer Termin;
United Ocean Transport Co._____Portacoma Pier;
Westfal-Larsen Co. Line (General S.S. Corp.)____Shaffer Term;
Weyerhaeuser S.S. Co._____Shaffer Term;

Shepard Line (General S.S. Corp.)_____Pier ;
Silver-Java Pacific Line (Burchard & Fisken) E. Waterway Doc;
States S.S. Co. _____Atlantic St. Doc;
Westfal-Larsen Line (Gen. S.S. Corp.)—East Waterway Docl;
Weyerhaeuser SS Co. (Interocean SS Corp) Milwaukee Ocean D;
Westfal-Larsen Co. Line (General Steamship Corp.)____4;

TACOMA

Alaska Steamship Co. _____Portacoma Pier;
Alaska Transportation Co. _____McCormick S.S. Terminal;
American-Hawaiian Steamship Co._____Baker Doc;
Arrow Line (Sudden & Christenson) _____Portacoma Pier;
Calmar Line (Swayne & Hoyt)_____Portacoma Pier;
Coastwise Line, Inc. _____Portacoma Pier;
California-Eastern Line _____Shaffer Term;
Coastwise Steamship Co._____Baker Doc;
Consolidated-Olympic Line _____Shaffer Terminal;
Donaldson Line (Balfour, Guthrie & Co.)_____Portacoma Pier;
Blue Funnel Line (Dodwell & Co.)_____Portacoma Pier;
Blue Star Line _____Portacoma Pier;
Border Steamship Line (Dodwell & Co.)_____Shaffer Terminal;
East Asiatic Line (European) _____Portacoma Pier;
E. K. Wood Lumber Co._____Baker Doc;
Fred Olsen Line (International Shipping Co.)_____Portacoma Pier;
French Line (General Steamship Corp.)_____Shaffer Terminal;
Furness Line (Burchard & Fisken)_____Portacoma Pier;
Grace Line _____Portacoma Pier;
Gulf Pacific Line (Swayne & Hoyt)_____Shaffer Terminal;
Hamburg-American Line (Sudden & Christenson) Portacoma Pier;
Hammond Shipping Co._____Baker Dock;
Holland-America Line (S. J. Maxwell)_____Portacoma Pier;
Interocean Line (Interocean S.S. Corp.)_____Portacoma Pier;
Isthmian Line (Norton, Lilly & Co.)_____Shaffer Terminal;
Italian Line (General S.S. Corp.)_____Shaffer Terminal;
Johnson Line (Grace Line)_____Portacoma Pier;
Kawasaki Kisen Kaisha _____Portacoma Pier;
Knutsen Line—U.K. Service(Inter'n S.S. Corp.) Portacoma Pier;
Luckenbach Steamship Co._____Portacoma Pier;
Matson Navigation Co. (Alexander & Baldwin)....Portacoma Pier;
McCormick Steamship Line._____McCormick Dock;
Mitsui Line _____Shaffer Terminal;
Nippon Yusen Kaisha _____Portacoma Pier;
North German Lloyd._____Portacoma Pier;
O. & O. Nav. Co. (Alexander & Baldwin)_____Portacoma Pier;
Pacific Coast Direct Line _____Shaffer Terminal;
Quaker Line _____Shaffer Term;
Royal Mail Lines, Ltd. (S. J. Maxwell)_____Portacoma Pier;
Shepard Steamship Co. (General S.S. Corp.)_____Shaffer Terminal;
Silver-Java Pacific Line (Burchard & Fisken)___Portacoma Pier;
States S.S. Co. _____Shaffer Terminal;
United Ocean Transport Co._____Portacoma Pier;
Westfal-Larsen Co. Line (General S.S. Corp.)____Shaffer Term;
Weyerhaeuser S.S. Co._____Shaffer Term;

Fig. 152. If a volume in which there is curvature of the text at the inner margin is placed at the edge of a glass exposing surface, the text is foreshortened and difficult to read.

Fig. 153. If the volume is placed as far in toward the center of the exposing surface as its size will allow, fore-shortening of the text at the inner margin is considerably reduced and legibility improved.

light source of great intensity is used to record images on 16 mm. Kalvar roll film.

Microtransparencies are produced in two forms—roll forms and sheet forms. The first of these is a linear succession of images on a ribbon of film usually 16 or 35 mm. in width and up to 100 feet in length. Longer rolls can be produced by joining two or more 100-foot rolls. Shorter lengths in the form of strips or even single frames can be obtained by cutting up the rolls. Sixteen mm. film is generally without perforations but 35 mm. film may be either perforated or non-perforated.

Depending upon the type of camera used, the image size may be of a fixed length or may be varied to suit the length of the document being filmed. With Kodagraph or Recordak Micro-File cameras, which are among the most widely used for the microfilming of research materials, the frame length can be varied from a minimum of $\frac{3}{8}$ inch to a maximum of $1\frac{3}{4}$ inches (Figure 154). Varying the frame length automatically changes the amount of film advanced so that film is not wasted. At the minimum setting of $\frac{3}{8}$ inch with $\frac{1}{16}$ inch spacing between frames, approximately 2,750 exposures can be made on a 100-foot roll of film. At the maximum setting, approximately 625 exposures can be made.

drum over which documents are transported and photographed while in motion. The moving document is "seen" by the camera lens through a narrow slit, and the recording is made by synchronizing the movement of the film to the movement of the document in accordance with the reduction ratio of the lens used. If, for example, the reduction ratio is 1:18, the film must move at exactly $\frac{1}{18}$ of the speed of the document.

Most rotary cameras record on 16 mm. film and are limited to the copying of loose-sheet materials at the reduction ratio of the lens used. They are also limited to the maximum document width the camera throat will accept but are not limited as to document length.

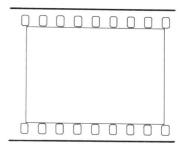

Fig. 155. Standard-size, double-frame image on 35 mm. perforated film (1 by 1½ inches).

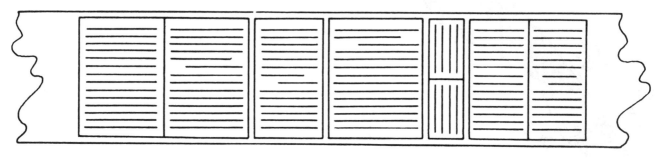

Fig. 154. Variations in image size on 35 mm. non-perforated film (Recordak Micro-File camera).

Microfilming can also be done with 35 mm. hand cameras of good quality, but such cameras are usually limited to a maximum of 36 exposures of a fixed size of 1 by 1½ inches (double frame) on 5½ feet of perforated film (Figure 155).

Microfilm cameras are of two principal types—"rotary" and "planetary." The component from which rotary cameras get their name is a rotary

Planetary cameras (the name is derived from the word "plane") consist of a camera head mounted on a vertical column, a baseboard, a set of lights, and appropriate electrical controls. A planetary camera thus is no different in its essential components from any other type of vertically mounted copying camera.

Planetary cameras usually can be operated

over a wide range of reduction ratios. They are usually equipped with some method of control over image format and can be used to copy documents varying greatly in size from very small to very large. Most planetary cameras use 35 mm. non-perforated film, but some are also capable of recording on 35 mm. perforated film or on 16 mm. film.

The orientation of images on a roll can be controlled by either turning the document or the camera head and adjusting the reduction ratio accordingly. Four positions, designated 1-A, 1-B, 2-A, and 2-B, are thus possible.[2]

by its trade name of Micro-Folio and the third as microfiche.

All forms make provision for the inclusion of an eye-legible title along the top edge of the sheet. With jacketed film and Micro-Folio, titling is usually done by adding either a translucent or opaque strip of paper bearing the title. Micro-fiches are usually titled photographically by means of a separate titling camera or a separate optical system within the microfiche camera itself. In some applications, titles on microfiches are also backed by "striping" them with a white opaque substance to make them more easily legible.

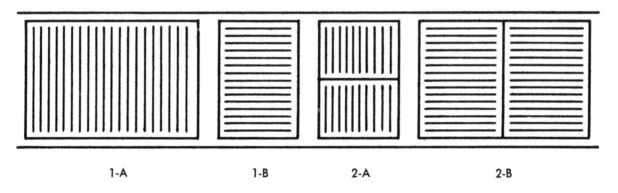

1-A   1-B   2-A   2-B

Fig. 156. Roll-microfilm image positions.

Exposed rolls of film can be processed either by hand methods or by means of continuous automatic equipment. Duplicate rolls of film can be produced on roll-to-roll printers of various types, depending on the process employed.

Sheet forms. Microtransparencies in the form of sheets are of three kinds. The first of these is a clear acetate sheet containing pockets in which strips of either 16 or 35 mm. film can be inserted. The second also entails the use of sheets of clear acetate but, instead of using pockets, strips of either 16 or 35 mm. film are affixed to the acetate by means of an adhesive. The third kind is a sheet of sensitized film on which successive images have been either printed or recorded. The first kind is usually referred to as "jacketed film," the second

JACKETS. Jackets are cellulose acetate sheets containing one or more pockets arranged horizontally and are obtainable in a number of standard sizes from 3 by 5 inches to 5 by 8 inches. The number of pockets will vary with the size of the jacket and according to whether the jackets are to be used with 16 or 35 mm. film strips. Micro-images in sheet form thus can be produced from roll forms simply by cutting rolls into strips of appropriate lengths and inserting the strips in the jacket pockets. While enlarged prints (hard copy) can be made from jacketed film without removing the film from the jacket, contact duplicates, with one exception, cannot. The one exception is a type of jacket recently introduced by the Recordak Corporation which is called "Micro-Thin." The jacket material is so thin that high-resolution contact duplicates can be made without removing the film from the jacket. A special device for the Micro-Thin system, called a "Reader-Filler," is

---

[2] *American Standard Specifications for 16-mm. and 35-mm. Microfilms in Reels or in Strips,* PH5.3–1958–6.1. (New York: American Standards Association).

provided that projects film images to a screen for inspection and automatically inserts the film in the jacket pockets at a speed of 400 strips per hour. A useful feature of jacketed film is what is called "add-on" capability. Additional frames can be added as needed to the capacity of the jacket.

MICRO-FOLIO. Another system for converting roll microfilm into sheet form is called "Micro-Folio," a product of the Atlantic Microfilm Corporation. Two specialized pieces of equipment are used in the Micro-Folio system. The first, which is called a "Micro-Folio Applicator," bonds a very thin strip of a transparent adhesive to the outer edges of a roll of film at a rate of 33 feet per minute. The second machine is called a "Micro-Folio Film Mounter." The mounter removes a protective coating from the thin adhesive strips and automatically advances and positions the strips in successive rows on sheets of clear acetate which can range in size from 3 by 5 inches to 5 by 8 inches. Both devices can be obtained for use with either 16 or 35 mm. film. Stripped-up Micro-Folio masters can be used for the production of microfiche duplicates by either the Kalvar or diazo processes. Micro-Folio also has "add-on" capability.

MICROFICHES. Microfiches are produced by two methods—by printing from appropriately jacketed film or Micro-Folio masters or by recording in specially modified roll-film cameras or "step-and-repeat" cameras. The method employing the use of roll-film cameras is called the "strip-up method." In the strip-up method, the cameras are modified to provide space automatically between each series of frames making up one row of images. When the film is processed, the individual strips are cut apart and either placed in a jig, which will hold the strips in position for contact printing to another sheet of film, or simply taped to a sheet of clear acetate. With both jacketed film and Micro-Folio, the height of images, and hence the number of rows, is determined by the film width of either 16 or 35 millimeters. In the strip-up method, maximum use of the available space on the sheet is obtained by setting the reduction ratio for a predetermined image height and then cutting off the excess film on both edges. Strips of 16 mm. film, for example, might be trimmed to 13 mm. to eliminate wasted space and gain one additional row of images. Microfiches may be produced directly from these masters, or the master may be used only for the making of a second-generation intermediate to be used as the master for the production of distribution copies.

In the step-and-repeat method, special cameras are employed which record images in a series of rows either on single sheets of film or on large rolls of film on which a succession of microfiches can be made.

Microfiches can be produced in a variety of sizes ranging from 3 by 5 inches to 5 by 8 inches or even larger. The sizes most widely used for reproducing research materials are 75 by 125 mm. (3 by 5 inches), 105 by 148 mm. (actually $4\frac{1}{8}$ by 6 inches but usually referred to as 4 by 6 inches) and 90 by 120 mm. ($3\frac{1}{2}$ by $4\frac{3}{4}$ inches), which is usually referred to as 9 by 12 cm. The latter size is a standard European sheet-film size. The first two are sizes approved by the International Standards Organization (ISO) and the Microfiche Standards Committee of the National Microfilm Association (U.S.).

There has been a strong tendency in this country to standardize not only the over-all size of microfiches but image size, placement, reduction ratio, and other factors as well. Three formats widely used in this country are the 60-frame format adopted by government agencies for technical reports (Figure 159), a 72-frame format used both for research materials and industrial catalogs (Figure 161), and a 98-frame format used for industrial catalogs (Figure 162). The latter two deviate slightly from the international size because they measure 105 by 152.4 mm.

In Europe, on the other hand, the step-and-repeat cameras principally used are capable of as many as 42 different formats ranging from two rows of four images for large materials—8 images in all—to 7 rows of 10 images for small documents—70 images in all—(Figures 163 and 164).

Roll film used for the production of microfiche by the strip-up method is processed by means of roll-film equipment. Microfiches produced by means of step-and-repeat cameras may either be in the form of single sheets or in rolls 75 mm. or 105 mm. in width carrying 200 or more microfiches. Both the single sheets and the rolls can be processed by manual or machine methods.

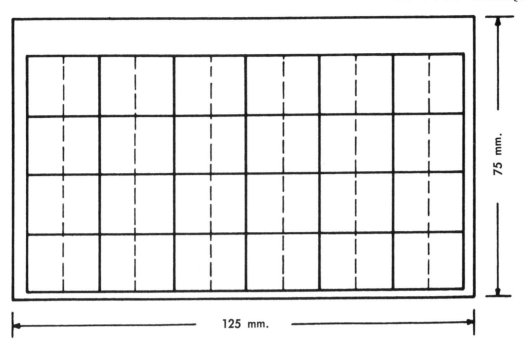

Fig. 157. Typical 75 by 125 mm. microfiche format (48 images).

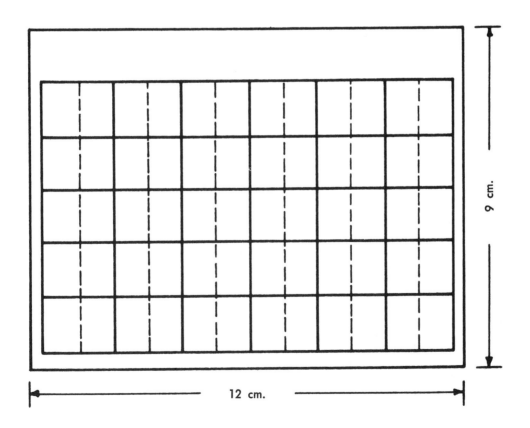

Fig. 158. Typical 9 by 12 cm. microfiche format (60 images).

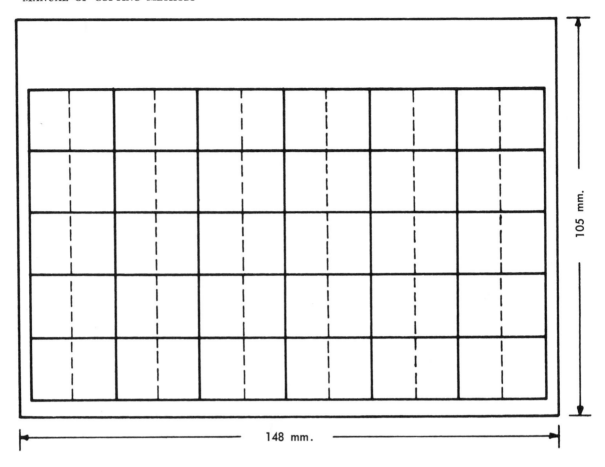

Fig. 159. Typical 105 by 148 mm. microfiche format (60 images).

Microfiches can be duplicated by contact printing using a number of different types of machines and processes.

VARIANT FORMS OF THE MICROFICHE. Standardization of over-all size, image size, and reduction ratio is, of course, of great importance where microfiches are being used to disseminate information widely. There are certain types of microfiches, however, that are very different in size but that have been designed expressly for a closed system. An example of such a closed system is that used by government land offices in the Netherlands. In this system, a strip-up method using 35 mm. film is employed to produce microfiches on sheets of film measuring 148 by 210 mm.—a standard D.I.N. size.[3]

Each microfiche contains 16 frames (32 pages)

of micro-images of large handwritten land registry records (Figure 165). Duplicates of these microfiches are distributed to each of the land offices in various cities in the Netherlands, and each office is equipped with a reader-printer that will accept this large microfiche. Property owners may consult the records at the land offices and may obtain hard copy of needed pages. Since the system is closed—i.e., microfiches are not distributed beyond the offices where suitable reading and printing equipment is available—the fact that the microfiches are of a non-standard *microfiche* size is in no way an inconvenience.

Another specialized form of the microfiche is the Eastman Minicard. The Minicard system is a high-speed, information-retrieval system entailing the use of small film chips measuring 16 by 32 mm. that can contain up to a maximum of 12 images plus a coding pattern of dots for high-speed, photoelectric sorting. This, too, is a closed system

[3] Deutsche Industrienormen (German standards organization).

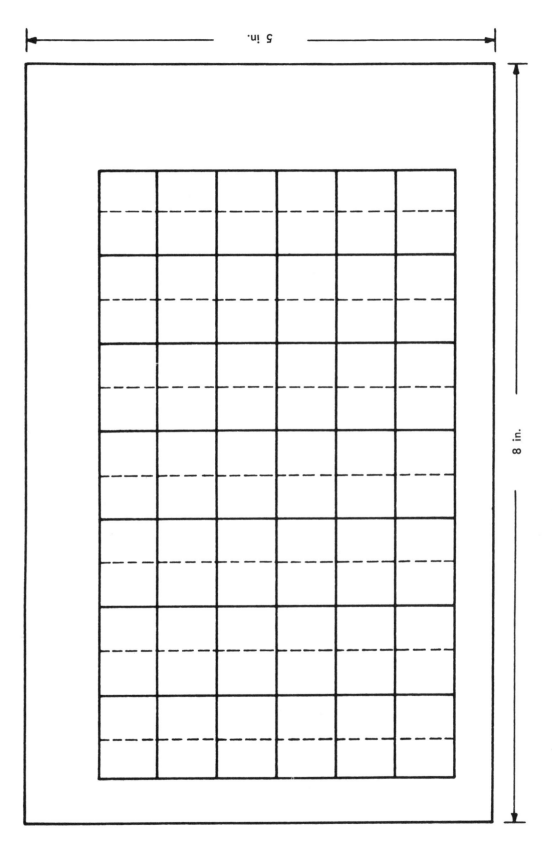

Fig. 160. 5- by 8-inch microfiche format used at one time by the United States National Aeronautics and Space Administration. Although this size is no longer being produced, several million such microfiches are in existence (84 images).

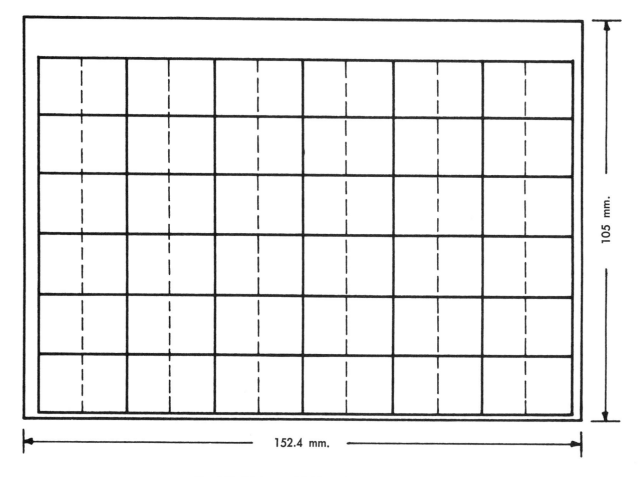

Fig. 161. 72-image 105 by 152.4 mm. microfiche.

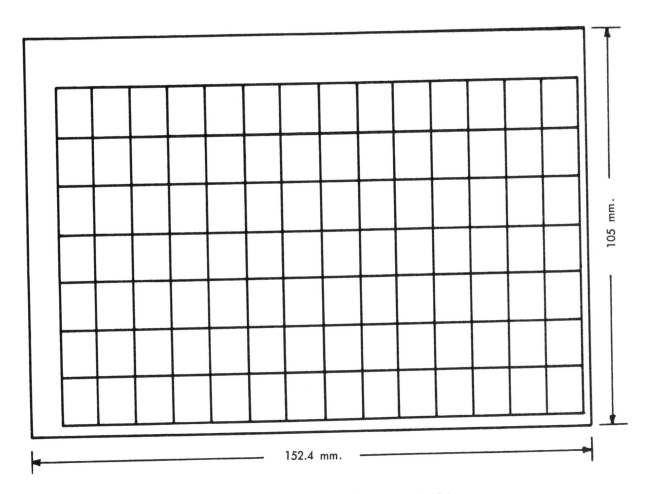

Fig. 162. 98-image 105 by 152.4 mm. microfiche.

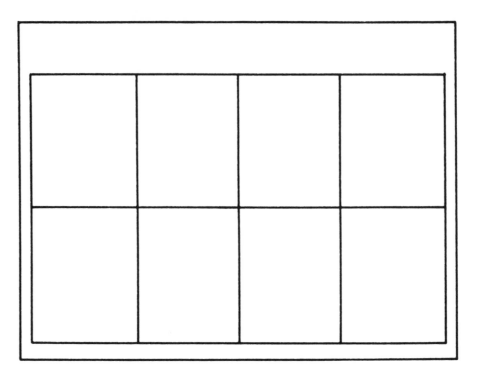

Fig. 163. 8-image format on 9 by 12 cm. microfiche.

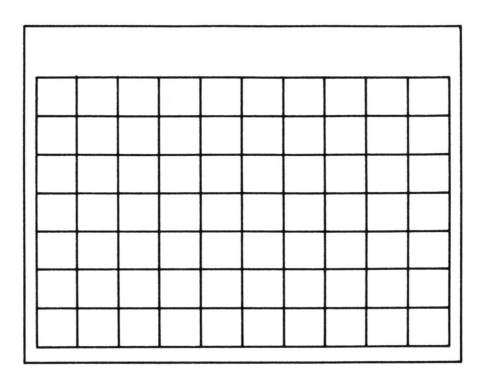

Fig. 164. 70-image format on 9 by 12 cm. microfiche.

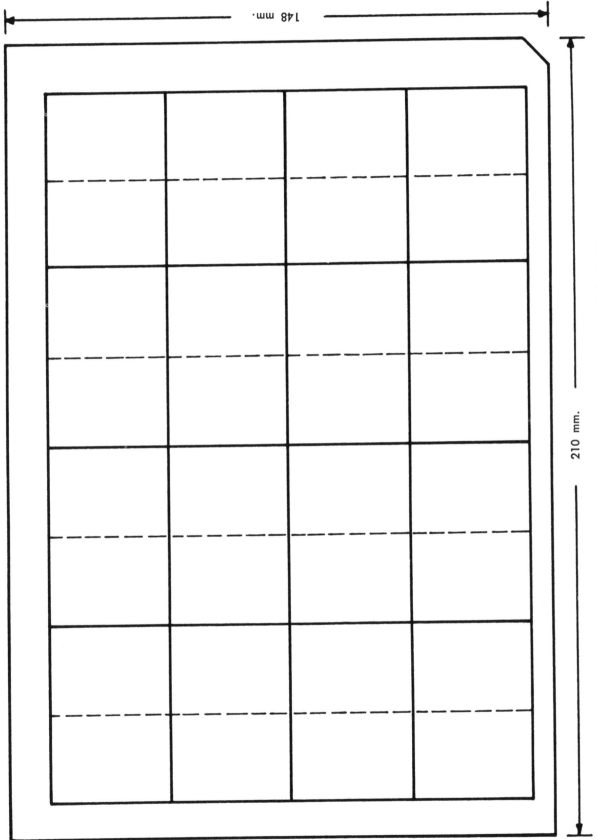

Fig. 165. 148 by 210 mm. microfiche format used by the Dutch land office.

since the Minicards can only be used in conjunction with Minicard sorting, reading, duplicating, and hard copy equipment. Other information-retrieval systems, such as Filmorex and Magnavox Media, also use small-sheet forms.

Still another variant of the sheet form is the Microcite system developed by the National Bureau of Standards. The Microcite system employs a 15-inch sheet of film carrying 18,000 images of abstracts on 3- by 5-inch cards filmed at a reduction ratio of 1:37. A special indexing system provides for the rapid location of desired images which are projected on a screen for reading or from which hard copy can be obtained.

Techniques: bibliographic considerations

Bibliographic units. One of the primary bibliographic considerations in the production of microtransparencies of research materials is the problem of bibliographic units. A bound volume may be 100 pages long or 1,000 pages long and still be a single unit. Microforms do not possess this quality of variable extensibility. Roll microfilm is limited by the capacity of storage reels and microfiche is limited by the number of frames that can be contained on a sheet of any given size. Microfiches, for the most part, are limited to materials which are relatively short in length, such as journal articles and technical reports, which can be reproduced on a single sheet. If, however, more than one sheet is required, each sheet is not treated as a unit separately titled, cataloged, and stored. Rolls of microfilm, on the other hand, chiefly because of their greater capacity, are treated as separate units. When roll microfilm first began to be used for the recording of research materials, the unit was frequently the 100-foot roll of film contained in the camera. In the filming of a newspaper file, for example, the first reel contained as many issues and pages as the film could hold, and the second reel began where the first reel left off. This practice resulted in extremely awkward bibliographic units such as:

Reel 1: *The Oakland Press* (1933)
    Jan 1–Oct 9, p. 3
Reel 2: *The Oakland Press* (1933–34)
    Oct 9, 1933, p. 4–July 17, 1934, p. 2

Current practice is to divide materials in advance of filming in more orderly and systematic ways so that each reel contains a conveniently handled unit of the material being filmed. The maximum practical capacity of a microfilm storage reel is 110 feet. If, for example, the number of frames required to film one month's issues of a newspaper will use 50 feet of film, the file can be divided for filming so that each reel contains the issues for two months. If, however, one month's issues require 75 feet of film, this then becomes the largest bibliographic unit feasible.

In filming materials in which the bibliographic unit is less than 100 feet, the usual practice is to complete the filming of the first unit and then continue with the second unit until the film supply is exhausted. The second unit is then continued on a second roll of film until it is completed and the third unit begun, and so on (Figure 166). After the film is processed, the parts of each bibliographic unit are spliced together and wound on separate reels. Typical bibliographic units for newspaper files in common use are shown in Table 25. Serials should be divided so that all of the issues for one or more complete volume or volumes are contained on one reel of film, or, if lengthy, into half volumes, quarter volumes, etc.

TABLE 25

TYPICAL BIBLIOGRAPHIC UNITS FOR NEWSPAPER FILES

10 days (with a maximum of 11 for 31-day months)
    January 1–10
    January 11–20
    January 21–31
15 days (with a maximum of 16 for 31-day months)
    January 1–15
    January 16–31
Full month
    January 1–31
Two months
    January 1–February 28
Three months
    January 1–March 31
Four months
    January 1–April 30
Half year
    January 1–June 30
Full year
    January 1–December 31
Two full years
    January 1, 1960–December 31, 1961

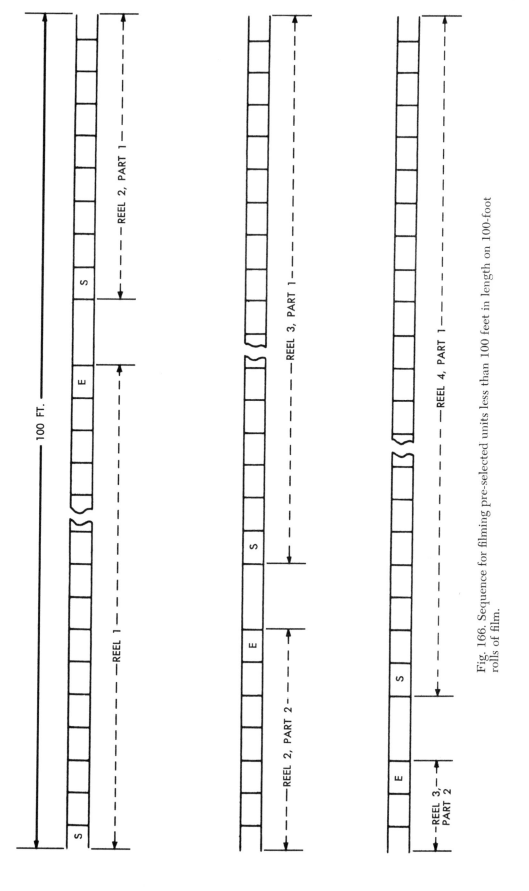

Fig. 166. Sequence for filming pre-selected units less than 100 feet in length on 100-foot rolls of film.

Collation of originals. Microfilms of research materials fall into two main classes depending upon their function. The first class, which, numerically, is quite large, includes microfilms of journal articles or of a few pages of a longer work. Such microfilms are usually made simply to disseminate in an inexpensive form information needed by a scholar or research worker which is not available to him locally. Often such microfilms are only a few frames long and are discarded after they have served their purpose. The second class of microfilms are those made of complete works or of extensive runs of serial literature for purposes of acquisition or preservation.

Microfilms of journal articles or short runs of consecutive or random pages should be collated by the personnel responsible for the delivery of the material to the photoduplication service to make sure that no pages are missing, out of sequence, or in too poor condition for filming. A missing page from a journal article may render it useless. In filming long runs of materials for acquisition or preservation, however, a different kind of situation often prevails. A file of a 19th century newspaper, for example, may be the most complete file extant, but still may have missing pages, missing issues, issues bound in incorrect sequence, and various forms of damage. Materials of this kind should be carefully collated before filming and a list prepared of all missing or damaged pages, which then can be filmed at the beginning as a table of contents. If a file is largely incomplete, a listing of issues filmed, instead of issues missing, can be used. If pages or issues are out of order and if the material is bound, instructions should be given for the camera operator to follow so that the sequence in filming is correct.

In addition to instructions about sequence, other physical conditions must also be brought to the attention of the camera operator before filming. This can be done either by using printed notes or by using sheets of paper of different colors inserted in the file to signal the presence of common, recurrent flaws.

A portion of a page may occasionally be missing because of accidental damage or vandalism, but this may not always be evident to the camera operator until he has filmed the page and turns it. This is particularly true of newspaper pages from which an article has been cut. Such pages should be backed with a sheet of colored paper to show that a portion is missing and should be filmed with the backing sheet in place to cover the text of the page beneath. Paper of a different color can be used to indicate missing pages or incomplete issues so that appropriate targets can be filmed. Sheets of other colors can be used to call attention to changes in year date, change in size, or to the presence of defects that the camera operator must remedy before filming. Typical of the latter is the presence of wrinkles or creases, which should be removed by means of a hand iron set at low heat.

One type of crease, which occasionally is encountered and which should not be removed, is the "river." Rivers occur when a sheet becomes creased before it is printed. Removing it would cause separation of the letters and words of the text, thus impairing legibility.

Preparation of manuscripts. The preparation of manuscripts for filming often requires different procedures than those used for printed material. In preselecting the material into convenient bibliographic units, attention must be paid to the fact that the number of documents, and hence of frames, may vary considerably between different chronological units. The number of frames per roll may also vary if there is a considerable variation in the size and shape of the documents.

If large collections of manuscript material are arranged alphabetically, the material should be divided so that breaks between rolls fall between letters of the alphabet. In the case of bound volumes of manuscripts that are cataloged in accordance with the content of each volume, it is preferable to include one or more complete volumes on each roll of film.

In filming miscellaneous collections of material, a brief listing of the contents of each roll should be prepared in advance and filmed at the beginning of the roll as a finding aid.

Manuscript collections also frequently contain duplicates. Duplicates should be removed from the file before filming or identified so that they will not be filmed.

A very useful publication, which gives a number of recommendations and examples for both the preparation and the filming of manuscripts, is

Staff Information Paper Number 19—The Preparation of Records for Publication on Microfilm, published by and available from the National Archives, General Services Administration, Washington, D.C.

Titling, and other preliminary identification data. To indicate the beginning and the end of a microfilm, the practice universally followed is to use START and END targets as the first and last frame of each film. To identify short runs of material on microfilm, two practices are in common use. One is to film, immediately after the START target, a copy of the order form, which lists author, title, source, date, and inclusive page numbers. A second practice is to film the title page (and, if needed, the verso of the title page) to indicate the source of the material.

In filming complete works or extensive runs, a title block is usually prepared in letters large enough to be read from the microfilm with the unaided eye. The letters used should be large enough so that, when filmed at the required reduction ratio, their height on the microfilm will be at least 2 mm. (0.08 inch) high.

Practice varies as to how detailed title blocks should be, ranging from place, title and inclusive dates to information in greater detail (Figure 167).

In addition to the information given in the title block, there is general agreement on the inclusion of additional information at the beginning of each reel, but not on which of the preliminary frames this information should appear. This additional information includes: (1) a scale to indicate the reduction ratio used in filming, (2) the name of the organization or institution responsible for the actual filming, (3) the name of the institution for whom the filming is being done (in cases where the producing institution does not retain the master negative), (4) cataloging information (e.g., the inclusion of a Library of Congress catalog card), (5) the location of the material filmed (if not that of the producing institution), (6) notice of restrictions on reproduction or use of the film, and (7) National Bureau of Standards test charts to indicate resolution.

The use of targets. In the course of the filming itself, a number of different targets should be included where necessary to make various conditions clear to the user, such as: PAGE(S) MISSING, ISSUE(S) MISSING, and ISSUE INCOMPLETE. Occasionally, newspapers issue supple-

Egypt. Cairo

AREV

January 1, 1963

through

January 31, 1963

State: California

County: Mono

City: Bodie

Title: Weekly

Standard-News

Frequency: Weekly

Reel: 1

Dates: 1880–1892

(Broken File)

Fig. 167. Title blocks.

ments which may be missing from a file. In such cases, a target reading ISSUE INCOMPLETE —SUPPLEMENT LACKING should be filmed. It should also be noted that supplements are sometimes printed on one side only in the form of broadsides. In such cases, the blank verso should always be filmed to indicate to the user that nothing has been omitted.

If, due to stains or discolorations, it is impossible to record the text of a page in its entirety at a normal exposure but possible to record the text in the darker portions at a higher exposure, the second exposure should be accompanied by a target reading RETAKE OF PRECEDING FRAME.

In many instances, pages that have been poorly printed may have the appearance, when filmed, of having been improperly photographed. A double impression, for example, may have the appearance of a page that was moved during exposure. To indicate to the user that the condition is in the original, and hence irremediable, targets such as ORIGINAL DEFECTIVE or FILMED FROM BEST COPY AVAILABLE should be used.

In serial publications, changes in page size occur from time to time. If a change in the reduction ratio is required, a target reading CHANGE OF PAGE SIZE should be filmed with an inch and millimeter scale to show the new reduction ratio used.

If more than one year of a serial is included on a reel of film, a target indicating the year should precede the issues for each year. Another kind of targeting that is helpful to the user in locating pages on films of large metropolitan newspapers is a running title at the top or side giving the year, month and day (Figure 168).

Restriction notices are sometimes in the form of targets appearing on every frame in cases in which it is important to keep the user informed of the restrictions.

A very useful addition to microfilm frames of unpaged materials, such as manuscript collections, is frame numbering. With electrically operated microfilm cameras, this is accomplished by wiring an electric counter into the shutter circuit and placing the counter in one corner of the field.

Each time the shutter is actuated, the counter advances one number. Cameras such as those in the Recordak Micro-File line are already wired for accessory counters which can be plugged into the camera control panel. With manually operated cameras, a manually operated counter can be used, which must be tripped by a lever each time an exposure is made.

Techniques: technical considerations

In the following sections, a number of the techniques necessary for the successful production of microcopies in roll form of many kinds of originals are described. These techniques, by and large, also apply to the production of microfiches and the microtransparencies used for micro-opaque production and to the production of optical copies by methods and equipment other than microfilming.

Reduction ratio. One of the first considerations in converting research materials to microtransparency form is the determination of the reduction ratio to be employed. The over-all size of the page and the type size, type design, and line width of the text are primary factors affecting the choice of a reduction ratio that will be appropriate for the purpose for which the film is being made. This, in turn, will affect the position of the images on the film if roll film is being used. Commonly accepted practice is to limit the filming of finely printed texts to a maximum reduction ratio of 1:14.

The maximum frame size of 35 mm. non-perforated film as used in a typical camera, such as the Recordak Model MRD-2, measures 1¼ by 1¾ inches. The maximum sizes of documents that can be filmed within these frame limits at reduction ratios ranging from 5 to 21 diameters are shown in Figure 169. If a bound volume having a page size of 6¾ by 9½ inches is to be filmed, it can be positioned one page per frame in position 1-A at a reduction ratio of 1:6, two pages per frame in position 2-B at a reduction ratio of 1:8, or two pages per frame in position 2-A at a reduction ratio of 1:11 (Figures 170, 171, and 172). Even if the type size were quite small, the higher reduction for position 2-A, which would also be the most economical, could be used without danger of loss of legibility.

JAN 25, 1963

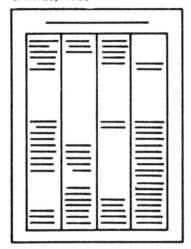
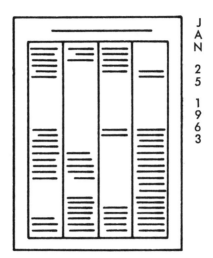

Fig. 168. Running titles for microfilms of newspapers showing year, month, and day of issue.

If, in another instance, a journal having a page size of 10 by 13 inches is to be filmed, it can be positioned one page per frame in position 1-A at a reduction ratio of 1:8, two pages per frame in position 2-B at a reduction ratio of 1:12, or two pages per frame in position 2-A at a reduction ratio of 1:16 (Figures 173, 174, and 175). If the type face is small, or if the type impression is weak, broken, or lacking in contrast, or if unusually fine lines and small characters appear on reduced-size maps or drawings, position 2-B at the 1:12 reduction ratio would be preferable. Whenever position 2-A is used, the frame can be shortened to suit the page height.

In the examples given, the problem has so far been limited to the establishment of an optimum reduction ratio solely on the basis of the physical characteristics of the original. But, because the use of micro-images requires reading and/or enlarging equipment, compatibility with the use-equipment may have a decided bearing on the choice of reduction ratio. While most cameras can be set to any desired reduction ratio, many readers and reader-printers offer only limited control over magnification. In such cases, the reduction ratio used may have to be lower or, if the physical characteristics of the original will permit it, higher, to provide for a satisfactory image on the reader screen or on an enlarged print.

Still another factor affecting the choice of reduction ratio has to do with the end use to which the microfilm will be put. If, for example, a positive film duplicate will be made that will be used for the making of positive hard copy in an electrostatic reader-printer, it must be remembered that some loss in definition will occur with each generation. A negative produced at a reduction ratio of 1:20 may yield an acceptably sharp screen image on a reader, but hard copy produced from a positive duplicate of the film may not be acceptably sharp. In such cases, the choice of reduction ratio must be based on the definition requirements of the ultimate-use copy and not on the camera-produced copy.

Another compatibility problem arises if the reader to be used is not equipped with a mechanism for rotating the image. This usually limits the position of the images on film to positions 1-B or 2-B, and hence to the reduction ratios that can be used for these positions. In another case, if high-quality enlargements must be made from the film, any loss in definition that may occur in the enlarging process must be taken into account in establishing the reduction ratio to be used.

It can thus be seen that no fixed rules for the establishment of reduction ratio can be made on the basis of any single criterion. An optimum choice can be made only if all the relevant factors

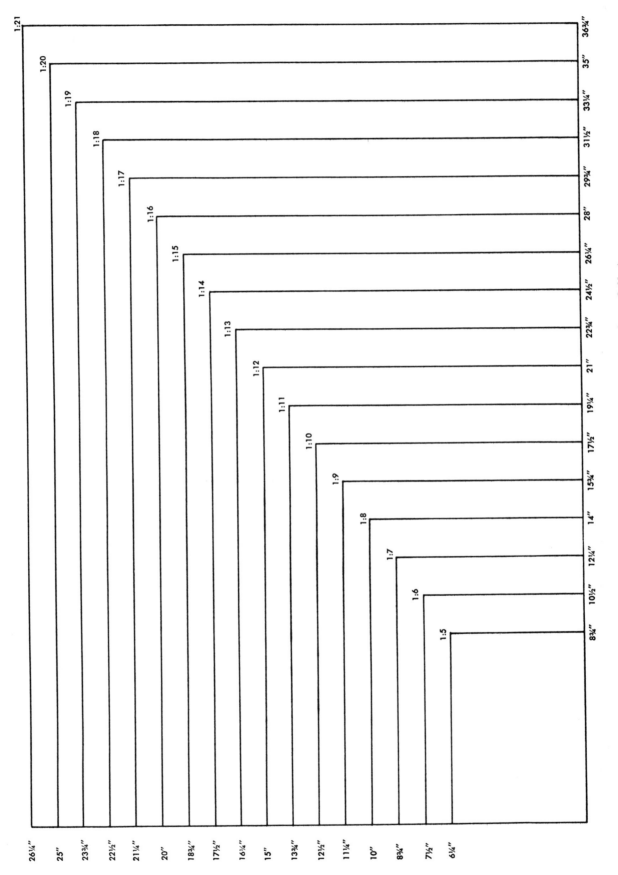

Fig. 169. Reduction Ratio Chart (35 mm. non-perforated film).

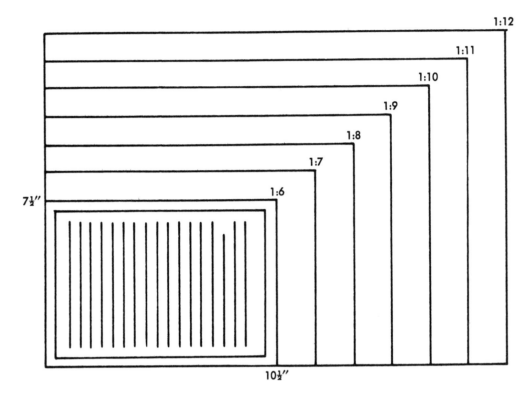

Fig. 170. Page size: 6¾ by 9½ inches; Position 1-A; Reduction: 1:6.

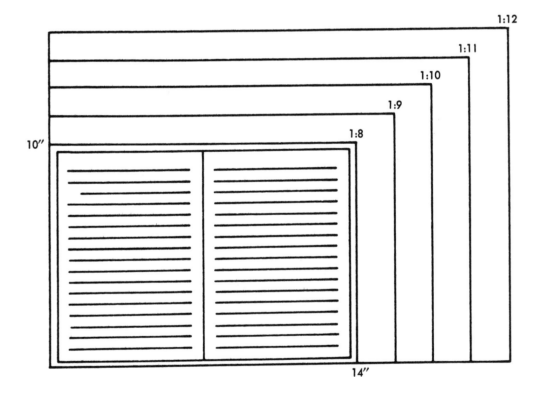

Fig. 171. Page size: 6¾ by 9½ inches; Position 2-B; Reduction: 1:8.

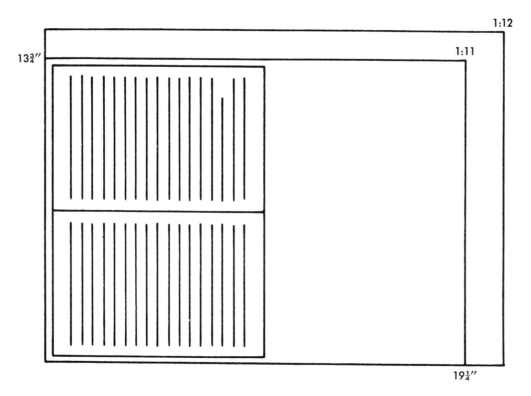

Fig. 172. Page size: 6¾ by 9½ inches; Position 2-A; Reduction 1:11.

are taken into consideration, and the choice, to some extent, will depend on the experience and judgment of the camera operator.

Fromm, in a recent paper,[4] describes a method for simultaneously evaluating factors affecting the choice of reduction ratio, including letter height, type face, and line density. The method, now under development at the Eastman Kodak Research Laboratories, employs a simple measuring device consisting of "a random-grain-pattern step tablet, in which the grains in each step differ in size from the grains in the adjacent step, but the integrated density of each step is approximately the same." Measurement of the characteristics of the text of a document for determining not only reduction ratio but also relative exposure is made by placing the step tablet in contact with the document and examining the text at a normal

viewing distance to determine the highest step in the tablet through which the text can be read. Fromm points out that, at the present stage of investigation, the practical application of this measuring device has yet to be established.

Plane of focus and depth of field. Although theoretically perfect sharpness is only possible on a single plane of focus, practically speaking there is some latitude wherein the subject being copied can be somewhat closer to or more distant from the plane of focus without an appreciable loss of sharpness. This is important in copying pages from tightly bound volumes in which curvature at the inner margin may be quite pronounced.

Depth of field for any given lens or lens opening is not a constant but a variable, which changes as the reduction ratio changes. The higher the reduction ratio, the greater the depth of field will be and vice versa.

"Usable" depth of field will depend, in turn, on the size, line width, and space width of the characters making up the text. Boldly printed texts can be out of focus to a considerable degree and still record well enough for satisfactory legibility.

[4] Harold J. Fromm, "Methods for Controlling the Quality of Microimages in Microreproduction Systems," *Proceedings 1965 Convention,* ed. Vernon D. Tate (Annapolis: The National Microfilm Association, 1965), Vol. 14, pp. 103–15.

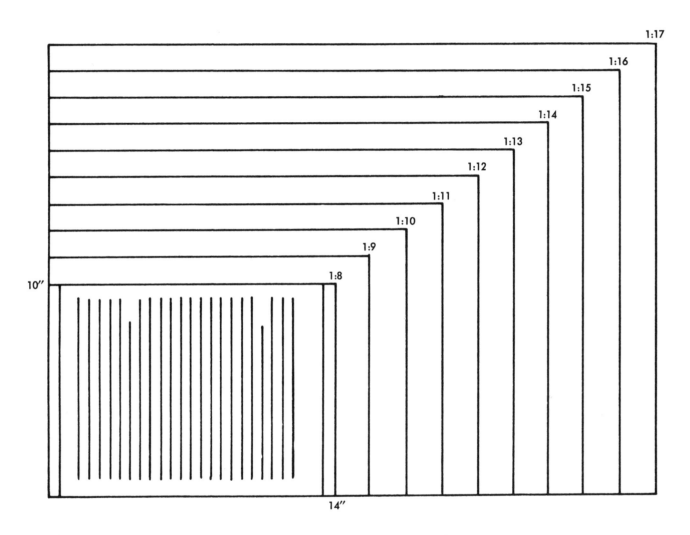

Fig. 173. Page size: 10 by 13 inches; Position 1-A; Reduction: 1:8.

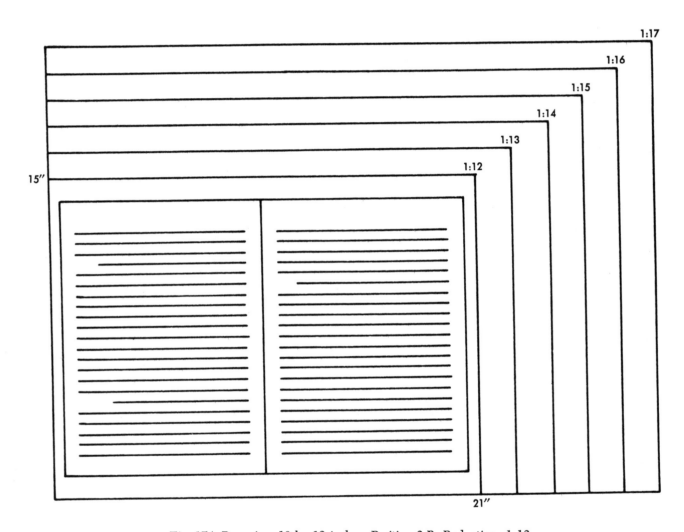

Fig. 174. Page size: 10 by 13 inches; Position 2-B; Reduction: 1:12.

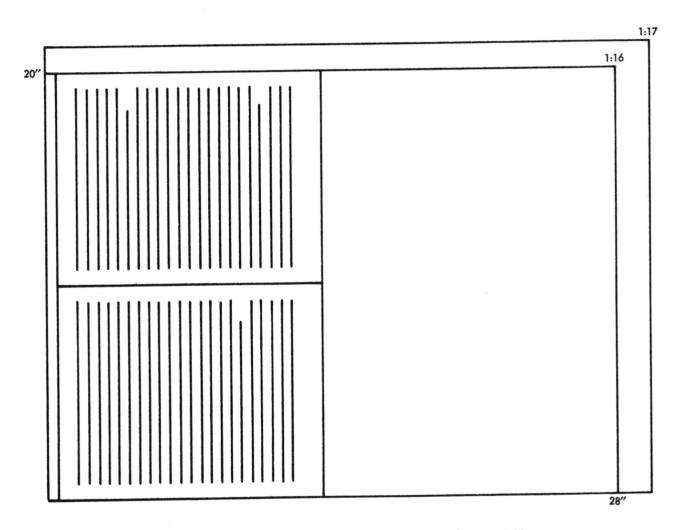

Fig. 175. Page size: 10 by 13 inches; Position 2-A; Reduction: 1:16.

With finely detailed texts, however, the limits are much more critical.

Exposure. If high-quality duplicates are to be readily produced from roll-form microtransparencies, the exposure must be such as to provide a background density that will be suitable for the materials in question and that must be as consistent as possible from frame to frame. Materials that are low in contrast or that have very fine lines are more readily reproduced if the background density is relatively low (1.00 to 1.20). High-quality duplicates from bolder and more contrasty materials are usually obtained at background densities ranging from 1.30 to 1.60. It is important that the exposure selected be suitable for the least contrasty and finest lines in the original. For example, if a volume is being filmed that contains important marginalia written in pencil, the exposure should be set for the best recording of the pencil lines.

Most planetary microfilm cameras are equipped with a photoelectric exposure meter mounted on an arm that can be swung over the copy to determine its reflectance. In theory, increasing or decreasing the amount of light by means of a rheostat so that a constant meter reading is maintained will provide satisfactorily consistent background density, but, in practice, this is not always true. Printed originals having closely set lines of type will have little white-paper area from which light will be reflected to the photoelectric cell. Others, such as advertisements in newspapers, may have large open white areas, or, in half-tone illustrations, almost no white areas at all. The use of a photoelectric meter, therefore, requires some experience and judgment on the part of the operator if the background density of negatives from varying originals is to be kept within acceptable limits. In filming originals that are difficult to meter but that have a fairly uniform background area reflectance, uniform background density can often be more readily controlled by using a fixed voltage setting rather than using a meter.

Processing. The processing of microfilm must be precisely controlled if negatives or positives of proper density, contrast, and permanence are to be obtained. Furthermore, the films must be free from scratches, abrasions, or other physical defects. Solution temperatures must be held within close tolerances, and the time the film is in each solution and the degree of agitation must also be closely controlled. In general, it is preferable to use the formulae for the chemical solutions recommended by the manufacturer of the film used, but there are situations in which this may not be practicable. In such cases, tests must be run to determine the developing times that will give optimum results with films and developers of different manufacture.

Equipment for processing microfilm ranges from simple and relatively inexpensive hand-operated equipment for low-volume work to highly complex and very costly equipment where high volume is required.

One type of hand-processing equipment consists of a reel having metal guides constructed in a spiral pattern and a set of shallow circular tanks for the solutions. A 100-foot length of film is loaded on the reel and the reel then placed for the required length of time and with the requisite degree of agitation in the developer, rinse bath, and fixer. The film is then washed and wrapped around a rack or a squirrel-cage drum and allowed to dry. The use of equipment of this type requires a photographic darkroom.

Another type of hand-processing equipment, which is partially automated, consists of an oblong tank having two electrically driven spindles located near the opposite ends of the tank. A reel of film is loaded onto one spindle and threaded to a second reel on the second spindle. A cover is then placed over the tank and processing can be done in the light. Developer solution is then poured into the tank through a light-tight well. A small electric motor rotates the spindles so that the film is wound from one reel to the other. The motor then reverses itself to wind the film back to the first reel. This operation is continued for the duration of the required developing time, at which point the developer is emptied from the tank and the rinse bath poured in. The rinse bath is followed by the fixing bath and, after fixation, the cover can be removed and the film washed in a stream of running water. Drying is done on a rack or a squirrel-cage-type drum.

Automatic processing of microfilm is done on machines patterned after the machines used for processing motion picture film; they are called "continuous processors." These machines consist of a series of large tanks for the chemical solutions and are equipped with banks of rollers that drive the film through the tanks and through a drying cabinet. A "leader" film is used to keep the machine threaded when not in use. When film is to be processed, the solution tanks are filled, and the first roll of exposed film is attached to the end of the leader film. The leader film then tows the exposed film through the machine. The second roll of exposed film is attached to the end of the first roll, the third roll to the end of the second, and so on. At the end of the processing run, the leader film is attached to the end of the last roll processed to re-thread the machine for the next processing run.

Until fairly recently, continuous processors were large and costly machines the use of which could only be justified if the volume of film to be processed was very large. Users of microfilm whose volume was too great to be met by hand methods but well below the volume needed to justify the cost of installing a continuous processor had to rely on commercial services. Because of improvements in the technology of microfilm processing, the need for equipment between these extremes is now being met by very small continuous processing devices, such as the Recordak Prostar.

One of the principal requirements in microfilm processing is that the processed films have archival permanence. This means that, not only must all the exposed but undeveloped silver halides be removed by the fixing bath but, in particular, that the final washing of the film be sufficient to reduce the quantity of residual chemicals resulting from fixation to an extremely low level (0.005 milligrams per square inch).[5] With hand processing, a fairly prolonged wash is required to bring films to the level of archival permanence, but, with modern continuous processors, the design of their wash systems is such that the wash time is quite short.

Regardless of the method or type of equipment used, the processing of microfilm should follow the recommendations of the film manufacturer as to solution formulae, time, temperature, and procedural steps. A further recommendation resulting from research into the causes of aging blemishes in microfilm is that the fixing solution contain a small amount (0.2 grams per liter) of potassium iodide. Also, according to the Eastman Kodak Company, the use of hypo-eliminating solutions to reduce the wash time is "not recommended for microfilm because they contain oxidizing agents that can contribute to the formation of emulsion blisters and microscopic blemishes."[6]

Inspection. The inspection of microfilm negatives is the final step in the production process of preserving documents on film. The usual procedure is to examine the film frame by frame on a microfilm reader to make sure that nothing is missing and nothing is out of sequence, and that all frames are of a quality level suitable for reading, duplicating, or making hard copy. Since many original files, especially newspapers, may be dispersed or destroyed after filming, failure on the part of film inspection personnel to note and report defective frames or missing material can result in the permanent loss of such material. There are many kinds of possible defects, some of which will be in the original material and thus are irremediable, and others that occur in the photographic process, which will be remediable. Hence, experience and judgment are necessary in the work of inspection. Close cooperation between camera operators and film inspectors is helpful in expediting the work of inspection. The most practical working situation is one in which microfilm personnel trade off between camera work and inspection so that each operator becomes conversant with both phases of the work. Because the frame-by-frame inspection of microfilm is a time-consuming and hence relatively costly operation, a system of spot inspection has occasionally been used by some laboratories for large filming projects. The reasoning behind this has been that, if

[5] *American Standard Practice for Storage of Microfilm,* PH5.4–1957 (New York: American Standards Association).

[6] *Storage and Preservation of Microfilms,* Kodak Pamphlet Number P.108 (Rochester, New York: Eastman Kodak Company, 1965).

the camera work has been done by careful and competent operators, the percentage of frames that might be defective or the number of pages that might have been omitted is too low to justify the labor cost of frame-by-frame inspection. Such a procedure may be justified if the loss of the material from the film does not constitute a permanent loss of the information. If, however, the material is unique, fragile, subject to rapid deterioration, or scheduled for destruction, then frame-by-frame inspection rather than spot inspection is the procedure that should be followed. The total cost of preparing a microfilm from the bibliographic and physical preparation of the material for filming through camera work and processing can be quite high. Frame-by-frame inspection, although adding still further to the costs, should be regarded as necessary protection of the investment thus far. For the same reason, the handling of the film during the inspection must be done with great care.

Scrupulous attention must be given to the maintenance and to the cleanliness of the reading equipment used for inspection. Processed film, except in leader and trailer areas should not be touched or handled. Inspection and editing personnel should work with soft, lintless cotton gloves because perspiration, oil, or other substances on hands may attack the emulsion.

Since the work of frame-by-frame inspection is tedious, monotonous, and also entails some eye strain, inspection work should not be scheduled for long periods of time.

Duplication. For the most part, the duplication of roll microforms involves the production of one or more positive copies from a master negative. Only occasionally, such as in cases in which the negative is unavailable or has been lost, is it necessary to produce a duplicate negative from an existing positive. One situation in which a duplicate negative may be required is in the printing of hard copy by processes such as Xerox Copyflo.

Roll-to-roll film duplication requires, in addition to a continuous-contact printer, the use of various other pieces of ancillary equipment, such as an inspection bench consisting of a sub-surface illuminator and a pair of rewinds, a footage meter, a densitometer, and a splicer.

The making of high-quality duplicates de-

pends not only on good equipment but also on care in the preparation of the film for duplication. It must first be examined from end to end for overall quality, particularly for changes in density, which may require changes in the exposure used in printing. Secondly, all splices must be carefully examined to make sure they are strong enough to travel through the printer; any weak ones must be remade. Thirdly, the film must be carefully cleaned to remove any dust or foreign matter that might interfere with image quality.

Ideally, positive duplicates intended for use on reading devices should have no splices. While splices can readily be remade in a microfilm laboratory, this is rarely possible at the point of use.

Storage. The physical nature of film—usually a chemically produced image in a gelatin layer coated on an acetate support—is such as to require much more carefully controlled storage conditions than are usually accorded to printed materials. Extremes or marked fluctuations in temperature or humidity, the presence of atmospheric gases or dirt particles—all are inimical to the longevity of film records. Detailed recommendations for the storage of microfilm—covering such factors as temperature, humidity, air-entrained impurities, fire protection, reels, storage containers, storage housing, storage rooms, air conditions, and periodic inspection procedures—are set forth in *American Standard Practice for Storage of Microfilm*, PH5.4–1957.[7]

Since the publication of the American Standard, however, the whole question of storage conditions has come under intensive scrutiny following the discovery of "aging blemishes" on certain films years after processing and storage. The investigation of the nature, causes, and effects, and the prevention of these blemishes has resulted not only in certain changes in the recommendations for storage practices set forth in PH5.4–1957, but also in other recommendations affecting the exposure and processing of microfilm.[8] Where PH5.4–1957, for example, recommends a relative humidity of 40 to 50 percent and a temperature of

[7] Copies of this document can be obtained from the American Standards Association, 10 East 40th Street, New York, New York 10016.

60° to 80° F., the National Bureau of Standards' recommendations are for a relative humidity of 30 to 35 percent at 50° to 60° F. for active files and a relative humidity of 15 to 20 percent at 50° to 60° F. for inactive files. The NBS studies also indicate that high densities are undesirable and that the addition of a small quantity of potassium iodide (0.2 grams per liter) to the fixing solution appears desirable. Since research in this area is continuing, additional recommendations or changes may appear.

Nitrate film. When microfilms were first in use, motion picture films on a cellulose nitrate rather than on a cellulose acetate (safety) base were still obtainable. Cellulose nitrate is not only quite flammable but is also unstable and subject to decomposition. Partially decomposed nitrate film can be explosively flammable and there are instances in which spontaneous combustion of decomposing nitrate film has occurred resulting in explosion and fire. The presence of a small amount of nitrate film thus poses a threat to an entire collection. The National Bureau of Standards study cited states that "Since the gaseous decomposition products evolved by nitrate-base film are very corrosive, such materials should be removed from any building housing permanent records."

It is known that the manufacture of nitrate film continued in this country at least as late as 1951 but the film may have been manufactured in other countries even more recently. In some cases, the film may be edge-marked as nitrate film or, if the film is in its original box or can, the label may state that it is nitrate film. In other cases, there may be no indication as to whether the film is on a nitrate or acetate base. The Eastman Kodak Company suggests the following test to determine the type of base:

"A simple, reasonably foolproof test to distinguish nitrate and any cellulose ester safety film is to punch a ¼-inch sample from the film [the film must be dry] and place it in a test tube or a small bottle of trichloroethylene. The liquid should be shaken to make sure that the film punching is completely immersed. If the punching sinks it is nitrate film; if it floats to the surface it is acetate film. This is because trichloroethylene has a specific gravity between that of nitrate film and cellulose ester safety films. . . .

"Trichloroethylene is non-flammable but its vapor should not be breathed, its toxicity being about half that of carbon tetrachloride (a somewhat hazardous solvent sometimes used for cleaning film)."[9]

Another method of testing is a burning test recommended in the *American Standard Specifications for Safety Photographic Film,* PH1.25–1956.[10]

If, in examining a collection of microfilms, some films are found to be on a nitrate base, they should be duplicated to acetate base film. Great care should be used in the duplicating operation because of the flammable nature of the material. *In particular, nitrate film or any other film not positively known to be on a safety base should not be spliced with thermal splicers.*

When the duplicates have been made, the nitrate film should not be simply discarded. The Eastman Kodak Company points out that "unstable or deteriorated nitrate films present hazards similar to explosives and must be handled with the same respect" and suggests that "safe disposal should be arranged with the proper city or fire prevention authorities."[11]

Techniques: specific types of research materials

Bound-volume copying. One of the most common problems in filming arises from the manner in which volumes are bound. Full-sewn volumes with ample inner margins may present no problems at all (Figure 176). Many such volumes

[8] C. S. McCamy and C. I. Pope, *Summary of Current Research on Archival Microfilm,* National Bureau of Standards, Technical Note No. 261, April 16, 1965. (Copies are obtainable for 25¢ from the Superintendent of Documents, U.S. Government Printing Office, Washington, D.C. 20402.)

[9] *Storage and Preservation of Motion-Picture Film* (Rochester, New York: Motion Picture Film Department, Eastman Kodak Company), p. 67.

[10] Copies can be obtained from the American Standards Association, 10 East 40th Street, New York, New York 10016.

[11] *Hazard in the Handling and Storage of Nitrate and Safety Motion Picture Film* (Rochester, New York: Motion Picture Film Department, Eastman Kodak Company). p. 15.

readily open to a position which is flat enough for easy filming. Oversewn bindings, especially if the inner margins of the pages are narrow, can, at times, be quite difficult to film. When such volumes are opened to their fullest extent, they are often far from flat. In extreme cases, portions of the text at the inner margin may be completely lost to view (Figure 177).

Ideally, a volume to be filmed should be opened and held as nearly as possible in a flat plane. Curvature of the text at the inner margin

achieve the necessary conditions for filming bound materials, various types of bookholders are used.

Bookholders are usually in the form of a box containing a spring-loaded platen or one or more sheets of foam rubber and a hinged glass cover. The function of the springs or foam rubber is to create pressure that will force the material being copied upward against the undersurface of the glass cover where it will be held in a flat plane.

Because pressure against the glass, depending

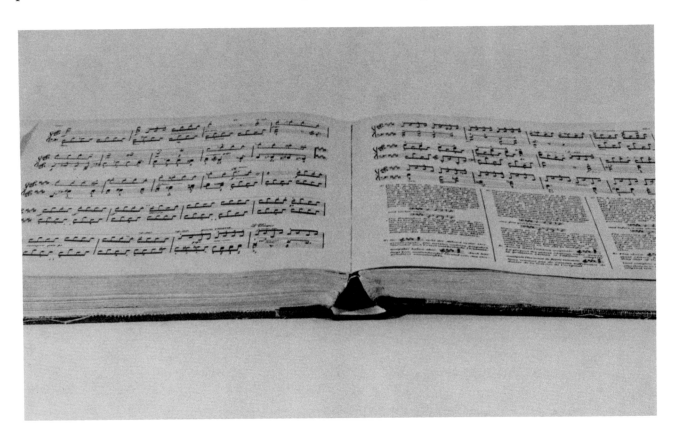

Fig. 176. Full-sewn binding which permits pages to lie flat.

causes foreshortening of the text and should be eliminated or reduced as much as possible. Curvature may also introduce undesirable reflections which can partially obscure portions of the text. With tightly bound volumes, a certain amount of pressure must be applied to hold the pages in a position flat enough for filming, but, at the same time, the amount of pressure must not be great enough to cause damage to the binding. To

on the size and thickness of the volume being filmed, will not be uniform over the entire surface, the glass must be strong enough to withstand local pressure without bending or breaking. Double-strength plate glass is recommended for this purpose.

In copying bound volumes with a bookholder, provision must first be made for leveling the volume so that both pages are held against the under-

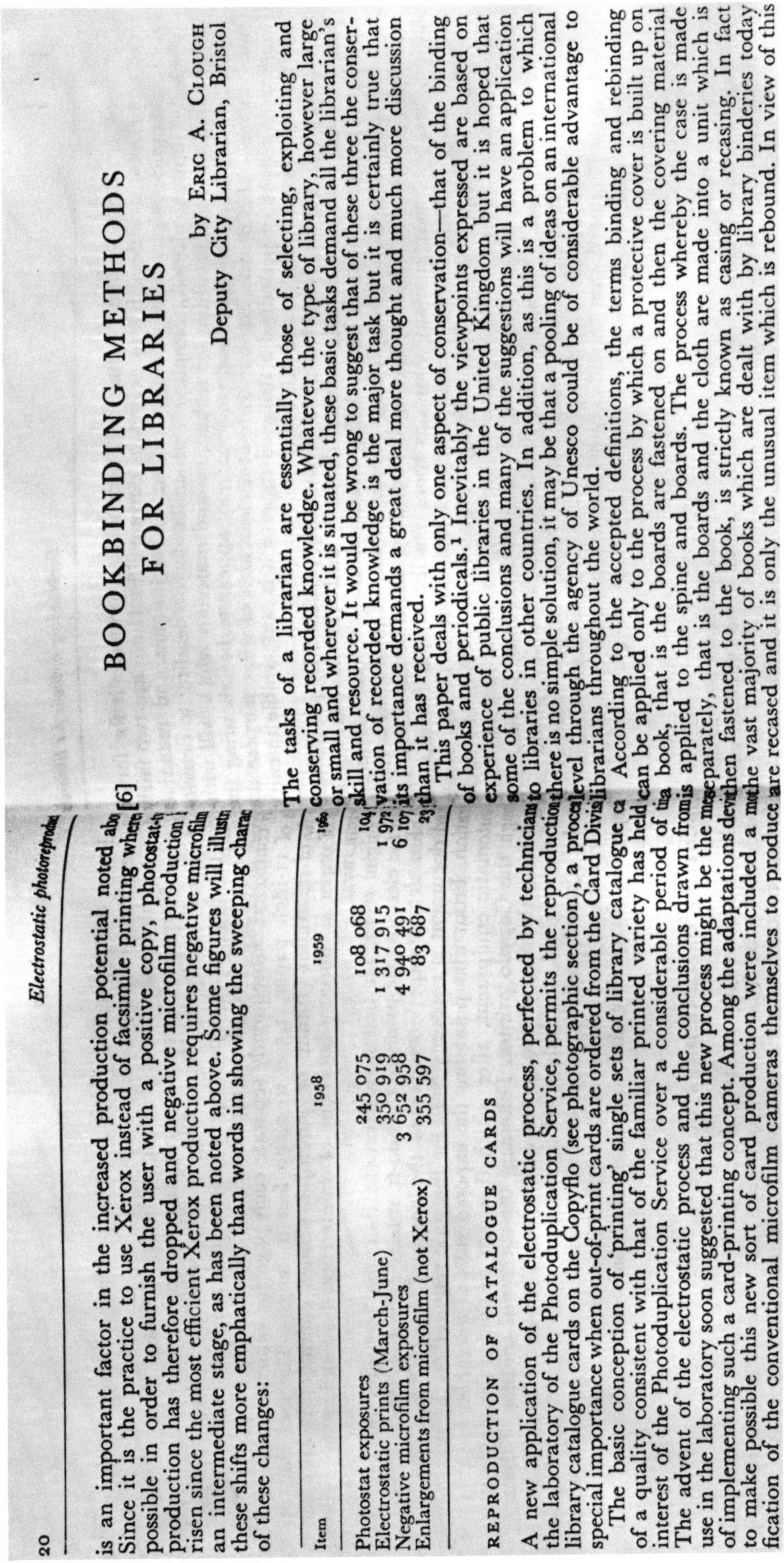
20 Electrostatic photoreprodu

is an important factor in the increased production potential noted abo Since it is the practice to use Xerox instead of facsimile printing where possible in order to furnish the user with a positive copy, photostat-r production has therefore dropped and negative microfilm production risen since the most efficient Xerox production requires negative microfilm an intermediate stage, as has been noted above. Some figures will illustr these shifts more emphatically than words in showing the sweeping charac of these changes:

Item	1958	1959	196
Photostat exposures	245 075	108 068	104
Electrostatic prints (March-June)	350 919	1 317 915	1 972
Negative microfilm exposures	3 652 958	4 940 491	6 107
Enlargements from microfilm (not Xerox)	355 597	83 687	23

REPRODUCTION OF CATALOGUE CARDS

A new application of the electrostatic process, perfected by technicians the laboratory of the Photoduplication Service, permits the reproduction library catalogue cards on the Copyflo (see photographic section), a proce special importance when out-of-print cards are ordered from the Card Divis

The basic conception of 'printing' single sets of library catalogue ca of a quality consistent with that of the familiar printed variety has held interest of the Photoduplication Service over a considerable period of ti The advent of the electrostatic process and the conclusions drawn from use in the laboratory soon suggested that this new process might be the me of implementing such a card-printing concept. Among the adaptations dev to make possible this new sort of card production were included a mo fication of the conventional microfilm cameras themselves to produce

[6]

BOOKBINDING METHODS FOR LIBRARIES

by Eric A. Clough
Deputy City Librarian, Bristol

The tasks of a librarian are essentially those of selecting, exploiting and conserving recorded knowledge. Whatever the type of library, however large or small and wherever it is situated, these basic tasks demand all the librarian's skill and resource. It would be wrong to suggest that of these three the conservation of recorded knowledge is the major task but it is certainly true that its importance demands a great deal more thought and much more discussion than it has received.

This paper deals with only one aspect of conservation—that of the binding of books and periodicals.[1] Inevitably the viewpoints expressed are based on experience of public libraries in the United Kingdom but it is hoped that some of the conclusions and many of the suggestions will have an application to libraries in other countries. In addition, as this is a problem to which there is no simple solution, it may be that a pooling of ideas on an international level through the agency of Unesco could be of considerable advantage to librarians throughout the world.

According to the accepted definitions, the terms binding and rebinding can be applied only to the process by which a protective cover is built up on a book, that is the boards are fastened on and then the covering material is applied to the spine and boards. The process whereby the case is made separately, that is the boards and the cloth are made into a unit which is then fastened to the book, is strictly known as casing or recasing. In fact the vast majority of books which are dealt with by library binderies today are recased and it is only the unusual item which is rebound. In view of this

Fig. 177. Oversewn binding in which text is lost at inner margin.

surface of the glass cover with approximately equal pressure. This is usually accomplished by building up one side of the volume with sheets of fiberboard or other suitable materials, as shown in Figure 178. As filming progresses, the cardboard sheets are successively withdrawn to correct the level. When the mid-point in filming the volume has been passed, the cardboard sheets are used to build up the level of the other side of the volume.

If a bookholder is not being used, it is virtually impossible to keep both pages exactly in plane. The use of cardboard sheets between the pages of the volume often helps to ameliorate this condition.

A simple bookholder developed at the library of the United States Department of Agriculture (see Figure 181) consists of a slideable board (1), with a handle (2), and three layers of cloth-covered foam rubber (3), each of which is 2½ inches thick. The glass cover (4) is spring-loaded and is brought to a level position by the two stops (5) at the front.

Bookholders are relatively slow to use. When filming long runs of material that can be opened fairly flat without the need for pressure afforded by a spring-loaded bookholder, a simpler type of holder can be used. It consists of a series of wooden blocks fastened together to form a series of steps, each of which is approximately one-half inch in height, and a sheet of glass. The volume is placed as shown in Figure 182, and the glass is placed on the lowest step above the volume. The glass is then simply lifted to turn each page. As filming progresses, the height of the volume above the copyboard will diminish, and the glass will have to be brought down to lower steps and later raised again to higher steps as the height increases. The fact that the glass is at a slight angle does not affect image quality, provided the angle is not great enough to produce unwanted reflections.

Still another type of bookholder, called the "Berceau," which was developed by the Association pour la Conservation et la Reproduction Photographique de la Presse (A.C.R.P.P.) in Paris, is designed for the filming of volumes having fragile bindings and that cannot be opened flat without endangering the binding (Figure 183). Provision

has been made in this bookholder for adjusting the angle to accommodate volumes having bindings of various degrees of tightness or fragility. As is shown in Figure 184, this causes some foreshortening of the text.

RARE BOOKS. The technique for filming rare or valuable bound volumes will, of course, be different from those techniques used for filming the ordinary run of bound materials. In some cases, it may not even be possible to film rare materials because of their fragility or the manner in which they are bound.

The condition of the binding and the condition of the paper may be such as to preclude the possibility of using an ordinary book cradle. With some volumes, it may not be possible to open them to an angle greater than 90° without damage either to the paper or to the sewing. To keep pages reasonably flat and to prevent movement of pages during filming, sheets of thin, light-weight glass can often be used to advantage.

Since a rare book is a physical entity whose many characteristics may be as important or more important than its subject matter, the usual practice is to film all pages including blanks and to film the pages in their entirety so that the full border of each page shows. Page size in itself can be important to the scholar. For this reason, precise use of an inch and millimeter scale should be employed.

FOLDING PLATES. Several techniques for filming volumes containing folding plates may be used, depending upon the characteristics of the particular volume and the end use to which the film will be put.

Ordinarily, bound volumes are microfilmed with the use of a bookholder. If a folding plate is small enough to be accommodated in the bookholder, backing it with a sheet of stiff cardboard, plywood or masonite will usually suffice to hold it flat against the glass surface of the bookholder for filming. More often than not, however, folding plates are too large for a bookholder. If they must be filmed in the sequence in which they occur in the volume, the bookholder must be removed and the volume and plate opened out on the copyboard. If only a legible recording of the data on the plate is required, it may not be necessary to completely flatten out all of the creases. If, on the other hand, the subject is a map that must be true

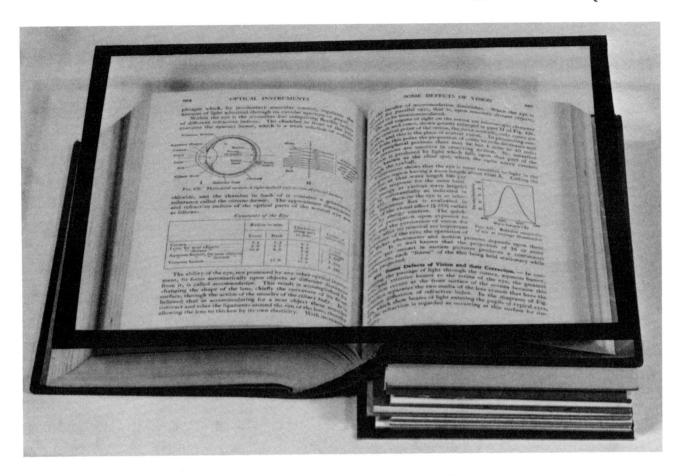

Fig. 178. Leveling a volume with cardboard sheets.

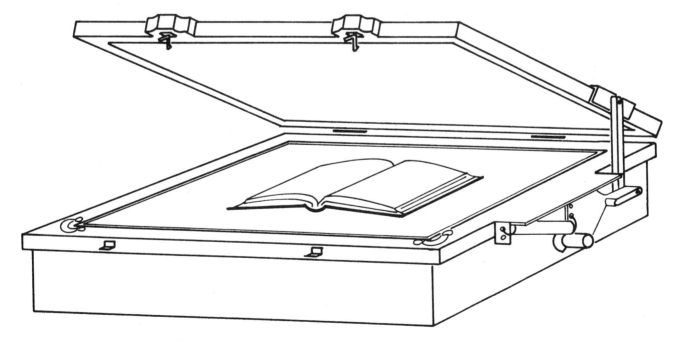

Fig. 179. Typical bookholder in open position.

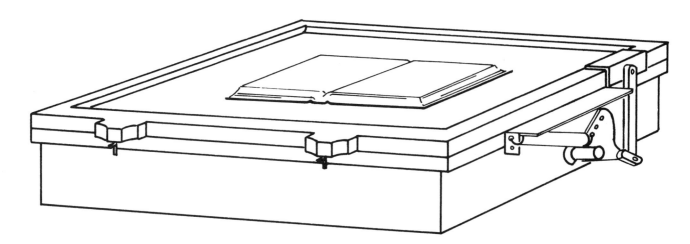

Fig. 180. Bookholder in closed position for filming.

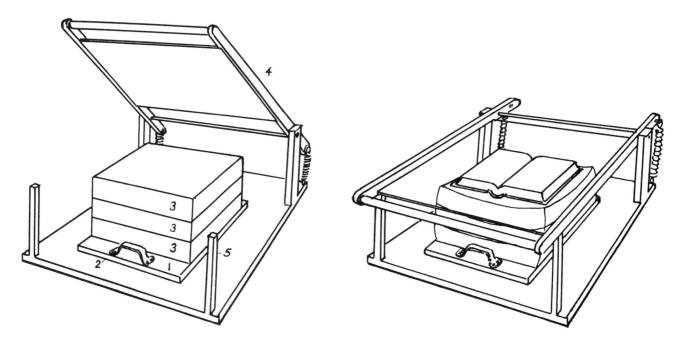

Fig. 181. Bookholder used at the United States Department of Agriculture library. (Reproduced with the permission of *American Documentation,* official publication of the American Documentation Institute.)

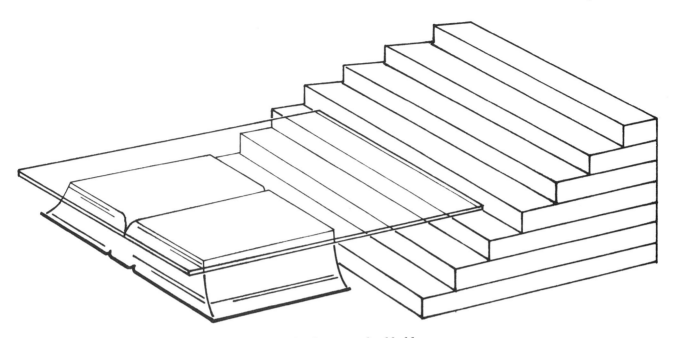

Fig. 182. Step-type bookholder.

Fig. 183. The "Berceau" angle bookholder used for filming bound volumes that cannot be opened flat without endangering the binding. (Photograph courtesy of Association pour la Conservation et la Reproduction Photographique de la Presse [A.C.R.P.P.] Paris, France.)

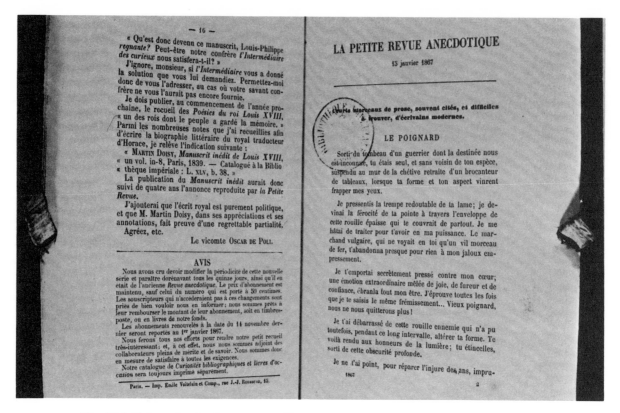

Fig. 184. Enlarged print from a microfilm negative of two pages from a volume filmed in the angle bookholder. Note the foreshortening of the text. (Print courtesy of Association pour la Conservation et la Reproduction Photographique de la Presse [A.C.R.P.P.] Paris, France.)

and square in the copy, then care must be taken to ensure that the subject is quite flat. This may entail the use of some kind of platform beneath the plate to raise it to a height equal to the thickness of the pages beneath it. Such a platform can be made of boxes of different areas and thicknesses covered with a sheet of cardboard or other suitable material (Figure 185). A sheet of glass can then be placed over the plate to flatten out the folds.

Occasionally folding plates are encountered that are so large they cannot be filmed on a single frame in position 1-A, because of equipment limitations or because of the excessive reduction in size that may be entailed. In such cases, the accepted practice[12] is to film the plates in sections from left to right and from top to bottom, as

shown in Figure 186, with at least one inch of overlap. A 30- by 40-inch plate filmed in four sections would thus be made up of 16- by 21-inch sections, which, depending upon whether the plate was in a horizontal or vertical format, would appear on film as shown in Figure 187.

If a large plate can be filmed on a single frame in position 1-A, but at a higher reduction ratio than is desirable, it is helpful to the user if the plate is first filmed in its entirety and then filmed in sections.

If a volume contains a number of folding plates, the amount of time required for repeatedly removing the bookholder to make the setup for a folding plate and then returning the volume to the bookholder may increase the cost of filming the volume considerably. A compromise can be effected by first filming the text in its entirety and then filming all of the plates at the end of the text.

---

[12] Stephen R. Salmon, *Specifications for Library of Congress Microfilming* (Washington, D.C.: Library of Congress, 1964). See also: Peter Scott, *Microfilm Norms* (Chicago: Library Standards for Microfilm Committee,

Copying Methods Section, Resources and Technical Services Division, American Library Association, 1966).

Fig. 185. Folding plate with supporting material to bring it to the height of the volume and held flat with a sheet of glass.

Targets should be used, of course, to indicate the location of the plates to the user of the film.

If a different reduction ratio is used to film a folding plate, an inch and millimeter scale should be introduced to indicate the new scale.

Newspaper files. Material relevant to the filming of newspaper files has already been presented in connection with the preparation of materials for filming and the use of targets. In addition, however, there are specific problems in the filming of newspaper files that require special consideration.

A problem of fundamental importance is that of reduction ratio and format. The sizes of newspaper pages in common use are often on a borderline between one- and two-page-per-frame filming. A 17- by 24-inch page, for example, can be filmed one page per frame in position 1-A at the relatively low reduction ratio of 1:14, whereas two-page-per-frame filming in position 2-B would require a reduction ratio slightly greater than 1:19. The maximum practical reduction ratio for good quality is generally agreed to be 1:20. This, however, does not mean that over-all page size is the only criterion. Films of modern, well-printed newspaper pages might be quite satisfactory when filmed two pages per frame at the higher reduction ratios, whereas poorly printed, lightly inked pages of the same size, or pages printed or partially printed in unusually small type faces will not. The decision as to whether one- or two-page-per-frame filming can be done must be made carefully. This is because too high a reduction ratio may impair quality, whereas too low a reduction ratio may double the amount of film required. In cases where there is any question, actual tests should be made and analyzed.

Because the microfilming of newspapers frequently entails a combination of relatively high reduction ratios and small type faces, precise control over every phase of the work must constantly be maintained.

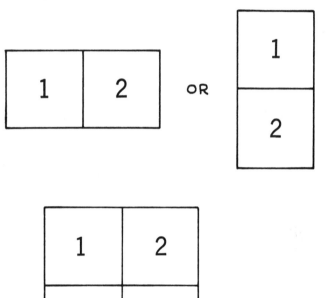

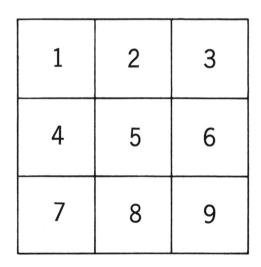

Fig. 186. Sequence for filming oversize plates.

While the following techniques are described in relation to the filming of newspapers, they also apply generally to the filming of other large originals such as maps.

LIGHTING. Because of the large area covered, especially when newspapers are being filmed two pages per frame, particular attention must be given to evenness of illumination. When the lamps

DENSITY. To eliminate undesirable density variations between frames, cameras should be operated on electrical circuits free of other equipment that might cause variations in voltage, or they should be equipped with constant-voltage transformers. Processing should be rigidly controlled to ensure that the background density of every roll is within acceptable limits for the production of

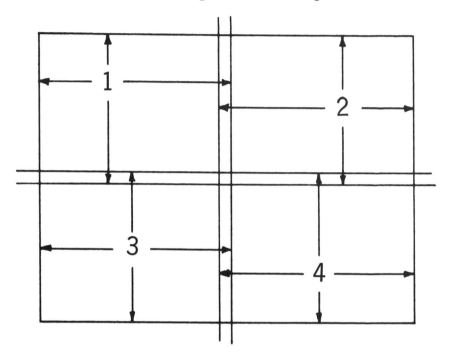

Fig. 187. Sequence for filming a 30- by 40-inch plate in four sections.

have been adjusted as well as possible, a blank sheet of white paper having a matte surface should be placed on the copyboard and photographed. The corners, edges, and center of this frame should then be read on a densitometer. If variations in background density within the frame exceed ± .10, the lights should be readjusted and a new test should be run.

RESOLUTION. National Bureau of Standards Microcopy Resolution Test Charts should appear on every roll so that a constant check can be maintained on the optical performance of the cameras. Camera lenses should be inspected and cleaned at regular intervals. If a noticeable difference in the resolution obtained at the center and corners appears, the lens should be recalibrated by a service representative of the manufacturer.

high-quality, positive duplicates or hard copy.

CREEP. Because of the large page size of newspapers, bookholders or sheets of glass are seldom used in the microfilming of newspapers. The normal procedure in filming newspapers two pages per frame is to film page one in the right half of the frame and then to turn the page and flatten it to photograph pages two and three. Because of the "pull" of the center fold, the page that has been turned and flattened may not remain perfectly flat but will tend to "creep" slightly toward the center fold. Two or three seconds should be allowed for this creeping movement to stop before the exposure is made.

ONE-PAGE-PER-FRAME FILMING. In filming newspapers one page per frame, a device is needed that will transport the opened pages back and forth for the alternate filming of versos and rectos. Some cameras such as the Recordak (or Kodagraph) Model C-1 are equipped with electrically operated, sliding subject holders. For cameras that are not so equipped, a sliding subject holder can be constructed by mounting a sheet of plywood on casters or bearings that move on a track. As an aid in positioning alternate pages, the base or frame on which the track is mounted should have a series of holes at ½-inch intervals into which pins can be placed to stop the movement of the sliding subject holder at the right point. Ordinary door pulls can be used as handles for moving the subject holder (Figure 188).

Creep must also be avoided in filming newspapers one page per frame. A simple method for doing this is to turn a page and flatten it before moving the subject holder. By the time the subject holder has been moved, creep will have stopped.

COLORED PAPER STOCK. Many newspapers regularly use paper stock of a particular color for certain sections. Because the response of a photoelec-

poor-quality, wood-pulp paper often show a marked tendency to discolor from exposure to light. If, for example, a weekly newspaper is received and stored for binding near a window where it is exposed to sunlight, the top page of each issue may be somewhat yellowish or brownish in color. This discoloration reduces the reflectance of the paper base and, if not corrected for, will cause a drop in background density. In filming newspapers one page per frame, evenness of density can be maintained by increasing the exposure for the discolored pages. In two-page-per-frame filming, this cannot be done, because the increase in exposure for the discolored page would result in overexposure of the adjacent page. If the discoloration is slight, an average exposure, which will result in a slight degree of overexposure of the non-discolored page and a slight degree of underexposure of the discolored page, may be used. If, however, the discoloration is more marked, the pages must either be photographed separately or photographed twice—once at the ex-

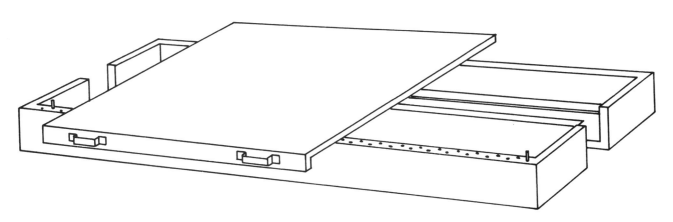

Fig. 188. A simple sliding copy holder mounted on tracks on a wooden frame.

tric exposure meter to color may be different from that of the film, variations in background density may occur. It is desirable in such cases to make a series of test exposures of the colored pages to determine how much of an increase or decrease in exposure over that indicated by the exposure meter must be made.

DISCOLORED PAPER. Newspapers printed on

posure setting required for the non-discolored page and once again at the higher exposure setting required for the discolored page. Whenever a second exposure is made, a target reading "RETAKE OF PRECEDING FRAME" should be included. A similar situation exists when microfilming pages that are partially discolored. One exposure will suffice if the discoloration is slight, but two successive different exposures must be used if the discoloration is marked. Tests should be run to determine how much of a difference in reflectance can be tolerated before two exposures are necessary.

BOUND VOLUMES OF NEWSPAPERS. When newspaper files are being microfilmed for preservation, it is highly preferable that they be removed from their bindings before filming. Bound volumes of newspapers are often quite thick. This can create serious problems in the foreshortening of the text occurring on the curving inner margin and in depth of field. There are instances, however, such as when only a portion of a newspaper file is being filmed (to supply another library with copies of issues it lacks), when removing the binding would be impractical. In addition to the depth-of-field problem, still another problem may have to be overcome if the volume is tightly bound. The lighting on microfilm cameras is usually positioned for flat or shallow copy. The depth of the inner margin of a tightly bound volume of newspapers may be such that portions of the text at the inner margin are in shadow. In such cases, it may be necessary to use an auxiliary lighting arrangement which will permit the lamps to be raised high enough to illuminate the shadow area (Figure 189).

DAMAGED AND MENDED PAGES. Because of their large page size and the relatively poor quality of the paper used, newspaper files often exhibit a greater number of instances of damaged pages than other types of research materials. Creased, wrinkled, or torn pages and pages that have been mended are a commonplace. Wrinkles and creases can be removed by ironing them with an ordinary electric hand iron set at moderate heat. Moistening deep creases with a damp sponge before ironing is often helpful. Creases that leave rivers in the page if removed should not be removed unless they cast shadows on the adjoining text. Clean tears can often be simply laid together. Rough tears with curling edges should be ironed or dampened slightly with a sponge so that the edges can be butted together. For severe tears where the edges are frayed or broken, a small sheet of very thin glass can be used to hold the edges flat. Care should be used in placing the glass so that the horizontal edges of the glass do not lie directly on a line of text.

Two types of mending tape are commonly used for mending newspaper pages. One is a glassine tape that is sufficiently transparent to permit filming without special handling. The other type is a tissue that is fairly transparent when it is closely bonded to the page but that is semi-opaque if the bond is poor. Poorly bonded tissue can be rendered transparent by moistening it with a damp sponge just before filming. Occasionally, pages are encountered that unfortunately have been mended with transparent cellulose tape. Often the tape will have become discolored and require the making of two exposures as is done with other forms of discoloration. A more serious hazard is caused by the fact that some types of cellulose tape tend to "bleed" and become tacky at the edges. This can cause the page on top of the mended page to stick to it and possibly become torn when the page is turned.

Volumes having reversed pagination. Most books in oriental languages, as well as some others, have their pages arranged in a sequence that is the reverse of that used for Western languages. The title page in such books corresponds in its position to what would be the last page in Western pagination. When such materials are filmed in position 2-B, successive pairs of pages will not be in sequence because, instead of the right-hand page following the left-hand page, the reverse is true. This results in a pagination sequence of 1–3–2–5–4–7–6–, etc., or 2–1–4–3–6–5–8–7–, etc. Such materials can be filmed in proper sequence simply by starting with the "end" target, filming the volume starting with the last page and ending with the first page, and then filming the "start" target. Another method is to turn the volume so that the pages are upside-down and film from the first page through the last.

Manuscripts. Manuscripts may occur either in the form of collections of loose-sheets or in the form of bound volumes that have been created by pasting or "tipping-in" the material on blank sheets. The materials in loose-sheet form are generally much easier to film. Frequently, manuscript collections include correspondence written on two sides of a single sheet or on both sides of a folded sheet, thus making it a four-page document. When in loose-sheet form, such originals can easily be positioned for filming. A two-sided original can

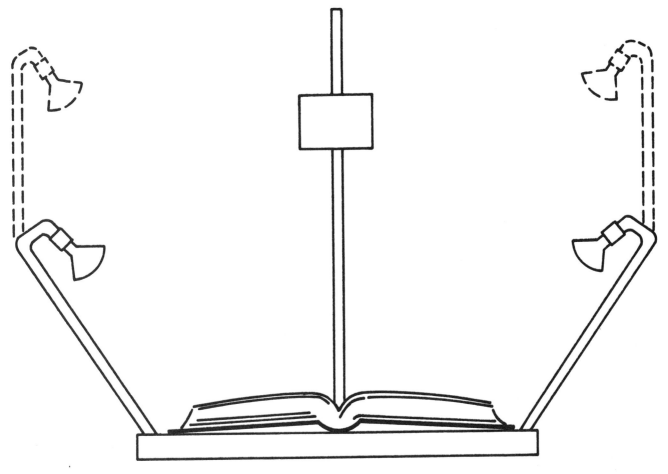

Fig. 189. Extension arms on light standards used to eliminate shadows in the inner margin area.

simply be turned over to film its verso and a four-page original can be filmed in the same fashion as any normal sequence of four pages. Two- or four-page manuscripts tipped into a bound volume become equivalent to small folding plates with all the problems attendant thereon. If a two-page letter has been turned over vertically for the writing of the second page, it must be tipped-in along its top edge and folded out vertically to film the verso. Since bookholders are not designed to handle such oddities, even a small page which must be folded out vertically may be beyond the capacity of the bookholder.

Another problem, often encountered in filming pasted or tipped-in manuscripts, is partial discoloration (which in some cases can be quite severe) from the interaction of the adhesive substance used and chemical components in the paper base.

These stains are usually brownish in color and, if not too dark, their effect on the legibility of the text can be minimized somewhat by the use of an orange filter, or by making a second exposure at a higher light intensity or of longer duration.

Procedures for microfilming manuscripts will in some cases be different from those used for printed material. If, for example, only an occasional verso is blank, it should be filmed to indicate that nothing has been accidentally omitted. If, however, a collection of manuscript materials contains a large number of documents having blank versos, these should not be filmed; a note stating this fact should appear at the beginning of the film.

When filming a manuscript collection made up of documents of many different sizes, the reduction ratio and frame size should be set to accommodate the largest size occurring and changed only for exceptionally large documents. When this procedure is followed in filming loose-sheet material, it is often possible to group two or more small documents on a single frame. Whenever the reduction ratio is increased for oversized documents, an inch and millimeter scale should be included in the frame to indicate the exact reduction.

Bound manuscripts on vellum often exhibit a significant difference in reflectance between each verso and recto. In some cases, an average exposure for each pair of facing pages may suffice, whereas, in others, two exposures may have to be made. Where the difference in reflectance is marked, the material should be filmed one page per frame and the exposure changed as needed.

Because manuscript collections are often unpaginated or may have broken series of internal pagination, the inclusion of an automatic frame numbering device to number photographically each frame is useful, not only for locating and identifying particular frames, but also as an indexing aid.

In general, manuscripts do not exhibit the contrast or evenness of impression common to the bulk of printed materials. For this reason, both high density and high contrast should be avoided.

Loose-sheet manuscript materials that are rare or fragile should not be filmed on rotary cameras.

Continuous-tone originals. Because of the high contrast of microfilm emulsions, continuous-tone illustrations usually show considerable loss of both highlight and shadow detail. Where a complete volume or an extensive run of continuous-tone illustrations must be microfilmed, alternative procedures are possible. The first is to use a motion picture-type negative film instead of microfilm. Such films have a long tone scale, can be developed to a moderate contrast, and are available in 100-foot lengths. Because films of this type do not have as fine a grain structure as microfilms, their resolution is not as high.

A second method is to overexpose conventional microfilm by a large factor and then to underdevelop the film in a diluted developer solution. For any particular film, the amount of overexposure and the degree of underdevelopment must be determined by exposing and developing test strips. The tone scale of copies made by this method is not as good as that obtainable with continuous-tone motion picture film but is greatly superior to that of conventionally exposed and processed microfilm.

Card files. There are a number of methods for reproducing card files on microfilm; the choice of method will depend on the purpose which the microfilm is intended to serve. In instances where an entire catalog or large segments are being filmed, either for preservation or to provide another library with a record of holdings, 16 mm. rotary cameras with automatic feeding devices of proven efficiency can be used to advantage. Where hard copy is to be made from the microfilm, the use of planetary cameras is preferable, because image placement can be controlled quite precisely. A useful device for accurate placement is a plexiglass jig used in conjunction with a subsurface illuminator to eliminate shadow lines around the edges of the cards and the tray-rod holes. Depending on the method to be used and the kind of hard copy to be produced, cards can be filmed in various multiples and in two or more rows. Book-type catalogs can be produced by shingling groups of cards as shown in Figure 190, microfilming them, and then printing offset mats by Xerox Copyflo.

Details for methods of producing catalog cards in small, various-sized editions by xerography for library use are described in the section on "Xerography," pages 148ff.

"CATALOGER'S CAMERAS." These cameras are devices designed principally for photographically recording the reduced-size entries in the book-form National Union Catalog (NUC) to provide catalogers with enlarged copy to work from without the labor of manual transcription. One such camera (Figure 191), which is in use at the University of Victoria (Canada), consists of a 35 mm. hand camera employing a half frame (1 by ¾ inches) instead of a normal full frame (1 by 1½ inches). The camera is arranged on a vertical stand and is equipped with an adjustable masking device for recording entries of different lengths. This mask is positioned a short distance below the lens at the focal plane on which the camera is focused.

Haines, George H 1912–
Sell your photographs, by George H. Haines. ₁London₁ Pelham Books ₁1964₁

90 p. illus. 21 cm.

Hajek-Halke, Heinz.
Abstract pictures on film; the technique of making light-graphics ₁by₁ Hajek-Halke. With an introd. by Franz Roh. ₁Translated by J. Maxwell Brownjohn₁ New York, Viking Press ₁1965₁

1 v. (chiefly illus. (part col.)) 31 cm. (A Studio book)

Translation of Lichtgrafik.

Hendricks, Gordon.
Beginnings of the biograph; the story of the invention of the mutoscope and the biograph and their supplying camera. New York, Beginnings of the American Film, 1964.

II, 78 p. plates, ports. 24 cm.

Horvitz, David, 1938–1963.
Photographs. ₁n. p., 1965₁

1 v. of illus. (incl. ports.) 22 x 29 cm.

Hütt, Wolfgang.
Landschaftsfotografie; ein Beitrag zu ihrer Geschichte und ihrer Theorie. ₁1. Aufl.₁ Halle, Fotokinoverlag ₁1963₁

151 p. illus. 28 cm.

Bibliography: p. 150–151.

Iofis, E   A   ed.
Цветная фотография. Изд. 2., испр. и доп. Москва, Искусство, 1961.

228 p. illus., plates, diagrs., tables. 20 cm. (Библиотека фото-любителя, вып. 13)

At head of title: Л. Ф. Артюшин ₁и др.₁

Institute of Office Management.
A guide to photocopying in the office; a report produced by a study group of the Birmingham Branch of the Institute for the Organisation and Methods Division. London ₁ᶜ1961₁

44 p. illus. 25 cm.

Jacobs, Lou.
Electronic flash, by Lou Jacobs, Jr. All photos. by the author unless otherwise noted. New York, American Photographic Book Pub. Co. ₁ᶜ1962₁

127 p. illus. 21 cm.

Jacobs, Lou.
Free-lance magazine photography; a guide to the working photojournalist. Philadelphia, Chilton Books ₁1965₁

160 p. illus. 24 cm.

Japan camera times. v. 1–   (no. 1–   );
Apr. 1958–
₁Tokyo₁

v. in   illus. 21–29 cm. bimonthly (irregular)

Vols. for Sept./Oct. 1959–   distributed by Rayelle Publications, Philadelphia.

John, David Hugh Oakley.
Photography on expeditions; recommended techniques for difficult surroundings ₁by₁ D. H. O. John. London, New York, Focal Press ₁1965₁

176 p. illus., ports. 25 cm.

Bibliography: p. 164–171.

Koeman, C
Photo, photomap, map. Delft, I. T. C., 1961.

8 p. illus. 24 cm. (Publications of the International Training Centre for Aerial Survey, ser. A/B, no. 7)

Kosar, Jaromir.
Light-sensitive systems: chemistry and application of nonsilver halide photographic processes. New York, Wiley ₁1965₁

xv, 473 p. illus. 24 cm. (Wiley series on photographic science and technology and the graphic arts)

Includes bibliographies.

Kühn, Fritz, 1910–
Sehen und gestalten; Natur und Menschenwerk. ₁6., verb. und erweiterte Aufl. Leipzig, E. A. Seemann, 1962₁

159 p. (chiefly illus.) 30 cm.

Kunfalvi, Rezső.
A fényképezőgép. Budapest, Tankönyvkiadó, 1950.

68 p. illus. 20 cm. (Tanulj jobban! Fototechnika 1)

Bibliography: p. 67.

Lacey, Peter.
The history of the nude in photography. Designed by Anthony LaRotonda. New York, Bantam Books ₁1964₁

215 p. illus. 18 cm. (A Bantam gallery edition, RG9)

Lange, Hellmuth, 1903–
Handbuch der Schmalfilm-Technik. 4., neubearb. Aufl. Berlin, Schiele & Schön ₁1962–

v. illus. 19 cm.

Larmore, Lewis.
Introduction to photographic principles. 2d ed. New York, Dover Publications ₁1965₁

ix, 229 p. illus. 22 cm.

Includes bibliographies.

Levitt, Helen.
A way of seeing; photographs of New York. With an essay by James Agee. New York, Viking Press ₁1965₁

78 p. (chiefly illus.) 20 cm.

Lilley, Geoffrey I
Make your own darkroom for colour printing. London, Fountain Press ₁1962₁

86 p. illus. 17 cm. (Fountain photobook series)

Fig. 190. Page of shingled proof slips.

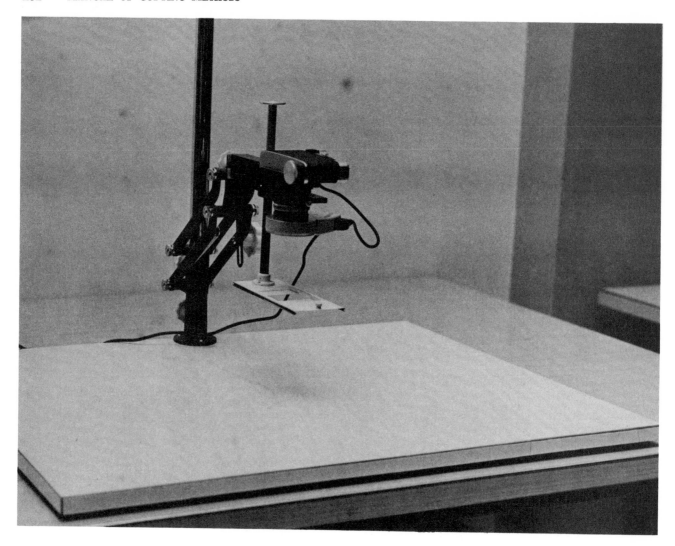

Fig. 191. "Cataloger's Camera" used at the University of Victoria (Canada) Library. (Don Ryan Photo courtesy of the McPherson Library of the University of Victoria).

Around the lens is a ring-shaped strobe light that illuminates the copy when exposure is made. To copy an entry, the page on which the entry appears is placed beneath the camera and the camera and mask are lowered so that the mask rests on the page. The mask is then adjusted for the length of the entry and the exposure made. Since the University of Victoria library does not have facilities for developing the film and making prints, these services are contracted for with a commercial studio.

Another type of cataloger's camera, which is not a microcopying device, is in use at Indiana University. It consists of a camera that accepts 4-by 5-inch sheets of sensitized paper, a tubular frame the length of the focal distance equipped with a glass plate to hold flat the entry to be copied, and a pair of lights. The camera works at a fixed magnification of 1.8 to 1. Camera-speed, stabilization-process paper is used that must be processed in a darkroom. From the camera-produced paper negatives, positives are produced by direct-contact printing for the cataloger's use.

Techniques: special problems

Offset. Little can be done to minimize the interference with legibility caused by offset. If the text on the page is bold enough to withstand some degree of overexposure and if the offset image is faint, the increase in background density resulting from an increase in exposure may help to make the offset image less apparent in the negative and even less so in positive duplicates or hard copy.

Showthrough. Showthrough in bound originals printed on one side only (e.g., typescripts on paper of insufficient opacity) can be eliminated by backing each page with a white opaque sheet of paper or cardboard. Showthrough in originals printed on both sides can be reduced or sometimes eliminated entirely by backing the page with a dark sheet of paper.

Colored paper stock. Colored paper stocks are widely used for covers of periodicals and often important data such as the table of contents is printed on the cover or on the inside of the cover. Colored stocks generally have a much lower degree of reflectance than white or off-white stocks and will require a higher light intensity if they are to be recorded at the same density. The use of a photoelectric exposure meter does not, however, always give a true indication of the light intensity required to produce this result. This is caused by the fact that the color response of the film is not equivalent to the response of the photoelectric cell to the reflected light rays. Colored stocks exposed correctly *according to the exposure meter* often show varying degrees of underexposure. In many cases, some degree of underexposure can be tolerated without seriously affecting the legibility or reproducibility of the film, but, in cases where the effect of underexposure is marked, a true exposure index must be sought by trial and error. This is done by making a series of exposures of the colored stock in question at progressively higher light intensities and recording the voltage readings for each exposure. When the exposures have been processed, the density of each can be read on a densitometer and logged against the voltage settings used.

When filming facing pages two at a time in which one is on colored stock and one on white, two exposures must be made—one at the predetermined voltage setting for the colored page and one at the normal exposure setting indicated by the exposure meter for the white page.

Color plates. The successful black-and-white recording of color plates depends primarily on the particular colors and relationships of colors appearing in the plate, rather than on technique. Where color coding is used, the colors may or may not record in sufficiently different tones of gray to make a black-and-white copy fully usable. The use of appropriate correction filters for the type of film used (e.g., a Wratten X-1 [green] filter with Kodak Micro-File film) will bring the response of the film to colors a little closer to that of the human eye, but there still will be instances in which quite different colors will record as the same shade of gray.

Foxed, stained, or discolored originals. If the degree of discoloration in foxed, stained, or discolored originals is not deeper than yellow to yellow-brown, a yellow or yellow-orange filter over the camera lens will reduce or eliminate the difference in background density that such discoloration causes. If the staining or discoloration is brown and fairly dark, as is often the case with glue stains or documents that have been left exposed for long periods of time to sunlight, filtering is of little help. In such cases, it is usually necessary to make two exposures—one for the non-discolored areas and a second at a much higher light intensity or longer duration for the discolored areas.

If a discolored original is in loose-sheet form and is not of a kind which would be adversely affected by heat, a copy made on thermographic materials (Thermo-Fax, Ektafax, and others) may be completely free from evidence of discoloration if the discoloring agent is non-infrared absorbing.

Brittle papers. Brittle papers must, of course, be handled with extreme care. In filming bound volumes containing brittle pages, a book holder should not be used. Instead, a light sheet of thin glass should be used to hold the pages open and flat enough for filming. Stiff backing materials between pages should not be used. In cases where the volume is also tightly bound, a 90-degree bookholder should be used. Papers that become brittle are usually of a composition that is also highly susceptible to discoloration from the action of light. In extreme cases, copying should not be attempted unless the binding can be removed.

Creased, folded, or wrinkled pages. Creased or folded pages often can be flattened sufficiently for filming simply by covering them with a sheet of glass or filming them, whether bound or unbound, in a bookholder. In other instances, it may be necessary to iron out the creases, folds, or wrinkles by using a hand iron set at low heat, which, with most irons, would be the "silk" or "rayon" setting. With dry, porous papers, slight moistening with a damp viscous sponge before ironing may make the task simpler. Shiny or clay-coated papers should not be moistened because the moisture may make the surface tacky and cause it to stick to the iron.

Damaged pages. The types of damage encountered in bound volumes are similar to those encountered in newspaper files and can be dealt with by the same techniques, with one important exception. Newspapers are often discarded after filming. For this reason, some types of damaged pages, such as torn pages, are temporarily and partially restored at the camera only to the extent required to obtain a satisfactory copy. Most bound materials, however, are part of a library's permanent collection and require a more permanent kind of repairing. Often the presence of damage is discovered only when materials are sent to a document reproduction service for microfilming or other forms of reproduction. They must then be sent to the library's mending department for repairs before copying is done. In other instances, the damage will be irreparable (e.g., a portion of a page missing or badly defaced). In such cases, notice should be given to the client that the material is incomplete or that it cannot be reproduced. If, however, extensive runs of material are being reproduced for preservation or dissemination from scarce or unique files, the presence of damage should be drawn to the user's attention by the use of appropriate targets.

Mended pages. Mended pages in bound volumes also have characteristics similar to mended newspaper pages and can be handled by the techniques already described for newspapers.

Additional techniques

Retakes. Retaking is a time-consuming and costly operation that can drastically affect the efficiency of filming. Because most retakes are the result of faulty camera work, great care should be taken in the selection and training of microfilm personnel to keep retaking to an absolute minimum.

Common examples of faults which will necessitate retaking are as follows:

(1) Omitted material caused by turning two pages instead of one or by failure to film versos of loose sheet material.

(2) Lack of sharpness caused by failure to adjust focus properly, or movement of the subject during exposure.

(3) Marked unevenness in density between frames caused by failure to use the exposure meter or to adjust the lighting in accordance with the exposure meter reading.

(4) Uneven density within frames caused by failure to adjust the lights properly or by the presence of some object between the lamps and the copy which casts a shadow. A retake for uneven density within a frame will also be required if a second exposure for a markedly discolored original is not made.

(5) "Hot spots" caused by failure to adjust either the lights or the subject in order to eliminate local surface reflections.

(6) Incomplete images caused by failure to position the original within the field of view of the lens.

(7) Partially obscured images caused by failure to remove creases or folds (e.g., a dog-eared corner) or foreign objects such as stray bits of paper.

In addition to retakes which are chargeable to the operator, there are others that are the result of faulty equipment or defective materials. Common examples of these are:

(1) Film scratches may be caused by dust in the camera, carelessness in processing (if hand processing is used), improper tension in continuous processing machines, or dust in the microfilm reader used to inspect the processed film.

(2) Light fogging caused by exposure of the film to light at some point prior to processing. Fog can occur in a camera if the door fastenings become worn to a point where the doors do not close tightly or if the flanges of a film take-up reel are slightly too wide. Fog can also occur, of course, because of carelessness in handling the film.

(3) Spots caused by tiny manufacturing defects in the film. If hand-processing is employed, spots may also occur from insufficient agitation of

the film when it is in the developer. Lack of agitation can also be a cause of uneven density.

A typical procedure for handling retakes is as follows:

(1) Obtain the material from which the retake is to be made.

(2) From the record or order form made at the time of the original filming, determine the reduction ratio, frame size, position used, and exposure used and set the camera accordingly.

(3) To identify the retake, a START OF RETAKE target should be filmed as well as pertinent information needed for editing.

(4) The START OF RETAKE target should be followed by one or two blank frames to provide enough film for splicing.

(5) The retake or retakes are then filmed and followed by blank frames for splicing.

(6) An END OF RETAKE target should then be filmed.

An important consideration in retaking is the distance between splices, particularly if overlap, cemented splices are used. When a film is duplicated on a continuous-contact printer, it is threaded over and between a series of rollers, some of which may be relatively small in diameter. The double thickness of overlap splices stiffens the film so that it bends less easily when traveling around rollers. This stiffening effect is greater if successive splices are close together and may cause one of the splices to break. If only a single frame needs retaking, it is preferable to retake several pages on either side of the page that needs retaking to space out the two splices needed.

When the roll of film containing the retake has been processed, the following steps must be performed:

(1) The retake must be located and cut from the remainder of the roll.

(2) The original film must then be retrieved and the place were the retake is to go located.

(3) Pagination must then be checked with a hand magnifier to make certain that the retake will be in proper sequence.

(4) The original film is then cut and the retake spliced in.

It will be evident from the enumeration of the steps entailed in replacing a defective frame with a retake that considerable labor time taken is required. There will be instances in which it will be less costly to retake entire orders, if they are relatively short, rather than retaking single pages and splicing them in. The crossover point between partial retaking and complete retaking can only be determined if adequate labor and materials cost studies are maintained. Care on the part of camera operators is of paramount importance if retakes, and the higher labor cost they entail, are to be avoided. The work of filming must never be rushed but always done at a pace commensurate with accuracy. If a camera operator knows a frame to be faulty (e.g., if a page moved during exposure), a retake should be made immediately. This same procedure should be followed if the operator even suspects that a frame might have been improperly photographed. It is vastly simpler and cheaper to take an extra exposure at the time, even if not needed (because it can be punched out), than to have to go through the retake procedure.

Filling in missing materials. The cost of preparing a microfilm negative of an extensive run of material, such as a newspaper file, is usually quite high, and the microfilm negative becomes not only the preservation copy of the material in question but also the medium by which additional copies can be made for distribution to other libraries. It is highly desirable, in such a situation, to attempt to obtain the loan of copies of any missing or damaged issues before the filming is undertaken. In some cases, this may not be possible, due to time, cost, or the reluctance of a library to risk loss of or damage to rare or unique material. An alternative solution to this problem is to obtain, wherever possible, a microfilm negative of the missing material that can be incorporated by splicing into the main negative. If this is done, however, it is essential that the microfilm negative of the missing material be made as closely as possible to the specifications of the main negative in terms of image position, image size, reduction ratio, density, and resolution. Space, of course, should be provided in the main negative for the subsequent splicing in of the missing material.

In ordering microfilm negatives of missing pages, it should be remembered that the number of splices in a roll of film should be kept to a minimum, that splices should not be too close together, that overlap splices affect contact, and that splices occasionally break. If, for example, pages 1 and 2, 5 and 6, and 11 and 12 are missing, the entire sequence from 1 through 12 should be ordered. This will provide adequate space between the two necessary splices and eliminate four closely spaced unnecessary splices. Ample leader and trailer should also be requested for the film of each missing section so that overlap splices will not be too close to adjacent frames where they would cause breaks in contact when the negative is duplicated to positive form. Because splices do occasionally break and must be cut and remade, a small amount of leader and trailer between the splice and the frames on either side of it should be provided.

Filming for hard-copy production. Microfilms made only for the purpose of reading may be of any image size or format up to the largest in common use because most microfilm readers are capable of projecting the full *width* of 35 mm. microfilm. If the full length of the film does not appear on the reader screen, this is seldom a problem since the film can simply be advanced to read the portion that does not appear. In filming for subsequent hard-copy production, the situation is different. The maximum image size that can be used will be determined by the maximum film area that can be projected in the particular printing device to be used. If, for example, an enlarger is being used that has a maximum frame size of 1 by 1½ inches (the standard frame size of 35 mm. cameras employing double-perforated film), the reduction ratio used in filming must be such that the entire text area falls within these dimensions. The same holds true if filming is being done for subsequent hard-copy production on reader-printers, but, with reader-printers still another limitation may be imposed. With many reader-printers, the size of the image—i.e., the degree of magnification—can be changed by using different lenses, each of which works at a fixed magnification. If the lens-to-screen distance is fixed, the higher the degree of magnification, the smaller the film area that can be presented on the screen will be. Hence, both the image size and the reduction ratio used in filming must be compatible with the performance characteristics (area covered and magnification ratio) of the lens that will be used for making hard copy.

When microtransparencies that will be used on a particular model of reader-printer are ordered from outside sources, specific instructions must be given the producing laboratory so that usable films will be obtained.

The density of negatives will vary with the characteristics of the original being filmed. Originals having very fine or faint lines, such as manuscripts, may require a relatively low background density in the neighborhood of 1.0 if all of the lines are to be printable, and some background tone in the print may be unavoidable. Microtransparencies of well-printed originals can have a background density in a range from 1.2 to 1.8. If hard copy is to be made by the electrolytic process used in Filmac reader-printers, high background density is usually preferable because the contrast of the electrolytic process is low.

Still other requirements must be met if hard copy is to be made by the Xerox Copyflo method. The preparation of microtransparencies for Copyflo printing is described in the section, "Eye-legible Copies from Microtransparencies."

In general, it is much easier to make satisfactory hard copy from negative microtransparencies than from positives. With negatives, there is a considerable degree of exposure latitude. Under- or overexposure may make the image lighter or darker without significantly affecting legibility. With positives, however, exposure latitude is much more limited. Underexposure results in lines that are too broad, with a consequent filling up of spaces within letters. Overexposure causes a narrowing and veiling of fine lines.

Sheet-form techniques. The techniques for dealing with the various problems presented by originals, which have already been discussed in connection with roll film, will, of course, be essentially the same for microfiche regardless of the method of production. There are other differences, however, when the sheet form is used instead of the roll.

In the first place, the splicing in of retakes is not possible. If the strip-up method is used, the additional length of film required for a splice would extend the length of a row beyond the length of the sheet. If a faulty frame appears on a microfiche produced by the step-and-repeat method, the entire microfiche must be retaken.

Secondly, in printing roll film, it is possible to vary the light intensity of the positive printer to compensate for differences in density, provided the changes in density are neither too abrupt nor too frequent. In duplicating microfiches, no such compensation is possible.

Still another important difference lies in the fact that the limitations imposed by row length and the number of rows in a microfiche place restrictions on variations in frame size. With roll microfilm, it is possible to lengthen or shorten frame size as needed to suit the dimensions of the documents being copied and to vary the reduction ratio at will over a wide range. While some step-and-repeat microfiche cameras offer a slight degree of control over frame length, this is of little importance because the sheet form is most practical if the frame size is uniform throughout.

The quality requirements for microfiches, regardless of the production method used, are somewhat higher than the requirements for roll film. The reason for this is that roll microfilm is seldom duplicated past the second generation, whereas distribution copies of microfiches may be of the third, fourth, or even higher generation. Because a slight loss of sharpness occurs in the printing of each successive generation, the master microfiche must have very high resolution indeed.

Because of their relatively short capacity as compared with one-hundred foot lengths of roll film, microfiches do not lend themselves to division into convenient bibliographic units. This limitation, however, is an advantage if relatively short originals, such as journal articles or technical reports, are being reproduced because, in a great many cases, a single article or report can be reproduced on a single microfiche. This provides both a physical as well as a bibliographic unitization, which offers a number of advantages over roll film in duplicating and filing.

Depending upon the equipment used, the addition of an eye-legible title is either done within the step-and-repeat camera itself or by means of a separate titling camera. Depending on the method of production, the title may be either negative or

positive. Positive titles are often backed with a white or tinted opaque stripe. Because, in duplicating microfiches, the opacity of the stripes interferes with the reproduction of the title, the striping material should be of a substance which can be readily removed with a film cleaner or other suitable solvent.

If diazo films are used to make duplicate microfiches, tinted stocks can be used for color coding purposes.

A duplicate microfiche of any generation may be either negative or positive, depending on the process used. Printing on silver halide materials usually yields a positive duplicate from a negative original and vice versa. If reversal processing is used, or, if duplicates are made on diazo or Kalvar films, negative duplicates from negatives and positives from positives can be made.

EYE-LEGIBLE COPIES FROM MICROFORMS

Enlargements from microforms to eye-legible size are usually referred to as hard copy and can be made with a variety of different types of equipment and by means of a number of different processes. Enlargements on sheets of paper or film from roll-form microtransparencies can be made with enlargers such as the Recordak Model MEB, which is equipped with high-resolution lenses and a pair of spindles to hold the supply and take-up reels. Continuous webs of enlargements can be made by using Xerox Copyflo enlargers. Enlargements can also be made with great rapidity and under conditions of ordinary room light by means of reader-printers. Enlargements from sheet form microtransparencies can be made with photographic enlargers, if the throat of the enlarger is deep enough to accept the sheet size used. For producing hard copy from microfiches of technical reports, certain government agencies use a specially designed step-and-repeat enlarger, which is capable of automatically producing hard copy of an entire microfiche. Rapidly produced enlargements from sheet forms can also be made by means of reader-printers.

The processes that can be used for making hard copy include conventional silver halide with wet (darkroom) processing or stabilization processing, and autopositive, DTR, diaversal, diazo, Dry Silver, Electrofax, xerography, and the electrolytic process.

Enlarger-produced hard copy

Enlargements on silver halide materials. Before the advent of many of the newer processes now used for making enlarged prints from microtransparencies, virtually all hard copy was made on silver halide materials. Silver halide materials of many types are available, and a great degree of control over size and image quality is possible. When desirable, prints may be substantially larger or smaller than the original documents. Microfilms of card files can be printed on card-weight stock. If a number of copies are needed, prints can be made on thin, translucent stocks or on film for subsequent diazo printing. "Use copies" are ordinarily made on relatively inexpensive "document weight" stocks (e.g., Kodagraph fast projection paper), which can be folded without cracking. Papers of this type are fast enough to be printed at exposures of only one to two seconds' duration. Processing follows the usual steps of development, rinsing, fixation, washing, and drying. The papers, however, are quite durable and developing times are not critical. This makes it possible to process substantial numbers of prints at one time. If prints are being made of paginated materials, sorting the finished prints can be done, of course, by the page numbers. When printing unpaginated materials, such as manuscripts, the prints should be stamped on the back with an automatic numbering machine after exposure and before processing.

A disadvantage of silver halide materials is their tendency to curl. This is very marked when "thin" and "ultra-thin" stocks are used. Also, the tendency of card-weight silver halide materials to curl makes card files printed on such materials rather difficult to use.

When printing from negative microtransparencies having a fairly high background density (1.3 to 1.7), there is ample latitude in both exposure and processing time. When printing from negatives having lower background densities, exposure times are more critical if a gray background tone is to be avoided.

In printing from positive microtransparencies,

exposure times are quite critical. Underexposure results in a widening of the lines of the image, while overexposure causes a narrowing and filling of the lines. If enlargements from a roll of positive microtransparencies are to be made, it is preferable to make a duplicate negative from the positive and make positive enlargements from this negative. Because positive microfilms are usually fairly high-contrast copies made from high contrast negatives, the contrast of the duplicate negative should be kept relatively low.

Enlargements can also be made on other types of silver halide coatings, such as stabilization process and DTR materials. Stabilization materials for enlarging from microtransparencies have characteristics that are quite similar to ordinary silver halide materials made for this purpose. In addition, however, there are many other types of stabilization process materials that can be used. Not only are other surfaces and weights available, but many stabilization process papers can be obtained in several degrees of contrast or in which contrast can be controlled by the use of filters. Stabilization process papers are also available in a wide range of speeds. Some are suitable for printing under incandescent room light but not under fluorescent light. Others are quite high in speed and must be used in a photographic darkroom. In general, the cost of stabilization process papers is somewhat higher than that for ordinary silver halide coatings.

Projection-speed DTR materials can also be used for enlarging from microtransparencies, but, unlike ordinary silver halide or stabilization process materials, DTR materials yield negative prints from negatives and positive prints from positives. Because DTR materials are quite high in contrast, exposure latitude, especially when printing finely detailed subjects, is quite limited. Because two specially coated sheets of material are required in making DTR copies, the materials' cost is higher than the cost of ordinary silver halide or stabilization process materials.

Enlargements by Xerox Copyflo. Another type of enlarger employing the xerographic process is the Xerox Copyflo. Unlike the other enlargers described that make a single print at a time, Xerox Copyflo enlargers print from roll-form microtransparencies on a continuous web of paper at a rate of 20 paper feet per minute. Three models are available, one of which—the Copyflo 11 Model 1 —is widely used for the reproduction of research materials of many kinds. Not only can complete rolls of microtransparencies be rapidly converted into relatively inexpensive hard copy, but, if needed, prints can also be made on continuous rolls of translucent paper stock for diazo printing, on 100 percent rag content or other permanent card stocks for reproducing library catalog cards, or on offset master stock. If maximum advantage is to be taken of the considerable potential offered by the Copyflo method, a number of factors must be taken into account that will affect the production methods and techniques used in making the microtransparencies used for printing.

PREPARATION OF MICROTRANSPARENCIES FOR COPYFLO. In Copyflo printing, a roll of microfilm 16 mm. or 35 mm. in width is used to produce a roll of enlarged paper prints ranging in size from 4½ to 11 inches wide with a maximum image width of 11 inches. The format of the pages and frames on the completed roll of paper prints is exactly that of the microfilm. The size of the original documents and the format, framing, spacing, and alignment of the successive images are therefore factors that must be considered in the production of microfilms for subsequent printing with Copyflo equipment.

Documents may be filmed in any one of the four standard formats shown in Figure 156. The selection of the best filming position will be determined by the size of the reproduction desired, always keeping in mind that dimension "A" cannot exceed 11 inches in the final print.

Single pages 11 inches in width and of any length, filmed in position 1-A, can be reproduced full size by Copyflo. Wider pages, capable of yielding an acceptable reproduction when reduced to 11 inches, may also be reproduced in this format.

Filmed in positions 1-B and 2-B, single or double pages 11 inches in height can be reproduced full size; larger pages can be reproduced in reduced size.

If the width of two pages does not exceed 11 inches, material filmed in position 2-A can be reproduced full size. Larger materials will be reduced to the 11-inch maximum. In filming loose-sheet material, doubling the frame length will permit the filming of four pages per exposure in this format.

FRAMING AND SPACING. Even at moderate ratios, the reduction in size achieved in microphotography is so great that film space is frequently used carelessly and wastefully. It is not uncommon, for example, to see a film of a series of twenty short articles separated from each other by a foot of blank film. If such a film were enlarged ten diameters, the 19 one-foot spaces would become 190 feet of waste paper which would add considerably to the cost. Excess film used for spacing should be spliced out before printing.

Framing and spacing between frames should be carefully controlled. One-eighth inch of excess frame space on each side of 600 frames enlarged twelve diameters would require almost 150 feet of additional paper. In using cameras such as the Recordak or Kodagraph Micro-File Models C and D, in which the spacing between frames is controllable, the spacing should be adjusted to a minimum.

ALIGNMENT OF IMAGES. Careful alignment of successive images on microfilm will reduce both labor and material costs. As shown in Figure 192, a microfilm of 3 by 5 cards properly aligned can be reproduced on a roll of 5-inch paper, whereas cards filmed without regard to alignment may require 7- or 8-inch paper. It will also be seen that prints of unaligned images will require more labor in cutting and trimming.

BINDING MARGINS. While lateral control for positioning the projected image on the roll of paper is possible with Copyflo equipment, the best practice for obtaining additional paper area for binding margins is to provide for it in the positioning, spacing, and alignment of images during filming (Figure 193). In photographing large pages from bound volumes in position 1-A, the pages should be offset to the right. Using positions 1-B and 2-B, increasing the length of the frame will provide the desired margins. Using position 2-A, the volume can be offset to the right if only a left-hand margin is required. If a folded format is to be used, the magnification of the image can be controlled to provide a margin. A 9-inch width for the two-page format, when printed on 11-inch paper, will provide an additional inch on both sides. An 8-inch

Fig. 192. Cards poorly aligned in filming (left) require wider paper stock and are more difficult to cut than cards which are carefully aligned on film (right).

image width will provide 1½ inches of margin on each side, and so on. In filming materials that are to be bound folded, the centerline of the book must be precisely centered and perpendicular in each microfilm frame.

ENLARGEMENT RATIOS. The degree of enlargement obtainable with Copyflo equipment is not adjustable over a continuous range. There are ten fixed magnification steps for 35 mm. film—7, 7½, 8½, 9, 9½, 11, 12, 13, 14, and 15. Additional magnification steps of 17, 18, 19, 22, and 24 may be used for enlarging 16 mm. microfilm. If documents are to be reproduced to the exact size of the originals, the reduction ratio used in filming must correspond to one of the listed magnifications.

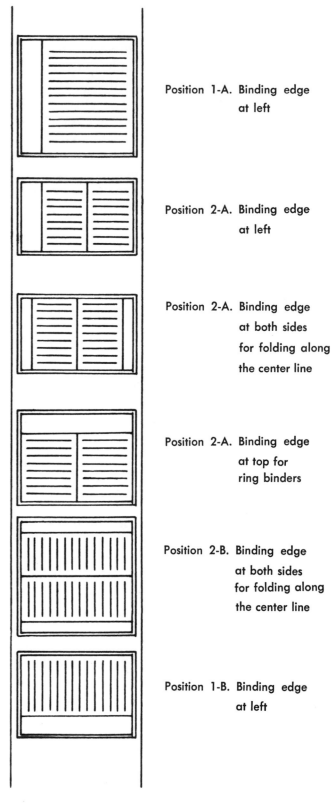

Position 1-A. Binding edge at left

Position 2-A. Binding edge at left

Position 2-A. Binding edge at both sides for folding along the center line

Position 2-A. Binding edge at top for ring binders

Position 2-B. Binding edge at both sides for folding along the center line

Position 1-B. Binding edge at left

Fig. 193. Filming positions for Copyflo printing to provide binding margins.

ELIMINATION OF SHADOW LINES. Shadows cast by the edges of cards or around the holes punched for tray rods can be eliminated by filming the cards on the glass surface of a light box to provide subsurface illumination.

Enlargements by other processes. Several enlargers are available that use processes other than silver halide for printing from microtransparencies. The Bruning Copytron, which was designed specifically for making enlargements from microtransparencies of engineering drawings, employs the Electrofax process. Two enlargers—the Xerox Models 1824 and 1860—were also designed for engineering-drawing reproduction and employ the xerographic process. The Dry Silver process is used in four enlargers—three models of the 3M Quadrant Dry Silver Printer and the Microcard Corporation's EL-4 microfiche enlarger. The Quadrant Printers are rather specialized enlargers: two are used for making 8½- by 11-inch enlargements from "A"-size engineering drawings or documents filmed in groups of four or eight on full-frame, nonperforated 35 mm. film mounted in aperture cards, and one is used for making enlargements up to 18 by 24 inches in size from "A," "B," or "C" drawings mounted in aperture cards. The Microcard EL-4 is a specialized and highly automated piece of equipment used to make complete hard-copy reproductions of the contents of microfiches prepared according to *Federal Microfiche Standards.*[13] Two enlargers—the Caps-Jeffree Ultra Violet Enlarger and the Keuffel and Esser *Helios*—are designed for printing on diazo materials or on photosensitive offset plates. Offset plates can also be made from microtransparencies by projecting an image onto the surface of the selenium plate used with the Xerox Number One and Number Four cameras. All of the enlargers mentioned, with the exception of the Caps-Jeffree, work at either a fixed, single magnification or within very narrow limits. The Caps-Jeffree offers a continuous range of magnifications from 5X to 25¾X.

---

[13] *Federal Microfiche Standards* (Document Number PB167 630), Second Edition, 1966. (Copies may be purchased for 50¢ each, postage prepaid, from the Clearing House for Federal Scientific and Technical Information, Springfield, Virginia 22151.)

Hard copy from reader-printers

A number of different processes are employed in various types of microfilm reader-printers, including the stabilization process, DTR, electrofax and an electrolytic process. The principal problem in making hard copy from microtransparencies of research materials on most reader-printers is one of compatibility between the reduction ratio used in filming and the magnification ratio of the reader-printer. The majority of reader-printers work at a fixed magnification that is compatible with the reduction ratios usually used for the filming of either office records or engineering drawings. A few offer some control over magnification by means of supplementary, interchangeable lenses. Both business records and engineering drawings are fairly well standardized in size, whereas research materials vary over a wide range of sizes and shapes. Because of this lack of standardization and other factors as well, the reduction ratios used in filming research materials vary greatly and, more frequently than not, are incompatible with the magnification ratios of most reader-printers. 18- by 24-inch engineering drawings, for example, are usually filmed at reduction ratios of around 1:14.5 to 1:15.5. Microfilms of newspapers that are approximately the same size as engineering drawings may, on the other hand, be filmed at reduction ratios that are either lower or higher. If a reduction ratio lower than the magnification ratio of a given reader-printer has been used, the screen image on the reader-printer will be over-magnified and will be too large for the available print area. If a higher reduction ratio has been used, the entire image area will appear on the reader-printer screen and on the print but will be reduced somewhat in size. With many newspapers, the size of the type faces employed and the quality of printing is such that even a relatively small reduction in size will impair legibility.

Examples of the limitations imposed by a fixed print size and fixed magnification ratios are given in Tables 26 and 27. Table 26 shows in the left-hand columns the dimensions of the area which can be filmed on a full frame of 35 mm. nonperforated film at reduction ratios ranging from 1:7 to 1:20. The right-hand columns show how little of this area can be reproduced on a single print made

TABLE 26

Reduction Ratio	Dimensions in Inches of Area Microfilmed on Full 1¼- by 1¾-inch Frame, Non-Perforated 35 mm. Film	Dimensions in Inches of Area Which Can Be Reproduced on a Single 7- by 8¼-Inch Print			
		7X Lens	9X Lens	13X Lens	19X Lens
7	8.75 x 12.25	7.0 x 8.25	5.44 x 6.42	3.77 x 4.44	2.58 x 3.04
8	10.0 x 14.0	8.0 x 9.43	6.22 x 7.33	4.31 x 5.08	2.94 x 3.47
9	11.25 x 15.75	9.0 x 10.61	7.0 x 8.25	4.85 x 5.71	3.31 x 3.9
10	12.5 x 17.5	10.0 x 11.79	7.77 x 9.16	5.38 x 6.35	3.68 x 4.34
11	13.75 x 19.25	11.0 x 12.96	8.55 x 10.08	5.92 x 6.98	4.05 x 4.78
12	15.0 x 21.0	12.0 x 14.14	9.33 x 11.0	6.46 x 7.62	4.42 x 5.21
13	16.25 x 22.75	13.0 x 15.32	10.11 x 11.92	7.0 x 8.25	4.79 x 5.64
14	17.5 x 24.5	14.0 x 16.5	10.88 x 12.83	7.54 x 8.88	5.16 x 6.08
15	18.75 x 26.25	15.0 x 17.68	11.66 x 13.75	8.08 x 9.52	5.53 x 6.51
16	20.0 x 28.0	16.0 x 18.86	12.44 x 14.66	8.62 x 10.15	5.89 x 6.95
17	21.25 x 29.75	17.0 x 20.03	13.22 x 15.58	9.15 x 10.79	6.26 x 7.38
18	22.5 x 31.5	18.0 x 21.21	14.00 x 16.5	9.69 x 11.42	6.63 x 7.82
19	23.75 x 33.25	19.0 x 22.39	14.77 x 17.42	10.23 x 12.06	7.0 x 8.25
20	25.0 x 35.0	20.0 x 23.57	15.55 x 18.33	10.77 x 12.69	7.37 x 8.68

on a reader-printer working at four fixed magnifications—7X, 9X, 13X, and 19X—and which yields a print having a maximum image area of 7 by 8¼ inches. Expressed in percentages, the 7X lens reproduces 54 percent of the area of a full frame, the 9X lens 32.6 percent, the 13X lens 15.7 percent, and the 19X lens only 7.3 percent.

Table 27 shows the reduction ratio that must be employed in the filming of four typical serials, if the entire text area of a single page is to be reproduced on a single print when using any one of the four lenses referred to above. If the reduction ratio is higher than that shown, the image will be correspondingly smaller in size on the print, and this may affect legibility. If, on the other hand, the reduction is lower than that shown for any lens, the entire text will not appear on the print, and more than one print may be required to reproduce a page.

Because journals of the sizes shown can be,

TABLE 27

Subject	Text Dimensions in Inches (Single Page)	Reduction Ratio Required in Filming to Permit Reproduction of One Page on a 7- by 8¼-inch Print			
		7X Lens	9X Lens	13X Lens	19X Lens
Unesco Bulletin For Libraries	4⅝ x 7⅞	7	9	13	19
College and Research Libraries	5³⁄₁₆ x 8	7	9	13	19
Photo Science and Technique	6⅞ x 9⅜	8.5	10.5	15.5	22.5
American Documentation	6¾ x 9¼	8	10.5	15	22

Of the processes suitable for the reproduction of research materials which are described in this section, some have been in use for a number of years, their characteristics are by now well known, and can be described in a fairly detailed fashion. Other processes, particularly the newer ones, are not so well known. In some cases manufacturers, understandably enough, are not willing to disclose details about their workings. In such cases every attempt has been made to make the description of these processes as complete, from a practical standpoint, as the available information will allow.

Fig. 194. Typescript material reduced to 60 percent of original size.

⁴ It is necessary at this point to indicate that I accept the definition of specialized information centers advanced by G. S. Simpson: "A scientific information center exists for the primary purpose of preparing authoritative, timely and specialized reports of the evaluative, analytical, monographic, or state-of-the-art type. It is an organization staffed in part with scientists and engineers, and to provide a basis for its primary function, it conducts a selective data and information acquisition and processing program." *American Documentation,* XIII (January 1962), 43. This definition can be supplemented by that of Cohan and Craven, who consider that an information center represents the unification of "library, patent, translation, report writing, archival, ab-

⁴ It is necessary at this point to indicate that I accept the definition of specialized information centers advanced by G. S. Simpson: "A scientific information center exists for the primary purpose of preparing authoritative, timely and specialized reports of the evaluative, analytical, monographic, or state-of-the-art type. It is an organization staffed in part with scientists and engineers, and to provide a basis for its primary function, it conducts a selective data and information acquisition and processing program." *American Documentation,* XIII (January 1962), 43. This definition can be supplemented by that of Cohan and Craven, who consider that an information center represents the unification of "library, patent, translation, report writing, archival, ab-

⁴ It is necessary at this point to indicate that I accept the definition of specialized information centers advanced by G. S. Simpson: "A scientific information center exists for the primary purpose· of preparing authoritative, timely and specialized reports of the evaluative, analytical, monographic, or state-of-the-art type. It is an organization staffed in part with scientists and engineers, and to provide a basis for its primary function, it conducts a selective data and information acquisition and processing program." *American Documentation,* XIII (January 1962), 43. This definition can be supplemented by that of Cohan and Craven, who consider that an information center represents the unification of "library, patent, translation, report writing, archival, ab-

Fig. 195. Footnote (top) enlarged to 100 percent (center) to 150 percent (bottom) to 200 percent of original size. (From *College and Research Libraries,* 25 [May, 1964], p. 201.)

and frequently are, filmed at a reduction ratio of 1:10, it will be seen from Table 27 that, if the 7X lens is used, all four journal pages can be reproduced on a single print, but all will be reduced somewhat in size. If the 9X lens is used, pages of the two smaller journals can be reproduced on a single print at a slight reduction in size but the larger two will not, and will require two prints each, if the entire text is to be reproduced. If either the 13X or 19X lens is used, no page can be reproduced on a single print, and increasingly large numbers of sectional prints will be required as the magnification is increased.

With the increased need for and use of hard copy from microtransparencies of research materials, it is important that microtransparencies that are to be used on reader-printers be produced to meet the limitations that reader-printers impose.

Sizes of eye-legible copies from microforms

When an optically produced intermediate, such as roll microfilm or microfiche, is used for the production of eye-legible copies, the copies, depending upon the type of enlarger or reader-printer, may be smaller, equal to, or greater in size than the original. This control over image size can often be used advantageously, depending upon the characteristics of the original and the function which the hard copy is intended to serve. Originals printed or typewritten in a fairly bold face can often be printed at a size substantially smaller, while still retaining a high degree of legibility (Figure 194). The legibility of originals that, at the other extreme, are printed in a very small type face can often be considerably improved if they are printed larger than the original size (Figure 195).

Appendix A

DOCUMENT REPRODUCTION SERVICES IN LIBRARIES

Until recently, the relatively high cost of photocopying equipment restricted its use to large or well-endowed libraries. This is no longer true. Simple photocopying devices can be leased or purchased outright for relatively small sums. Another type of device which is appearing with increasing frequency in libraries is the coin-in-the-slot photocopier. These devices are vending machines which are installed in library premises without cost.

Today, document reproduction equipment has become indispensable to library work at almost all levels, ranging from the photo-charging systems and vending machine copiers found in relatively small libraries to the vast array of equipment used in libraries such as the United States Library of Congress and in the larger research libraries both in this country and abroad. Although no complete statistics are available, the total production of library-operated document reproduction services in this country must run at least to hundreds of millions of copies annually.

In a manual such as this, it would be desirable to include fairly specific recommendations with respect to the establishment and operation of document reproduction services in libraries. Presumably it should be possible to codify the experiences of the many institutions which have operated such services over many years and to establish a firm corpus of recommended policies and practices. Such, however, is unfortunately not the case. The proliferation of low-cost copying through the use of new devices, the many purposes which copies can serve, plus profound differences in the character and purposes of libraries themselves create a situation in which it becomes increasingly difficult to make valid generalizations about the nature and operation of document reproduction services in libraries. It is possible, however, to isolate and examine some of the major factors which cause library-operated document reproduction services to differ markedly from non-library-operated services and which also cause wide variations in the policies and practices which govern the operation of such services.

Preliminary underlying factors

Four preliminary factors which are present in all libraries and which affect the nature and operation of document reproduction services are:

(1) Size of library
(2) Type of library
(3) Type of collection
(4) Type of clientele

Size of library. The size of a library expressed in volumes or other units will have some effect on the need for document reproduction services but by no means in proportion to size alone. Only among the largest libraries does there appear to be any rough correlation between the size of the library and the extent of its document reproduction activities.

Type of library. Whether a library is a tax-supported public library, a school library, the library of a corporation, a college library, an endowed private library, a university library, and so on, can have a marked effect on the kind and extent of document reproduction activities which might be appropriate to the library's functions. This, in turn, relates to size. Small or medium-size public libraries, for example, may offer nothing or very little in the way of document reproduction services or facilities whereas a college library equivalent in size to a public library may offer a great deal. In another comparison, a heavy demand for document reproduction may be present in a research library of a large corporation even though its collection may be no larger than that of a small public library.

Type of collection. The type of collection relates, of course, to the type of library and has its effect also on the nature and extent of document reproduction activities. The demand for photocopies will be lower in the case of a public library whose collection contains a substantial portion of fiction, belles-lettres and children's books whereas, if the library is a rare books library or the library of a scientific or an historical society, the demand will be much greater.

Type of clientele. The type of library and the type of collection will have a decided effect, of course, on the type of clientele the library serves. Different types of clientele will have different kinds of needs which will affect not only the types of document reproduction services but quality level and volume as well. The faculty of a university may make impressive demands on the library's document reproduction service for highly diverse types of reproductions whereas the patrons of a public library, although greater in number than the faculty of the university, may have needs which are quite limited.

Each of these factors—size and type of library, type of collection, and type of clientele—are thus seen to be an interrelated cluster of factors which will strongly affect the character of the document reproduction services needed. For example, a college library having an extensive collection of serials in microform can expect a considerable demand for hard copy—either made in a laboratory or by means of reader-printers—from its clientele whereas a university library holding originals of the same serials might adequately meet the photocopy demands of its clientele in this particular area by using one or more electrostatic copiers. Four other linked factors—type of document reproduction service, equipment, space, and personnel—are thus drawn into the total equation. The type of document reproduction service needed (e.g., hard copy from microforms vs. eye-legible copies from originals) will affect both the choice of equipment and the personnel skills required while the choice of equipment will, in turn, affect the space and installation requirements.

Document reproduction requirements

The mere existence of a need or a demand for document reproduction services does not necessarily mean, of course, that the services will be present. Photoduplication equipment, service, and supplies all cost money and in some cases a great deal of money. Large, well-supported libraries may be able to offer extensive document reproduction facilities and services whereas libraries with slender equipment budgets may have to make do with less efficient and versatile equipment and offer only a limited service. Assuming the availability of funds, a library considering the possibility of providing one or more kinds of document reproduction services or of revamping existing services will be better able to make appropriate decisions beforehand if answers or informed guesses can be provided for a number of questions. These questions are aimed at eliciting information covering two areas—internal service for the benefit of the library itself and external service for the benefit of the library's clientele. The relationship between internal and external service and fiscal policy is discussed under "Service factors vs. pricing," page 300.

(1) Is there sufficient demand for document reproduction services to justify the expense of acquiring, installing, and operating appropriate equipment? If so, what is the anticipated annual volume of the services contemplated?

(2) What kinds of materials are to be copied? Bound volumes? Newspapers? Manuscripts? Photographs? Catalog cards?

(3) What kind of service or services will meet the need? Microfilm negatives? Microfilm positives? Eye-legible copies from originals? Hard copy from microforms?

(4) For what purposes will copies be made? Acquisition? Preservation? Dissemination? Convenience? Classroom instruction?

(5) For whom will copies be made, and in what proportion to types of service and demand? The library itself? The library administrative staff? A faculty? A student body? Other libraries or institutions in the immediate geographical area? Outside the immediate geographical area?

(6) What kind of equipment will be needed to provide an adequate copying service? A coin-

in-the-slot photocopier? A Xerox 914? A microfilm camera? A positive printer for microfilm? Hand or continuous processing equipment for microfilm? A photostat camera? Equipment for making high-quality, continuous-tone copies? The answers to these questions will lead to further questions concerning the choice of ancillary equipment.

(7) What services should the library equip itself to provide and what services should be contracted for from commercial sources?

(8) Are local commercial sources capable of and willing to provide the kind of service in terms of quality and efficiency that the library and its clientele can afford to pay?

Business vs. service

The wide variance in the policies and practices of document reproduction services appears to derive in part from an area of ambiguity lying between the service aspects of the functions of libraries and the business aspects of operating a document reproduction service where a considerable cost factor is involved which must be recovered. This ambiguity is partially expressed in the widely used term "document reproduction *service*." Libraries often make the disclaimer that their document reproduction services are not selling copies but only a service. This in part is true, but nonetheless the patron of the service acquires, by paying a sum of money, a tangible object which becomes his property. A document reproduction "service" is thus not comparable in its methods of rendering service to other service departments of a library such as a reference service or an interlibrary lending service.

Business factors. If a satisfactory line is to be drawn between what constitutes an appropriate level of service to the library's clientele and sound business practice in the matter of recovering the substantial labor, materials, and overhead costs entailed in the making of photocopies, other facts must be known. These facts involve cost factors of various kinds. Although a library may not base the prices of its document reproduction services on all of the known costs for reasons indicated under "Service factors vs. pricing," a knowledge of what the true costs are can be useful in establishing over-all fiscal policies.

The principal cost factors may be classified as follows:

(1) Equipment costs
(2) Materials' costs
(3) Direct labor costs
(4) Direct overhead costs
(5) Indirect overhead costs

While there are many factors involved in full-scale cost accounting, only the principal ones will be dealt with here.

EQUIPMENT COSTS. Prices for the outright purchase or the lease or rental of document reproduction equipment are readily obtainable, of course, from manufacturers or their representatives. In the case of purchased equipment, the useful life expectancy of the equipment must also be ascertained. If an annual service contract is available, the cost of service to the machine will be predictable. If not, an estimate of service costs must be made. With some types of equipment, installation costs may be involved which must be added to the purchase price.

To calculate *annual* equipment costs, the purchase price of the equipment plus the costs of installation are divided by the number of years of useful life and the annual cost of service added to this sum. To calculate equipment costs *per copy*, the annual equipment cost is divided by the estimated annual volume of copies. If, in a hypothetical example, and using round figures, a large prism-type camera is acquired, the calculations would be as follows:

Purchase price:	$10,000
Installation costs:	1,000
	$11,000
Estimated useful life:	Ten years
Annual equipment cost:	$\dfrac{\$11,000}{10 \text{ years}} = \$1,100$
Plus annual service contract:	100
TOTAL:	$1,200
Estimated annual volume of copies:	20,000
Equipment costs, per copy:	$\dfrac{\$1,200}{20,000} = \$0.06$

If, however, the estimated annual volume of copies were significantly lower, the equipment costs per copy become substantially higher. At 5,000 copies per year, the equipment costs per copy would be $0.24 and at 1,000 per year, $1.20 per copy.

MATERIALS' COSTS. While materials' prices are also readily obtainable from suppliers, they represent only a part of what comes under the heading of materials' cost since another factor—waste—may be involved. With some processes and/or methods, waste will be relatively low but with others it may be quite high. Take, for example, the making of contact-reflex copies with diffusion-transfer-reversal materials. The list price of the materials, which includes the negative and positive sheets plus the developing solution, is approximately nine cents. The determination of what exposure to use with DTR materials is not, however, always predictable, especially if finely detailed originals or originals having uneven line density are being copied. The first copy made may show some breaking or loss of fine lines thus indicating overexposure. Reducing the exposure may then yield a copy in which small spaces within letters or numbers are filled thus indicating underexposure. A third copy is then made at an exposure setting between the settings used for the first two and is satisfactory. The materials' cost, obviously, is $0.27—not $0.09. In another example using DTR, the cost of a certain brand of developer solution for the making of one hundred 8½- by 11-inch copies is $0.50. Some DTR developers, however, oxidize on standing in the machine tray and soon become too weakened to function. If the useful life of the developer solution is one week and the one hundred copies are made within that time, the developer costs per copy would be $0.005. If, however, only ten copies are made during that particular week, the developer costs per copy would be ten times as great ($0.05) and an additional $0.045 must be added to the basic $0.09 cost of the raw materials making a total materials' cost of $0.135 per copy.

Some percentage of waste is inevitable in the use of sensitized materials and this cannot be ignored in figuring materials' costs. If waste is not carefully controlled, it can become quite a large factor in total materials' costs.

DIRECT LABOR COSTS. Direct labor costs are the salaries of the technicians engaged in the work of making reproductions. In the absence of actual studies made in a document reproduction service, what is required to estimate direct labor costs are production figures versus time. Here the experience of other document reproduction services can be helpful as can also the advice of qualified technical representatives of equipment manufacturers. For a microfilm operation, for example, it must be known how many exposures per hour or per day on the average can be expected in the filming of different types of library materials such as bound volumes, manuscripts, newspapers, and so forth. If hand processing is contemplated, it must be known how many rolls can be processed per day with different types of hand-processing equipment. Given the various production figures per time unit and the pay scale which such work commands in the area where the library is located, unit labor costs can be calculated. For the making of a single microfilm exposure, the direct labor cost will be a small fraction of a cent. For the making of a high-quality copy negative of a continuous-tone original, the labor cost may be as much as a dollar or more. In figuring direct labor costs, it is most important to recognize that scheduled working hours per week or per month divided into a weekly or monthly salary will lead to erroneous labor cost figures. The cost of nonproductive time must also be taken into account and this can be quite a sizeable factor.

Let us assume, for example, that a technician is being paid at a rate of $60.00 per week. On a 40-hour, five-day work week, his hourly rate would appear to be $1.50 per hour. If it takes him one hour to produce six enlargements, each from a different negative, the direct labor cost per enlargement would then be $0.25. But let us further assume that he is allowed three weeks' paid vacation, twelve days of sick leave, and seven paid holidays per year. This is a total of 40 working days per year or eight weeks. He thus works not 52 weeks each year but only 44, or a total of 220 days. If, on each of these days, he is allowed a fifteen-minute coffee break each morning and afternoon, this adds up to an annual total of 110 hours—an additional 2¾ weeks. His maximum annual productive time is 41¼ weeks or a total of 1,650 hours. His annual salary—52 weeks at $60.00 per week—is $3,120 which, divided by 1,650 productive hours shows a true hourly rate of $1.89—26 percent higher than the first figures showed. The unit labor cost of the six enlargements thus becomes $0.315 instead of $0.25.

Waste, which was mentioned in connection with materials' costs, is also a factor in labor costs. Here, too, a certain percentage is inevitable since no laboratory and its personnel are 100 percent efficient. Attitudes toward waste are, however, sometimes unrealistic. There seems to be an ingrained reluctance in people to jettison materials, perhaps because they are tangible and of a known value, whereas time is often taken for granted because it is there and wasted in efforts to save materials. An example of this is the making of retakes of microfilm frames to replace defective ones. If a microfilm is made of a fifty-frame (100-page) article at a unit cost of $0.04 per frame, the total price is $2.00. If one page is defective, a practice in common use is to retake the defective page and splice the retake into its proper position on the film. The 99 good pages are thus saved, but the labor cost entailed in completing the film with the one retake is prodigious. The steps involved include locating the volume from which the filming was done, locating the proper page to be retaken, making a camera set-up at the proper reduction ratio, identifying the retake with the order by making a target, filming the frame, locating and removing the frame after processing, locating the film to which it belongs, locating the position on the film where it must be spliced, splicing the frame into the film, and conducting a certain amount of clerical work necessary to the whole transaction. Studies of retakes made by the author have shown that the costs involved may easily be from 25 to 50 or more times higher than the per-frame price charged. To re-microfilm the entire 100 pages would seem at first glance to be quite wasteful, but when all the labor time for completing the retake is tallied, the complete re-microfilming of orders which are relatively short will often prove to be more economical.

DIRECT OVERHEAD COSTS. Direct overhead costs are principally the administrative, supervisory, and clerical costs entailed in the transaction of business by and with the document reproduction service. In a one-man, one-machine operation such as a xerographic copying service using a 914 Copier, this may involve making a slip to identify the order, entering the number of copies made on the slip, extending the number by the unit cost to get the total cost, adding sales tax, collecting money, making change, and making a daily summary. In the operation of a larger and more diversified document reproduction service, overhead may involve the services of a full-time administrator, supervisory personnel, and a clerical staff involved in a multitude of supporting operations such as over-the-counter order taking, the handling of incoming mail orders, the packaging and mailing of outgoing orders, invoice typing, bookkeeping, answering correspondence, preparing statistical and financial reports, and so on. In this area too, waste time and effort can be a significant cost factor. One of the important areas which should be thoroughly examined is the matter of records and how they are kept. In the first place, every effort should be made to keep paper work to an absolute minimum. The value of every record in terms of the time it takes to create it and keep it should be carefully assessed. Critical attention should be given to the design of forms to make sure that they are simple and functional and that needless duplication of effort and information is avoided.

Other areas of direct overhead cost would include such items as space, utilities, building maintenance, janitorial service, telephone service, stationery and office supplies, packaging and mailing supplies, and postage.

INDIRECT OVERHEAD COSTS. In a document reproduction service's function of disseminating materials held by the library, it serves to extend library service in ways which are useful to the library's clientele over and beyond the limitations imposed by circulation and use regulations and to extend the use of the library's materials to another and perhaps quite large clientele who are geographically removed from the library and hence unable to avail themselves of its resources in person. In this latter connection, two activities in particular are involved which relate to the supplying of photocopies and which, because of this, are different in certain ways from the usual activities of library service.

The first of these activities to consider is the matter of bibliographic searching on mail orders received by the document reproduction service. If, as is true with most libraries, a client is in need of a particular article for which he has a citation, it is usually his responsibility to use the library's card catalog to ascertain the call number of the publication in which the article appears and present a slip or card at the appropriate service desk where the volume can be paged for him. If he has stack privileges, he may obtain the volume himself. If he wishes to have the article photocopied, he must locate it, mark it with slips giving the starting and ending page numbers, and deliver it to the document reproduction service. It also may be his responsibility to return the volume to the department from which he obtained it after the copies have been made. If the citation he has is faulty or incorrect, it is his responsibility to correct the error and to obtain a proper citation. This is not always the case however. A situation could arise in which a client has written to the document reproduction service from a place 500 miles away requesting a copy of an article. In this case, all of the responsibilities detailed above which are assumed by or expected of the client who appears at the library in person devolve on the professional staff of the library department where the material is located or on a staff member, usually a librarian, attached to the document reproduction service.

A second activity which involves differences in library service where the end product is a photocopy is in the matter of price quotations. As in the first situation, the client can bring materials to the document reproduction service and ask for a price quotation or, if he has a copy of the document reproduction service's price schedule, he can figure the cost by himself. With requests for quotations received by mail, however, a staff member of the library or of the document reproduction service must look up the requested materials in the card catalog, locate the material, locate the article, check and perhaps correct citations, note the page size if this has a bearing on cost, count the pages, check to see if the article contains folding plates which will increase the cost, and finally write a letter to the client quoting prices, advising him of materials not held or not suitable for photocopying and of anything else relevant to the transaction. The situation would be complicated still fur-

ther if some of the requested materials were charged out to another borrower or were temporarily at the bindery. The steps which the client appearing in person usually performs must be performed by the library or the document reproduction service.

Let us further assume that the client, on receiving the price quotations, decides that the cost of the copies is more than he can afford. There the matter ends and the overhead cost of the time spent by library and/or document reproduction service personnel can in no way be recovered.

SERVICE FACTORS VS. PRICING. Since a document reproduction service in a library operates within an institution and may function in large measure as a medium for the dissemination in photocopy form of the materials the library holds, its character as a business is necessarily affected by this circumstance in ways which would not be true of a similar document reproduction operation outside of the institution. Examples of this have already been shown in the two instances in which indirect overhead costs were entailed. Another important difference involves the kinds of subjects which library document reproduction services are called upon to reproduce. Commercial document reproduction services deal largely with originals which are quite uniform in their characteristics. This makes pricing relatively simple since the labor and materials requirements for a large part of the copying done is fairly predictable. As was described in detail in Part 2 in the text of the *Manual*, the characteristics of the materials held by libraries vary widely. This complicates the problem of pricing since labor and materials' costs are not predictable by any formula for a substantial percentage of the work done.

Perhaps the largest single factor having to do with fiscal policy in general and hence of pricing in particular is that of external vs. internal service. While a document reproduction service may owe its existence, in part, to the fact that a library holds a collection of materials from which photocopies must be made for the benefit of the library's clientele, it also may owe another part of its existence— and in some cases a large part—to the fact that the library itself requires document reproduction services for administrative use or for the preservation of portions of its collection. For example, both the library administration and the library's clientele might be usefully served by the installation of a Xerox 914 Copier or some similar device which can be used for either the copying of administrative correspondence, reports, invoices and the like, and the copying of pages from bound volumes as well. Another situation which is not uncommon is where a library acquires microfilm equipment primarily for the preservation of materials in its collection such as deteriorating newspaper files. Since, in these and many other cases as well, the library is a user and often the principal user of certain types of photoduplication equipment for the performance of a purely internal service, it would hardly be fair to the library's clientele who avail themselves of the document reproduction department's external service to pay prices based on all of the cost factors previously described. Since the relative use of document reproduction services for internal and external service can be highly variable, a realistic pricing policy for external services is by no means easy to establish.

Another influential factor which will affect pricing is the library's concept of the extent to which the document reproduction service should be a service and the extent to which it should be a business. Many libraries—particularly college and university libraries—emphasize the service function and try to keep prices as low as possible for the benefit of students and faculty. This, in almost all cases, as Samuel Boone has shown,[1] results in failure on the part of the document reproduction service to meet all its operating costs with the deficit being made up by the library through some form of subsidy such as providing free space and

utilities; providing accounting services including bookkeeping, invoicing, and the collecting of large numbers of small bills; underwriting the costs of additional equipment or replacement equipment; underwriting the costs of bibliographic searching or the salaries of one or more members of the staff of the document reproduction service. No guide lines can be given as to the extent to which a document reproduction service should be self-supporting or should be subsidized since the factors involved will vary in almost every situation and will be subject to local opinion. While there appears to be general agreement that institutionally operated document reproduction services should operate on a non-profit basis, the break-even point will again be highly variable, depending, of course, upon the library's ultimate decision as to what operating costs or what percentage of operating costs is to be recovered and what percentage subsidized.

The question of subsidy vs. self-support is, of course, an important and fundamental one which has been analyzed and discussed for many years and answered in many ways—possibly in almost as many ways as there are library document reproduction services. Boone, in the only recent study of the operations of forty-five library-operated document reproduction services, sums up the situation as he found it as follows:

"The extent to which a library administrator may expect his photographic service to be self-supporting is a question which has never been fully analyzed, and the problems presented in making such an analysis are apparently insurmountable at this time. Such a variety of approaches are taken in administration that no single yardstick for determining the definition of "self-support" can be made to apply to all libraries operating such a service."[2]

---

[1] Samuel M. Boone, "Current Administrative Practices in Library Photographic Services" (Chapel Hill: University of North Carolina, 1964), 81 pp. Unpublished M.A. thesis.

[2] *Op. cit.*, p. 48.

Appendix B

THE ACQUISITION OF REPRODUCTIONS OF RESEARCH MATERIALS

The ever-increasing use of document reproduction processes and methods—especially microforms—for the preservation and dissemination of research materials has created vast new resources for the acquisitions librarian. During the past three decades, the number of current and out-of-print serials, newspapers, rare books, manuscripts, theses, and dissertations which have been micro-recorded has reached a figure of impressive magnitude. Most of the material which has been recorded is available in the form of duplicate micro-transparencies or micro-opaques. Copies of certain classes of materials can also be obtained in the form of xerographically produced hard copy.

Over the years not all of the work that has been done has been of good quality. Due to the absence of technical and bibliographic standards, microfilms of similar materials (e.g., newspapers) from different sources vary considerably in format, reduction ratio, contrast, density, sharpness, and other features. In some instances, the filming may have been done from a complete file in good condition while, in others, the original file from which the film was made may have been incomplete and in poor condition. In most cases, films are divided into reels which make up convenient bibliographic units but, in some cases, this has not been done. Bibliographic data may range from being quite complete to quite sketchy. There have been instances in which, because of lack of communication, the work of filming extensive runs of material has been duplicated by different institutions or commercial firms.

To bring about improvements in this situation, a Committee on the Photographic Reproduction of Documents was appointed by the Association of Research Libraries in 1947. One of the mandates to this committee was to develop a set of bibliographic and technical standards for the microfilming of newspapers. The work on standards was completed in 1949 and a proposed standard published in 1950.[1]

Continued and increasing attention to standards for microfilming since then have resulted in much greater attention being given to both the bibliographic and technical aspects of microfilm production; to the publicizing of filming projects contemplated, in progress, or completed; and to the reporting of the existence of master negatives through media such as the *Microfilm Clearing House Bulletin* of the Library of Congress and the *Union List of Microfilms* compiled by the Philadelphia Bibliographic Center. A major step forward in this area which was begun in 1965 with the aid of a grant from the Council on Library Resources, Inc., is the establishment of a *National Register of Microform Master Negatives* at the Library of Congress. This *National Register* will record the existence and location of master negatives (i.e., negatives not for reader use) of microcopied newspapers, serials, and books and make the information available to other institutions by the regular publication of reports. The *National Register's* operation will be in addition to that of the *Microfilm Clearing House*.

Sources of microform duplicates

The two principal sources for microform duplicates are from institutions holding master microforms produced by them or for them and from commercial microform agencies. Although institutions report projects and film holdings to the Mi-

---

[1] "A Proposed Standard for the Microphotographic Reproduction of Newspapers." *American Documentation.* Vol. 1, No. 1 (January, 1950), pp. 46–50.

crofilm Clearing House and the Philadelphia Bibliographic Center, the listings are not complete enough for the purposes of ordering. It is usually necessary to write to the institution holding the film for further information. Since films do vary in a number of important aspects, detailed information about the film file will often be useful and may save the acquiring library a good deal of time, trouble, and expense. In the first place, it should be ascertained beforehand whether the desired film is complete and, if not, how much is missing. If the file has serious gaps, this fact alone may contraindicate purchase. Secondly, it should be ascertained whether or not the film is of high enough quality to yield a fully satisfactory duplicate. With respect to compatibility between the film and the microform reading equipment used at the acquiring library, it is helpful to know what the image position and the reduction ratio of the film are. In purchasing materials from commercial firms who publish catalogs and lists of titles together with prices, the same data should be obtained beforehand. Such catalogs are not equivalent to the catalogs of antiquarian book dealers in which all important imperfections are noted.

A highly useful source of information on the availability of microform duplicates is Albert James Diaz' *Guide to Microforms in Print.*[2] The scope of the *Guide* is stated as follows:

"The *Guide to Microforms in Print* is a comprehensive guide, in alphabetic order, to materials which are available on microforms from United States publishers. Theses and dissertations are not listed.

"The *Guide is not* a union list of microforms— it is essentially a listing of microform publications offered for sale on a regular basis."

The offerings of fifty-two publishers—both commercial and institutional—are listed, the type and size of microform is indicated, and in many cases the price.

Individual catalogs which in some cases are annotated are offered by the following commercial firms:

---

[2] Albert James Diaz (ed.), *Guide to Microforms in Print* (Washington, D.C.: Microcard Editions, Inc., 901 26th Street, N.W.). Published annually.

Microcard Editions, Inc.
901 26th Street, N. W.
Washington, D.C. 20037
Microcard Microfiche Catalog

Readex Microprint Corporation
5 Union Square
New York, New York 10003
Readex Microprint Publications 1965–66

University Microfilms, Inc.
300 North Zeeb Road
Ann Arbor, Michigan 48103
Modern Periodicals on Microfilm

University Microfilms, Inc., also issues brochures describing other large collections of materials for which they hold master negatives, including:

English Literary Periodicals of the 17th, 18th and 19th Centuries on Microfilm

American Periodicals of the 18th and 19th Centuries on Microfilm

Early English Books 1475–1700 on Microfilm

Early American Books 1493–1875 on Microfilm

United States Government Documents on Microfilm

Another important collection of materials which University Microfilms, Inc., makes available in the form of positive microfilm or Xerox copyflo enlargements is theses and dissertations. Two publications are available on a subscription basis which list the titles available together with an abstract:

Dissertation Abstracts
Masters Abstracts

Still another publication of University Microfilms, Inc., is entitled *American Doctoral Dissertations* which is an annual list of all dissertations accepted by United States and Canadian institutions whether published on microfilm by University Microfilms, Inc., or not.

Micro Photo Division
Bell and Howell Company
1700 Shaw Avenue
Cleveland, Ohio 44112
Newspapers on Microfilm
Special Collections

Important listings of microforms but which are not catalogs include a publication which is also entitled *Newspapers on Microfilm* and is published by the Microfilm Clearing House of the Library of Congress. Interim listings of newspapers and other serials as well appear in the *Bulletins* of the Clearing House.

Important foreign publishers of microforms who publish catalogs include:

Micro Methods, Ltd.
East Ardley
Wakefield, Yorkshire
England
Micro Methods Catalogue

Inter Documentation Company A.G.
(Formerly International Documentation Center, Tumba, Sweden)
Poststrasse 9
Zug, Switzerland
Basic Collections in Microeditions
    India
    Slavonics
    Botany
    Zoology
    Humanities

These catalogs are brought up to date and reissued from time to time. Interim announcements of the availability of new material is made on occasion usually through newsletters. University Microfilms, Inc., publishes a newsletter entitled *Microcosm;* the Micro Photo Division of Bell and Howell has a newsletter entitled *The Micro Photo Reader;* Micro Methods, Ltd., issues *Micronews;* and the Inter Documentation Company periodically issues its *Progress Report.*

Another source of information on the availability of microfiches from both commercial and institutional sources in Europe is:

The Microfiche Foundation
101 Doelenstraat
Delft, The Netherlands
Microfiche Foundation Newsletter

One foreign publisher—Kodak Limited, London, England—offers only a single newspaper title —the *London Times* from 1785 to date. Copies can be ordered from:

Business Systems Markets Division of Eastman Kodak (Formerly the Recordak Corporation)
770 Broadway
New York, New York 10003

A comprehensive, annotated listing of Canadian newspapers on microfilm is published by the Canadian Library Association in loose-leaf form. Supplements are issued from time to time to keep the listing up to date.

Canadian Newspapers on Microfilm
(Compiled by the Microfilm Committee of the Canadian Library Association under the supervision of Sheila A. Egoff.)
Canadian Library Association
63 Sparks Street
Ottawa 4, Canada

Still another foreign institutional source is the Association pour la Conservation et la Reproduction Photographique de la Presse (A.C.R.P.P.) of the Bibliotheque Nationale in Paris, France, who publish a list of newspapers and selected serials for which they hold master negatives.

A commercial French source which holds master negatives of a variety of kinds of research materials and supplies lists of holdings upon request is:

Service International de Microfilms (S.I.M.)
9 Rue Commandant Riviere
Paris 8ᵉ
France

Sources of xerographic copies

Two firms in this country offer extensive collections of material in the form of Xerox copies made by Copyflo printing from roll form microtransparencies. The first of these—University Microfilms, Inc.,—issues a catalog entitled *OP* (for "out-of-print") and the second—the Micro Photo Division of the Bell and Howell Company—a catalog entitled *Duopage Out-of-Print Books.* The term "Duopage" refers to a technique developed by this firm for recording xerographic images on both sides of single sheets of paper.

To acquire copies of materials which are not already available in some form of reproduction, a source for the material must be found which is equipped to supply the type of reproduction needed. Institutional photocopying and microcopying services are listed in three important publications:

> *Directory of Library Photoduplication Services in the United States, Canada and Mexico.* (Chicago: University of Chicago Library Photoduplication Service, 1966).

> *Photocopies from Abroad; Directory of Photocopying and Microcopying Services.* Third Edition. International Federation for Documentation, The Hague, Netherlands, 1963. (FID Publication No. 347.)

> A *Directory of British Photoreproduction Services.* Second Edition. Council for Microphotography and Document Reproduction, London, England, 1964.

All three of these directories list for most sources the kinds and sizes of photocopies and microcopies available as well as the prices at the time of publication.

Notes on ordering

Perhaps the most important single factor in ordering photocopies and microcopies has to do with the purpose the copies are intended to serve. In some cases any kind of copy, as long as it is legible with or without optical aids, will suffice. In a great many other cases, however, what the copy is going to be used for, how it will be used, by whom and in conjunction with what equipment will have an important bearing on what kind of a copy must be obtained.

Where a duplicate from a master negative microtransparency is being ordered, the library must, of course, accept the specifications used in filming, but when new material is being filmed for the ordering library, it is quite important that adequate specifications or instructions be given to the producing laboratory. If, for example, microfilms are ordered to complete an existing microfilm file, the specifications for the added material should be the same as those used for the original film. If, in another example, microfilm is ordered by a library which has only one type of microfilm reader, it is essential that the film be compatible with the capabilities of the reading device. If microfilms are ordered from which Copyflo prints are to be made

and subsequently bound, the specifications must take into account the type of binding to be used and the position and size of the needed binding margin. (See "Eye-legible copies from microforms," page 287–94.) It must also be remembered that while text reproduces well by Copyflo, continuous-tone illustrations reproduce poorly. If a microfilm is to be used on a reader-printer, the reduction ratio and the position used in filming must be compatible with the magnification ratio and the maximum micro-image area of the reader-printer.

Some libraries reserve the right to retain negatives and to supply positives in their stead. If the film is to be used for the production of hard copy, negative film should be specified. While hard copy can be made from positives, most hard copy processes are negative-working and hence would yield negative prints. Good quality negative prints are somewhat more difficult to make and the results are seldom as satisfactory from the user's standpoint as positive prints.

In ordering eye-legible copies such as photostat-type copies, xerographic copies, or silver halide enlargements from microfilms, other use factors must be considered. Photostat-type copies are right-reading negatives. If a positive is needed, the negative must be recopied which substantially increases the cost. Xerography is unsuitable if the material contains important continuous-tone illustrations. Silver halide enlargements from microfilms are also seldom suitable for continuous-tone illustrations since the materials normally used are high in contrast.

If eye-legible copies are being ordered expressly for the purpose of replacing missing pages in a volume, not only must the copies be the same size as the original but they must have the same margins and additional marginal space for binding purposes. These requirements also apply to complete volumes in hard copy form.

In ordering document reproductions from institutional services, it should be borne in mind that rates among such services for identical types of photocopies vary widely. Also, some services impose a minimum charge per type of photocopy or per item handled. If a number of small items are being ordered, the total cost may be quite high. Price lists should be obtained beforehand, but here, too, a proviso is necessary. If, for example, a microfilm of a work known to be 100 pages in length is ordered from an institution that charges five cents per exposure, and two-page-per-frame filming is specified, the fifty exposures required should cost $2.50. If, however, the work contains several folding plates which slow the work of filming and require special handling, the cost may run to double or treble the anticipated amount.

When microforms of substantial runs of material are being ordered, whether from existing master negatives or produced to order, the films should be inspected before they are cataloged to make sure they are of satisfactory quality and, in the case of films produced to order, that the specifications given have been met.

Appendix C
COPYRIGHT

by Charles F. Gosnell

The right or permission to reproduce

In contrast to the problems posed by physical conditions in the reproduction of research materials are the legal problems. Given the technological ability to reproduce, consideration must be accorded to having the right or obtaining the permission to make the reproduction. Much material is protected by copyright, which is the right of authors and publishers to literary property, and to the exclusive duplication and sale of such literary property. Copyright is granted by the government as a limited monopoly or form of compensation for creativity. The value of copyright in terms of money is sometimes quite substantial, and correspondingly may be jealously guarded by its owners.

Material not subject to copyright restriction is known as in the "public domain." The "public domain" includes sometime-copyrighted material for which copyright may have expired or lapsed for technical reasons, and material on which copyright is not claimed (such as the great bulk of U.S. Government publications) or on which copyright may not be obtainable for other reasons.

If the material is in the public domain, copies can be made without hesitation. If the material is under copyright, there are certain situations in which reproduction is permitted. There is uncertainty and difference of opinion in a large area. Finally, there are situations in which permission to reproduce must be obtained and, if the copyright owner requires, a fee or royalty must be paid for the privilege.

This appendix is not intended to be a treatise on copyright law. Copyright is a very complex subject, and, with current (1966) attention to extensive revision of the federal copyright law, is now in a state of considerable flux. This appendix is intended to provide a frame of reference within which the reasonable man may make his judgments and try to decide whether he has the right to proceed in making his reproductions or whether he must obtain permission to do so. What follows is a series of observations on current practice in scholarly libraries of the United States and on the concepts which govern this practice. It must be remembered that most of the criteria offered will be little better than touchstones. Seldom are simple and absolute determinants available.

Whether material can be reproduced without legal hazard depends on the answers to an almost infinite series of questions, among which are:

Is the material free of restriction; i.e., is it in the public domain?

Is there a copyright claim?

If so, is the claim valid?

If the material is copyrighted, what are the circumstances under which one can go ahead anyway?

How many copies are to be made?

Is it to be copied in whole or part?

How large a part?

Is it "fair use"?

What is the ultimate purpose?

Is it "not-for-profit"?

Are the author's or publisher's profits affected?

Is it impossible to identify or locate the copyright owner?

A brief history of copyright

Copying was once considered a virtuous activity. St. Benedict endorsed it in his Rule. To this practice we owe the survival through the Dark Ages of many literary masterpieces of classical antiquity. The Bible itself has come down to us only through infinitely repeated copying.

The great Gutenberg never heard of copyright.

His development of printing was regarded primarily as an advance in the art of copying. His type was cut and cast to look like manuscript. The spread of the art of printing was duly opposed by the scribes, professional copyists, and amanuenses of the day.

As the history of law goes, copyright is a relatively new subject. It was not even thought of until long after the invention of printing over 500 years ago.

The roots of our present copyright law are found in England in the 1500's and 1600's when Crown and Church combined with the Stationers Company to maintain a tight monopoly of printing and bookselling for the purposes of censorship as well as of profit. The first specific English statute on copyright was enacted in 1710.

Our U.S. Constitution provides the following (Article I, Section 8) relating to the powers of Congress: "To promote the Progress of Science and Useful Arts, by securing for limited Times to Authors and Inventors the exclusive Right to their respective Writings and their Discoveries."

Statute law and court decisions thus provide that the essential effect of copyright is to give the author or his agent the exclusive right to multiplication of copies for sale. Its basic purpose is to provide compensation to authors for contributing to the common good by publishing their works. This compensation is something over and above the actual cost of manufacturing and distributing a book, but it is obtained only once, and no direct benefit accrues to an author (or publisher) from, for example, the resale of secondhand copies. Copyright is not primarily for the benefit of the author but primarily for the benefit of the public.

A careful distinction must also be observed between the words as written and the ideas or thoughts expressed. In writing the copyright clause in the Constitution, our Founding Fathers recognized that, while a string of words may be tangible and possible to protect, the idea or thought is intangible and cannot be exclusive property. For the good of all, ideas, thoughts, and knowledge must be freely available and uncontrolled by any monopoly.

Status of manuscript materials

Under the present system, unpublished manuscript materials have common law protection which lasts indefinitely, or until publication. Possession of the physical manuscript (paper and ink) does not automatically carry ownership of the copyright. Conversely, the owner of a manuscript can prevent the copyright owner from publishing simply by refusing access to, or use of, the manuscript. Where heirs of an author actively maintain the estate, permission to reproduce literary property must be obtained, and a royalty paid, if required. But if the material is available in printed form, and there is no copyright on the printed material, or if the copyright on the printed version has expired, it would be safe to reproduce the manuscript.

Reproduction of most unpublished material must be based on a series of calculated risks. Some material may be presumed to be in the public domain as a public record. But the greater bulk of manuscript material considered for reproduction is actually under common law copyright protection. For the greater portion, however, passage of time has so clouded or obscured the ownership of the copyright, that there is no one who can prevent reproduction or collect royalty for it.

By general consensus, the scholar or researcher has a moral right to reproduce when no one can be found able to grant the legal right. Otherwise a vast corpus of material would be under a perpetual blackout. The dilemma has been recognized by the Register of Copyrights who has proposed (1965) enacting limited statutory terms for unpublished materials. After the expiry of such a term, manuscript material would fall into the public domain and be free for all to use.

This idea of moral right is occasionally used to cover the need to copy materials on paper which is rapidly disintegrating. A further extension is the creation and dispersal of several copies as a precaution against loss through war or other physical hazards.

Copyright of published materials

Publication is an essential part of the copyright process, consisting of making a number of identical copies and offering them for sale or distributing them to the public. Under U.S. law, but not in many foreign countries, copyrighted material must bear a definite copyright notice of claim, identifying the owner and the date obtained. American copyright runs for 28 years, and may be renewed for another 28 years upon application to the Copyright Office in the Library of Congress. A recent study showed that only 15 percent of copyrights were renewed, but only specific inquiry to the Copyright Office can determine whether a given item is within the 15 percent. After copyright expires, the material falls into the public domain and is free for all.

Absence of the notice on all but foreign works may, with very few exceptions, be interpreted as meaning that the work is in public domain. Conversely, presence of the notice usually indicates a valid claim.

Thus the mechanism for determining what is subject to copyright seems fairly simple. In the case of a well-known author or publisher, contact for permission to reproduce may be easy. For an obscure or unknown author or publisher, it may be impossible. If the desired permission cannot be obtained, one must proceed to calculate, or rather guess, at the risk. In many cases, it may be assumed that if both author and publisher have disappeared, there is not much worth protecting, and unless some chance of great profit should suddenly appear, no one will come forward to challenge a reproduction.

Conditions of copyright in foreign countries and their effects in the United States vary widely and, because of space limitations, cannot be presented here.

Mention must be made of possible flaws in American copyright claims, which cannot be given in detail here. One of the best known and most controversial is the fact that under certain circumstances foreign manufacture of works by American authors may invalidate copyright.

A word of caution is necessary about certain extravagant claims of copyright.

The determination of what material may be actually subject to copyright is a very complex matter. The notice customarily printed on the verso of a title page is only the first step. Unlike the Patent Office, the Copyright Office does not rule on the validity of copyrights. Anybody can print a notice or claim on almost anything. Except for prosecuting infringements or for certain other technical reasons, it is not even necessary to deposit a copy or file a form with the Copyright Office.

Casual browsing in shelves of new books, particularly among the paperbacks and reprints, will quickly turn up centuries-old classics in modern format with brand-new copyright claims.

A typical example is the well-known *Fanny Hill*. Although the story first appeared in print in 1749, a recent edition bears the copyright date of 1963. It has been said that the copyright date may cover the introductory material, but this introduction is almost wholly taken from contemporary reviews and comment of over two centuries ago. The classics of Malthus, Adam Smith, Isaac Newton, and a host of others can likewise be found covered with this presumptive mantle of protection, although it is obvious that copyright on these works long ago expired.

Some publishers have resorted to extended definitions of what they conceive copyright restrictions to be or what they would like us to think them to be. For example:

All rights reserved. No part of this book may be reproduced or utilized in any form or by any means, electronic or mechanical, including photocopying, recording, or by any information storage or retrieval system, without permission in writing from the Publisher.

This claim suggests the following questions: Why buy a book if you cannot *utilize* it? What is the use if you are not allowed to read it and commit what you read to that most magnificent of all means of storing and retrieving information, the human brain?

Another notice apparently is intended to prevent libraries from putting a permanent binding on a paperback book:

For copyright reasons this book may not be issued to the public on loan or otherwise except in its original soft cover.

Fair use

The very purpose for which statutory copyright is granted requires that the public be permitted to make any and all uses of the copyright material, except for the limited monopoly granted to the author for a limited time to publish and sell. This leads us to the question of what is *fair use* and what is unfair, or infringement. Fair use is not, as it has been termed by some, a form of infringement which is condoned. The use of copyrighted material in all ways which do not interfere with the limited monopoly granted to the author is inherent in the copyright law and constitutes the justification for statutory copyright. Historically and basically, copyright is simply the right to sell multiple copies and to profit thereby.

The difference between infringement and fair use is a matter of purpose, degree, and the effect of the copying rather than the act of copying or publishing, as such. The differentiation between fair use and infringement is fundamentally a problem of balancing what the author must dedicate to society in return for his statutory copyright (which varies according to the nature of the works involved) against undue appropriation of what society has promised the author in terms of protection of his exclusive right to make merchandise of the product of his intellectual work.[1]

The meaning of "copy" in copyright is actually related to multiplication of copies and publishing for sale, and the courts have frequently ruled that copyright does not restrict the scholar from the taking of notes for individual and private use. Of course, as a matter of practicality, it would be impossible to prevent such note-taking, even if it were illegal.

The ultimate extension of this principle of fair use is found in the rights of reviewers and others to quote and republish in unlimited multiple copies extracts from copyrighted works.

Abe A. Goldman, general counsel for the Copyright Office, aptly writes:

Even more far-reaching in practical effect are the limits drawn around the exclusive rights of authors by the accretion of custom and pronouncements of the courts. A simple illustration is one so basic that we take it for granted and don't even think of it as a limitation on an author's rights—

namely, that anyone is free to read or recite a work privately, or to copy it down for his own private use. . . .

This brings us to what I have heard characterized as the "safety valve" of copyright, namely, the doctrine of fair use. If the author's exclusive rights were absolute—if they restricted every use of his work—then copyright could indeed become a roadblock to the growth and spread of learning and culture. To achieve the purposes stated in the Constitution, the works of authors must be made available for use by the public while, at the same time, the author enjoys such exclusive rights as will give him a just reward for his contribution to society. The underlying problem of the copyright law is to achieve both of these aims in some kind of fair balance. And one of the important elements in maintaining this balance is the doctrine of fair use.[2]

In a classic of understatement, the Register of Copyrights has reported that "fair use eludes precise definition."

Most librarians would define and practice "fair use" as that reproduction so limited in extent as not to harm the author or publisher by depriving them of profits from the sale of their publications.

On the one hand, the student or researcher who, instead of laboriously taking notes, uses a coin-in-the-slot photocopy machine does not deprive the author or publisher of a sale. On the other, the professor or librarian who makes multiple copies of chapters of books for class assignments is clearly "unfair" and violating or infringing copyright.

In the economics of scholarly publishing, the desire of the author to get his work widely known usually far outweighs any possible monetary return. The publications themselves are often subsidized, and the author's status in his profession is enhanced by the widest possible dissemination. Often the author sends out reprints of his journal articles to a wide circle. In such circumstances, the author's purposes are actually served by unrestricted availability of photocopies.

---

[1] Ralph R. Shaw, *Literary Property in the U.S.* (Washington D.C.: Scarecrow Press, 1950).

[2] L. H. Hattery and G. P. Bush, editors, *Reprography and Copyright Law* (Washington D.C.: American Institute of Biological Sciences, 1964), pp. 12–13.

Some contend that when a publisher lets a book or journal go out of print, he fails to meet the implied obligation to make copies available, and thus, by default, leaves the field open to others, especially to those who seek only single copies for their own use. Morally this argument is persuasive, but legally it has no basis. As a practical matter it usually works.

Recognition of the judicial doctrine of fair use has been incorporated in the current (1965) proposed revision of the copyright law. Case law on the subject has relatively little application to library photocopying.

An excellent study of "fair use" in general is that by Alan Latman, together with comments by leading members of the copyright bar. It is one of a series prepared for the Copyright Office, and printed for the Senate Committee on the Judiciary. The same volume contains "Photoduplication of Copyright Material by Libraries," by Borge Varmer.[3] This is a comprehensive study of the problems of regulation and law drafting.

The library consensus on fair use has been developed and stated by the Joint Committee on Fair Use in Photocopying.[4] Its findings have been summarized as follows:

1. The making of a single copy by a library is a direct and natural extension of traditional library service.
2. Such service, employing modern copying methods, has become essential.
3. The present demand can be satisfied without inflicting measurable damage on publishers and copyright owners.
4. Improved copying processes will not materially affect the demand for single-copy library duplication for research purposes.

While the principles of fair use as developed by the committee evolved from a "gentlemen's agreement" with the National Association of Book Publishers, and are still tacitly accepted by many publishers, they have not been formally endorsed by the publishers. Nor have they been formally challenged.

A similar statement has been issued by the Royal Society of London.[5]

Many groups other than librarians have manifested interest in the problems of copyright restrictions on reproductions for special uses. The strongest and most noteworthy is the Ad Hoc Committee composed of a number of educational organizations centering around the National Education Association. This group has included librarians and has worked closely with the ALA Committee on Copyright Issues. The Ad Hoc Committee has stoutly defended the needs of classroom teachers in the use of classroom projectors and in duplicating selections for teaching, testing, etc. It has pioneered in seeking to clarify issues of copyright in not-for-profit educational television. In television, the financial stakes are higher than in scholarly publishing, and consequently the issues are much harder fought.

The Ad Hoc Committee and its constituent groups have issued numerous press releases, reports, and working papers and have presented full statements at various official hearings.

The development of computers and electronic storage, retrieval, and transmission systems is bringing forth a multitude of new copyright problems and controversies. The solutions to these problems will surely have their impact on present practices, as reported here, but no firm predictions can be made at this writing. Yet it is obvious that, if the day ever comes when one storage copy can serve the nation or the world through transmission and expandable reproductions, our present system of copyright will have to be revolutionized.

The library as agent

Libraries generally, and particularly the larger research libraries that have fully developed photocopy services, seek to protect themselves in three ways. First, they admonish and endeavor to require their patrons to observe the principles of fair

---

[3] U.S. Congress. 86th, 2nd session, *Copyright Law Revision*. Studies 14–15. Prepared for the Subcommittee on Patents, Trademarks and Copyrights, Committee on the Judiciary, U.S. Senate (Washington, D.C.: U.S. Government Printing Office, 1960.) Committee Print.
[4] *ALA Bulletin*, Vol. 35 (February, 1941), p. 64; and Vol. 55 (June, 1961), pp. 571–73; *Special Libraries*, Vol. 55, No. 2 (February, 1964), pp. 104–106; *Library Journal*, Vol. 90, No. 15 (September 1, 1965), pp. 3403–405.

[5] *Science*, Vol. 150 (December 17, 1965), pp. 1534.

use. Second, they require the patron to assume all responsibility for any infringement by signing a statement on photocopy order blanks. Third, they contend that they are not selling photocopies, but merely acting as agents.

The first step is a wholesome manifestation of good intent. The second is a disclaimer upon which some doubt as to legal validity may be cast.[6] The third is an interesting piece of reasoning by analogy. If a library patron buys or borrows paper and a pen from the library and therewith proceeds to commit infringement can the library be held responsible? Is it any different when the library supplies sensitized paper and a lens? How can the library be held responsible for complicity in possible infringement, if it provides space for a push-button, coin-in-slot photocopy machine, which the reader can use at will?

Three typical statements, selected from forms issued by the New York Public Library, are as follows:

This is a request for reproduction of material listed on order number __ to be made by the New York Public Library under the following conditions:

1. I assume all responsibility for infringement of copyright.

2. I order these reproductions solely for editorial study and hereby affirm that neither these reproductions nor any further copies of them will be used in any way that would constitute publication in the legal sense before the right to do so has been obtained from the parties or party owning the copyright. I file this order in good faith that there is no infringement of copyright in ordering these reproductions solely for editorial study.

3. I understand that in making this reproduction, The New York Public Library sells nothing, acts merely as my agent on my responsibility, performs a service at my request without profit to itself; and I hereby agree to protect it against any claims for violation which may be filed because of its filling this order.

---

[6] Miles O. Price, "Photocopying of Copyrighted Material," *Bulletin of the Copyright Society of the U.S.A.*, Vol. 5, No. 6 (August, 1958), pp. 345–58. The foregoing is an abridgment of "Acquisition and Technical Processing," *Library Trends*, Vol. 6 (April, 1958), pp. 430–58.

4. I affirm that if I am acting for another I am authorized to give this assurance of indemnity against claims or damages for violation of copyright.

Signature ————————————

This service is intended for those readers who are in the building and having found what they want need a copy of a few pages to take with them. The following conditions (selected from the complete set) apply:

3. Library material only.

4. Copyrighted material will not be reproduced beyond "fair use."

5. The applicant assumes all responsibility for any questions that may arise in the making of the copy and in the use made thereof.

6. The Library does not sell copies. The fee is for the service of copying.

CONDITIONS

1. ONLY LIBRARY MATERIAL REPRODUCED

The Library will undertake the reproduction of only such material as is in its collections and is, in the opinion of the Library authorities, properly available for duplication.

2. FEE FOR SERVICE ONLY

The Library does not sell the photo-duplicates but merely performs the service of copying. The fee paid is exclusively for such service.

3. COPYRIGHT

All responsibility for questions of copyright that may arise in this copying and in the use made of the copies must be assumed by the applicant. Copyrighted material will not be reproduced beyond recognized "fair use" without the signed authorization of the copyright owner.

4. RESTRICTIONS

The Library reserves the right, at its discretion and without explanation, to limit the number of copies; to retain the negative; to restrict the use or further reproduction.

In the case of some manuscripts where the New York Public Library cannot determine the copyright owner, the Library will make a photocopy, but only lend it to the patron.

Alarmed by the rapid growth of quick and cheap photocopying as a possible threat to sales, or intrigued by it as a hopefully lucrative source of income, some publishers and authors groups have reacted sharply. They have sought restrictive legislation and have proposed a "clearinghouse" system to collect royalties on photocopying. Several studies have failed to show any considerable evidence of losses to publishers or authors due to photocopying.[7] No practical or effective way of operating a clearinghouse has been found.[8]

Useful references

There is an extensive amount of material on the subject of copyright, but very little of immediate application to the problems of reproducing research materials. In addition to the specific items already cited, the following may prove useful to the reader seeking broader background, or detailed information applicable to a difficult specific case. A standard text is by Howell, revised by Latman.[9] An excellent handbook, readable for the layman, and containing a number of practical helps is the monograph by Ringer and Gitlin.[10] The *Bulletin* of the Copyright Society of the U.S.A. (New York) is an excellent source of special articles. For general background and statements of various points of view, the symposium edited by Hattery and Bush is very useful.[11] Petre has written a helpful review.[12]

An interesting sidelight on publication of material sponsored by the U.S. Government is offered by the proprietor of the Public Affairs Press.[13]

Some influence on American policy and practice comes from abroad. A systematic and comprehensive comparative review of copyright laws has been compiled by the noted copyright authority, Arpad Bogsch.[14]

A survey of laws especially relating to photocopy has been issued by UNESCO.[15]

Most of the recent publications on the subject of reproduction and copyright are slanted toward revision of the present copyright law, which was enacted in 1909. The Register of Copyrights has issued an extensive series of studies, reports, and hearings and commentaries on proposed revisions of the law. These are good sources for information on current practice, interpretations of the present statutes, and court decisions.

The librarian's point of view and his concern that long-standing practices may be restricted or eliminated by adverse revisions in the new law has been stated by Gosnell.[16]

Forthcoming reports of congressional committee hearings should prove to be full and comprehensive sources. If and when a new copyright law is enacted, further study will be required.

[7] John C. Koepke, "Implications of the Copyright Law on the Dissemination of Scientific and Technical Information," *Special Libraries*, Vol. 54 (November, 1963), pp. 553–56. Curtis G. Benjamin, "Book Publishers' Interests in Reprographic Copyright," *Library Journal*, Vol. 88 (August, 1963), pp. 2837–41. Robert F. Clarke, "The Impact of Photocopying on Scholarly Publishing," *Library Journal*, Vol. 88 (July, 1963), pp. 2625–59.

[8] Committee to Investigate Problems Affecting Communications in Science and Education (Systems Committee, John Markus, McGraw-Hill Book Co., Chairman), *Proposals for Economical and Practical System for Establishing and Operating a Copyright Clearing House* (1963). 1,947 pp. Distributed by G. J. Sophar, Secretary, Jonker Business Machines, Gaithersburg, Maryland.

[9] Herbert A. Howell, *Copyright Law*, 4th ed., Revised by A. Latman (Washington, D.C.: Bureau of National Affairs, 1962). 358 pp.

[10] Barbara A. Ringer and Paul Gitlin, *Copyrights* (New York: Practising Law Institute, 1963). 162 pp.

[11] Lowell H. Hattery and George P. Bush, editors, *Reprography and Copyright Law* (Washington, D.C.: American Institute of Biological Sciences, 1964). 204 pp.

[12] David C. Petre, "Statutory Copyright Protection for Books and Magazines against Machine Copying," in *Copyright Law Symposium*, No. 14, sponsored by the American Society of Composers, Authors and Publishers (New York: Columbia University Press, 1966), pp. 180–225.

[13] M. B. Schnapper, *Constraint by Copyright: A Report on "Official" and "Private" Practices* (Washington, D.C.: Public Affairs Press, 1960). 154 pp.

[14] Arpad Bogsch, *The Law of Copyright under the Universal Convention* (New York: R. R. Bowker Co., 1964). 591 pp.

[15] Intergovernmental Copyright Committee, *The Photographic Reproduction of Protected Works by or on Behalf of Libraries, Documentation Centres and Scientific Institutions*, IGC/VIII/5 (Paris: UNESCO, 1965). 27 pp.

[16] Charles F. Gosnell, "The Copyright Grab-bag; Observations on the New Copyright Legislation," *ALA Bulletin*, Vol. 60, No. 1 (January, 1966), pp. 46–55.

At this point, it is interesting to note that Petre[17] has made a study of "computer copying" and reached the conclusion, from the analogy of player piano rolls, that "copyright protection for such appropriation is not available under the present statute."

[17] *Op. cit.*, pp. 215–19.

A word of warning

A final word of warning is necessary. The field of copyright law is broad and complex. It is changing constantly through new legislation and judicial interpretations of existing law. Accordingly, it is advisable for librarians to keep themselves informed about the current rules governing the reproduction of copyrighted materials.

Appendix D
STANDARDS RELATING TO DOCUMENT REPRODUCTION

The principal standards bodies are the International Standards Organization (ISO) and the national standards organizations in each country. While a great many countries have standards organizations, relatively few have promulgated standards relating to the reproduction of documents. Copies of all of the standards listed herein —international, domestic, and foreign—can be purchased from:

American Standards Association
10 East 40th Street
New York, New York 10016

INTERNATIONAL STANDARDS

International Standards Organization: ISO
Standards Relating to Document Reproduction

R5–1955
Diffuse Transmission Density (Photography) PH2.19–1959)

R169–1960
Sizes of Photocopies (on paper) Readable Without Optical Devices

R193–1961
Microcopies on Transparent Bases, Sizes of Recommended Bases (PHI.20–1963 and PH5.3–1958)

R218–1961
Microcopies, Scale of 35mm Microfilms for International Exchange

R260–1962
Terms Relating to Microcopies and Their Bases (PH.3–1958 and PH5.5–1961)

R417–1965
Methods for Determining Thiosulphate and Tetra-

thionate in Processed Black-and-White Photographic Film, Plates, and Papers

R435–1965
ISO Conventional Typographical Character for Legibility Tests (ISO Character)

DOMESTIC NATIONAL STANDARDS

American Standards Association: ASA
Standards Relating to Document Reproduction

PH1.28–1957
Photographic Films for Permanent Records, Specifications for

PHI.29–1958 (R1964)
Curl of Photographic Film, Methods for Determining the

PH1.31–1965
Brittleness of Photographic Film, Method for Determining the

PH1.33–1961
16mm 100-Foot Film Spools for Recording Instruments, Microfilm and Still Picture Cameras, Dimensions for

PH1.34–1961
16mm 200-Foot Film Spools for Recording Instruments, Microfilm and Still Picture Cameras, Dimensions for

PH1.35–1961
35mm 100-Foot Film Spools for Recording Instruments, Microfilm and Still Picture Cameras, Dimensions for

PH1.37–1963
Scratch Resistance of Processed Photographic Film, Methods for Determining the

PH2.17–1958
Diffuse Reflection Density

PH2.19–1959
Diffuse Transmission Density (ISO R5–1955)

PH3.8–1953 (R1965)
Contact Printers, Specifications for

PH4.1–1962
Manual Processing of Black-and-White Photographic Films and Plates, Methods for

PH4.8–1958
Determining the Thiosulphate Content of Processed Black-and-White Photographic Film and Plates, Method for

PH4.12–1954
(Partially revised by PH4.32–1965)
Stability of the Images of Processed Black-and-White Films, Plates, and Papers, Methods for Indicating the

PH4.20–1958
Photographic Filing Enclosures for Storing Processed Photographic Films, Plates, and Papers

PH4.29–1962
Manual Processing of Black-and-White Photographic Paper, Methods for

PH4.30–1962
Residual Thiosulphate and Thionates in Processed Photographic Papers, Method for Determining

PH4.32–1965
Evaluating the Processing of Black-and-White Photographic Papers with Respect to the Stability of the Resultant Image, Method for (Partial Revision of PH4.12–1954)

PH5.1–1959
Microfilm Readers for 16mm and 35mm Film on Reels, Specifications for

PH5.2–1963
Paper Sheets for Photo-Reproduction of Documents, Dimensions for

PH5.3–1958
16mm and 35mm Microfilms on Reels or in Strips, Specifications for (ISO R193–1961 and R260–1962)

PH5.4–1957
Storage of Microfilm, Practice for

PH5.5–1961
Micro-Opaques, Specifications for

PH5.6–1961
100-Foot Reels for Processed 16mm and 35mm Microfilm, Dimensions for

PH5.7–1964
Micro-Opaque Readers, Specifications for

Z38.7.5–1948
Printing and Projection Equipment, Methods of Testing

FOREIGN NATIONAL STANDARDS

Great Britain: British Standards Institute: B.S.I. Standards Relating to Document Reproduction

BS 1153:1955
Recommendations for the Storage of Microfilm

BS 1371:1956
Microfilm Readers and Reels (Amended Dec., 1958).

BS 1896:1960
Sizes of Sensitized Materials for Document Reproduction

Belgium: Institut Belge de Normalisation: NBN Standards Relating to Document Reproduction

NBN 289–1953
Terminologie de la reproduction photographique et héliographique (1re partie)

(Terminology on Photographic and Heliographic Reproduction [Part One])

NBN 320–1953
Documentation—Reproduction photographique de documents sur papier-copies lisibles sans intermédiaire optique—Formats

(Photographic Reproduction of Documents on

Paper—Copy Readable without Optical Devices—Formats)

NBN 360–1955

Microfilms de 16 mm ou de 35 mm en rouleaux (16 mm and 35 mm Roll Microfilm)

NBN 393–1956

Manipulation et conservation de microfilms de 16 mm ou de 35 mm

(Handling and Storing of 16 mm and 35 mm Microfilm)

NBN 423–1956

Reproduction documentaire. Microcopies sur supports transparents. Dimensions recommandées.

(Document Reproduction. Microcopies on Transparent Bases. Recommended Dimensions.)

Colombia: Instituto Colombiano de Normas Técnicas: Colombian Standards Relating to Document Reproduction

No standards have yet been issued by the currently official standards body. The previous Colombian Standards body, the Instituto de Normas Colombianas (INORCOL), has issued the following draft standards:

2–1.1–0.001

MICROFILM

Microfilmficha de 35 mm Especificaciones

(Microfilm: 35 mm microcopies specifications)

2–2.1–0.001

MICROFILM

Minifichas Bibliográficas Definicion y uso

(Microfilm: Bibliographical strips. Definition and Use)

2–2.1–0.002

MICROFILM

Microfilmficha de 35 mm Conservación y archivo

(Microfilm: 35 mm Microcopies Preservation and Storage)

2–2.1–0.003

MICROFILM

Microfilmficha de 35 mm Conservación y archivo Depósitos

(Microfilm: 35 mm microcopies Preservation and Storage Centers)

2–2.1–0.005

FOTOCOPIAS EN PAPEL

Para lectura a simple vista. Especificación

(Photocopies on Paper: For simple view reading. Specification)

2–2.1–0.006

MICROFILM

Microfilmficha opaca de 35 x 210 mm Especificaciones

(Microfilm: Opaque 35 x 210 mm microcopy. Specifications)

2–2.1–0.008

DIAPOSITIVAS

Diapositivas de 85 x100 mm Medidas

(Slides: 85 x 100 mm Lantern Slides. Measurement)

2–2.1–0.009

DIAPOSITIVAS

Diapositivas de 50 x 50 mm (Superficie útil 36 x 36 mm) Medidas

(Slides: 50 x 50 mm Lantern Slides (36 x 36 mm Effective Surface. Measurement)

2.1–0.010

FOTOMICROGRAFIAS

Aumentos

(Microphotographs. Enlargement)

France: Association Française de Normalisation: AFNOR Standards Relating to Document Reproduction

Document Reproduction: Photocopies

NF Z 42–001

Octobre 1961

Formats de photocopies (sur papier) lisibles sans intermédiaire optique)

(Paper sizes of photocopies readable without Optical Devices)

Document Reproduction: Microcopies

NF Z 43–001

April 1954

Supports recommandés-Dimensions

(Recommended Bases—Dimensions)

NF Z 43–002

December 1959

Vocabulaire de la microcopie-1° Microcopies et leurs supports

(Vocabulary of Microcopies—Microcopies and Their Bases)

NF Z 43–004

December 1959

Limitation du taux de réduction des microfilms de 35 mm pour appareils de lecture dans les échanges de documentation

(Limits in Reduction Ratio of 35 mm Microfilm used in Readers for Document Exchange)

NF Z 43–006

December 1959

Caractère typographique conventionnel AFNOR pour essais de lisibilité

(Standard AFNOR Type Characters for Readability Tests)

NF Z 43–007

December 1959

Description et utilisation de la mire AFNOR—Prise de vues

(Description and Use of the AFNOR mire—viewing)

NF Z 43–008

December 1959

Description et utilisation de la micromire AFNOR—Lecture

(Description and Use of the AFNOR micromire—Reading)

NF Z 43–010

April 1954

Microfilms de 35 mm

(35 mm Microfilm)

FD Z n° 43–020

April 1954

Microfilms de 16 mm

(16 mm microfilm)

NF Z 43–030

April 1954

Microfiches-films de format 105 mm x 150 mm

(150 mm x 150 mm Microfiche Film)

NF Z 43–031

Microfiches-films de format 75 mm x 125 mm

(75 mm x 125 mm Microfiche Film)

NF Z 43–040

February 1961

Caractéristiques essentielles des appareils de lecture pour microfilms de 35 mm

(Essential Characteristics of 35 mm Microfilm Reading Apparatus)

Germany: Deutsche Industrie-normen: DIN Standards relating to document reproduction

16542

Temperatur der Entwickler und Bäder für photographische Zwecke in der Reproduktionstechnik

(Temperature of developers and baths for photographic reproduction purposes)

19050

Entwurf; Aufnahme-Filmspulen für Reprographie für Film 16, 35 und 70 mm

(Draft; Film spools for repro-photography for 16, 35, and 70 mm film)

4518

Strahlungsempfindliche Papiere für die Vervielfältigung von bild-und Schriftvorlagen (Dokument en Papiere), Abmessungen

(Radiation-sensitive papers for the reproduction of illustrations and text [document-copying papers], dimensions)

Italy: Nazionale Italiano de Unificazione: UNI Standards Relating to Document Reproduction

UNI 5450–64

Carte fotografiche—Formati e rotoli per la riproduzione di documenti

(Photographic Paper-Formats and Rolls for Document Reproduction)

5451–64

Sopporti transparenti per microcopie-dimensioni

(Transparent supports for Microcopies—dimensions)

Netherlands: Stichting Nederlands Normalisatie-instituut: NEN Standards Relating to Document Reproduction

(NEN) Ontwerp 3236–1961
(Draft Standard)
Reproduceerbaarheid van getekende, geschreven, getypte en gedrukte documenten. Richtlijnen
(Reproducibility of printed written, typed and printed documents. Guides)
Voekje—1961 booklet
Toelichting bij Ontwerp 3236
(Explanation of Draft 3236)

Portugal: Reparticào de Normalizacáo: NP Standards Relating to Document Reproduction

NP—112 (1957)
Cópias fotográficas de documentos—Formatos
(Photographic Copies of Documents—Sizes)

NP—303 (1963)
Microcópias—Terminologia e definiciones
(Microcopies—Terminology and Definitions)

Spain: Instituto Nacional de Racionalización: UNE Standards Relating to Document Reproduction

UNE 1059
Microcopia
(Microcopies)

1060
Carretes para microfilme de 16 y 35 mm
(Spools for 16 and 35 mm Microfilm)

1061
Ejecución práctica de microfilme
(Practical Design of Microfilm)

1078
Reproducción fotográfica de documentos sobre papel
(Photographic Reproduction of Documents on Paper)

Federal Microfiche Standards

In 1962 the National Aeronautics and Space Administration began to use microfiches for the dissemination of technical reports. The size initially used was a 5- by 8-inch film sheet. Prior to this the Atomic Energy Commission had been distributing technical reports on 3- by 5-inch Microcards but later changed over to 3 by 5-inch microfiches. Because of the interest on the part of other government agencies in the use of microfiches for technical report dissemination and the discrepancy in the sizes of microfiches used by NASA and AEC, extensive studies were made which resulted in a set of standards which were adopted for government-wide use by the Committee on Scientific and Technical Information (COSATI) of the Federal Council for Science and Technology. The microfiche size which was finally adopted was the international standard size of 105 by 148 mm. (4⅛ by 6 inches). Copies of the *Federal Microfiche Standards* (Document No. PB 167 630) may be obtained for 50 cents each, postage prepaid, from:

Clearinghouse for Federal Scientific
and Technical Information
Springfield, Virginia 22151

Appendix E

ANNOTATED BIBLIOGRAPHY

by Allen B. Veaner

The annotated citations in this bibliography have been selected expressly for their current applicability to the bibliographic, technical, and administrative aspects of library reprography. Also listed—but without annotation—are additional titles of peripheral interest; these may be of value for supplementary reading, but they cannot be regarded as of primary importance, owing to their age, lack of library application, or other factors. Similarly, I have included a few general reference works on photography. A few works significant for their historical value or general durability have been included; an asterisk precedes the entries for those titles.

Owing to these selection criteria, several important works have been omitted. For instance, I exclude Harold Denstman's *Photographic Reproduction* (New York: McGraw-Hill, 1963) on the ground that it contains no library applications, and provides no information not obtainable elsewhere in a form better suited to library usage; I leave out Ralph Shaw's *The Use of Photography for Clerical Routines* (Washington, D.C.: American Council of Learned Societies, 1953) because its message has already been fully appreciated by the library community. I do not include Blanche P. McCrum and L. K. Born's *Microfilm and Microcards: Their Use In Research* (Washington: Library of Congress, 1950), because micro-opaques seem to be on the wane. For similar reasons, I omit Fremont Rider's *The Scholar and the Future of the Research Library*.

Readers interested in older books, or those having no modern library applications, are referred to the author's survey, *The Literature of Document Reproduction,* cited as No. 102 in the present bibliography.

CONTENTS

INDEX

GENERAL

1. *Basic Photography for the Graphic Arts* (Kodak Publication Q-1). Rochester, New York: Eastman Kodak Company, 1963. 45 pp. $.75.

Explains the techniques employed in the preparation of photomechanical printing plates for published illustrations. Although few library laboratories will actually prepare such plates, understanding the technical requirements of this specialized branch of photography will enable libraries to supply optimum camera copy for the platemaker. Well illustrated and written in clear, simple language with a minimum of technical jargon. Reference to more detailed works.

*2. BINKLEY, ROBERT C. *Manual on Methods of Reproducing Research Materials;* a Survey Made for the Joint Committee on Materials for Research of the Social Science Research Council and the American Council of Learned Societies. Ann Arbor: Edwards Brothers, 1936. 207 pp. Out of print.

The earliest comprehensive survey of this field by a humanistic scholar, and the most interesting incunabulum of library reprography. Binkley incorporated many actual specimens of various processes directly into his text, thus affording the future researcher source materials for the study of permanence and durability.

Note: A much less complete preliminary edition—without specimens—was issued by the author in 1931 under the title: *Methods of Reproducing Research Materials.*

*3. *The Photography of Library Materials.* Papers Presented at the Annual Meeting of the California Library Association, October 18, 1946. San Francisco, 1946. 51 pp. Processed. Out of print.

4. CROY, OTTO R. *Camera Copying and Reproduction.* London: Focal Press [1964]. 256 pp. $8.95.

Only one page of this text mentions book copying; the balance of the book details special techniques for handling nonbook materials: coins, manuscripts, paintings, porcelain, stained glass, wood, etchings, carvings, textiles, and other subjects.

There are very good chapters on camera setup, lighting, developing, printing, and enlarging. Several rather weak chapters on microphotography are oriented toward microfilming personal and business documents rather than scholarly materials. The author states in two places that commercial microfilm cameras are in no way better than 35 mm. hand cameras—a claim that certainly cannot be substantiated. Recommended for photographers principally concerned with copying artifacts and museum items rather than books or printed matter. Plain, straightforward prose makes this text very suitable for self-instruction for those who lack experience in photocopying. Well illustrated.

5. HAWKEN, WILLIAM R. *Full-Size Photocopying* (The State of the Library Art, Vol. 5, Pt. 3). New Brunswick; Rutgers, 1960. 397 pp. $8.00.

Presents a well-documented account of the technical processes employed in a variety of photocopying machines, from the early Photostat cameras through the xerographic equipment just predating the Xerox 914. This work is of particular value for its historical coverage of equipment and processes now being superseded by fully automated systems. Numerous references and citations.

6. HAWKEN, WILLIAM R. *Photocopying from Bound Volumes* (LTP Publication No. 4). Chicago: American Library Association, 1962. 208 pp. $4.00.

This is the first book to analyze explicitly those characteristics of research materials which make their copying so extraordinarily more difficult, expensive, and time-consuming than copying business correspondence, the purpose for which most copying machines are designed. It is also the first publication to set forth design criteria for a machine which could adequately and safely copy research materials. The author evolves principles of document copying which are derived from the subjects to be copied rather than from the copying machines themselves; hence, even though some of the machines and processes described in the text have been superseded, all of the author's assumptions and conclusions may be applied to any new process. Library administrators and heads of photoreproduction services should find the introductory and concluding portions of exceptional value in dealing with students and faculty who may have been misled or misinformed concerning the ease of copying research materials.

Three *Supplements* (see No. 53) have been issued since 1962. Continuously updated reports on new machines and new processes are published as part of the Library Technology Project's subscription information service, *Library Technology Reports* (see No. 54).

*7. *Manual on Document Reproduction & Selection* (F.I.D. Publications, 264). The Hague: International Federation for Documentation, 1953–57. 3 vols. Out of print.

8. VERRY, H. REX. *Document Copying and Reproduction Processes.* London: Fountain Press, 1960; New York: Morgan & Morgan, 1964. 317 pp. 63/–.

Provides clear, easy to understand explanations of the basic technical processes and materials used in copying. Although this book does not cover any library applications, it could be very useful as a staff training tool or self-instruction aid for laboratory personnel. Well illustrated.

REFERENCE BOOKS AND HANDBOOKS

9. AVEDON, DONALD M. *Glossary of Terms for Microphotography and Reproductions Made from Micro-Images.* 3d edition. (NMA Informational Monographs, 2.) Annapolis: National Microfilm Association, 1964. 67 pp. $3.50

This glossary, which defines hundreds of terms (including many trademarks), is oriented mainly toward the engineering drawing applications of microfilming. It is a fairly technical work and is recommended only for experienced microphotographers. In preparation for a fourth edition, several librarians have contributed comments and suggestions which may make the next edition more useful to library reproduction personnel. Spiral binding allows the *Glossary* to lie flat on desk or workbench; all alternate pages are blank for notes. An appendix lists a variety of international units used in scientific work by the National Bureau of Standards.

10. CRAEYBECKX, A. S. H. *Elsevier's Dictionary of Photography in Three Languages: English, French, and German.* Compiled and Arranged on an English Alphabetical Base by A. S. H.

Craeybeckx. Amsterdam: Elsevier, 1965. 660 pp. $30.00.

13,650 entries; German and French indexes refer to serially numbered English entries in the front. One of a large series of multilingual technical dictionaries published by Elsevier, this is a work of the first quality, but its high price may put it out of reach for many. Useful mainly to the professional staff of large laboratories where foreign help or foreign equipment are employed, or where the widest variety of techniques compel thorough acquaintance with foreign publications; it would also naturally belong in the reference section of any university science collection.

11. CRAEYBECKX, A. S. H. *Gevaert Manual of Photography.* 4th edition. London: Fountain Press, 1958. 459 pp. 25/–.

12. HORDER, ALAN. *The Ilford Manual of Photography.* 5th edition. Ilford: Ilford, Ltd., 1958. 725 pp. 30/–.

13. *Photo-Lab Index.* John S. Carroll (ed.). Hastings-on-Hudson, New York: Morgan & Morgan, 1 vol. (loose-leaf). Basic volume: $25.00; quarterly supplements: $5.00 per year.

None of these books (Nos. 11, 12, 13) does more than call attention to the existence of document reproduction. Each is written for the advanced amateur and professional photographer who does virtually everything except copy documents. However, they do include the basic technical and reference information which is common to all branches of conventional photography; since thorough familiarity with the techniques of conventional photography will enhance the competence of any technician, these works should be readily available to staff of the library reproduction service. *Photo-Lab Index* is a looseleaf handbook which can be kept continuously updated by subscription to supplements which add to the manual or replace outdated information. Keeping this handbook up to date is somewhat of a chore; if the reader is disinclined to this kind of updating, he can dispense with it in favor of the other two manuals.

14. *Focal Encyclopedia of Photography.* 2d edition. London: Focal Press, 1965. 2 vols. $39.50.

Going far beyond the expertise of even the

most widely experienced photographers, this modern reference work opens up to the laboratory manager or technician the complete spectrum of photographic knowledge. Four sections of particular interest to the copyist are found under the entries, Copying, Manuscripts and Old Documents, Micro-copying, and Document Copying. The principal contributors to these sections are H. W. Greenwood, author of *Document Photography* (London: Focal Press, 1944), H. R. Verry, and D. A. Wilson, Chief of the Photographic Service of the British Museum. These articles are good primers for new laboratory employees; the balance of the encyclopedia will be most useful to those in charge of photographic services. Excellent illustrations are provided, and the accompanying text is written in clear, straightforward English. Some articles contain brief bibliographies.

For those unable to afford the latest edition, the earlier 1956 version, published at $20.00, is still of considerable basic value. The even less expensive desk edition issued in 1960 at $7.00 is an outstanding bargain if still obtainable—it is identical to the 1956 edition except for paper, binding, and omission of photographic illustrations.

15. *Glossary of Photographic Terms, Including Document Reproduction* (Military Standardization Handbook, 25; Department of the Army Technical Manual, TM-11–411). Washington D.C.: Govt. Printing Office, 1961. 128 pp. Out of print.

This compilation of definitions embraces the whole of photography and is drawn from seven professional sources, including the NMA *Glossary*. About 6500 terms are defined, including many trade-marks and proprietary names. While this glossary may be faulted for lacking illustrations, its definitions are clear and sufficiently discursive to convey full meaning. The work is well printed and the paper binding is punched to fit a 3-ring binder. Although one of the soundest bargains in photographic publications, it is now out of print; a revised edition is said to be in preparation.

16. DESSAUER, JOHN H. *Xerography and Related Processes.* London: Focal Press [1965]. 520 pp. $38.00.

An important beginning chapter written by Chester F. Carlson, inventor of modern xerogra-

phy, traces the two-hundred-year history of electrostatic recording. Carefully outlining and acknowledging the contributions of his many contemporaries, Mr. Carlson traces the long evolution of xerography. A second chapter outlines the basic principles of the xerographic process, and the balance of the book is devoted to a technical treatment of photoconductors, charging systems, development techniques, image transfer, miscellaneous imaging phenomena, and applications. Except for the first chapter, the book will appeal mainly to physicists and photographic engineers and to libraries enjoying generous book budgets.

17. UEHLEIN, ERHARD. *Concepts of Reprography: Terms and Definitions in German, English, and French.* Frankfurt a.M.: Deutsche Gesellschaft fuer Dokumentation e.V. [1963]. 71 pp.

This little pamphlet was distributed without charge at the First International Congress on Reprography, and is the only multilingual glossary devoted entirely to reprography. About 150 terms are briefly defined; the quality of the English definitions is not up to the Department of Defense *Glossary* but the work could be useful to a library photographic service which deals extensively with foreign students and scholars. As it is short and not copyrighted, it could be photocopied inexpensively.

PERIODICALS
(Library Applications)

*18. *Journal of Documentary Reproduction.* A Quarterly Review of the Application of Photography and Allied Techniques to Library, Museum, and Archival Service. Chicago: American Library Association, 1938–42. 5 vols. Out of print; no more published. (Positive microfilm is available from the Library of Congress Photoduplication Service at a cost of $15.00, postpaid in the United States.)

19. *Library Resources & Technical Services.* Chicago: Resources & Technical Services Division of the American Library Association. Quarterly. $5.00 per year.

Each Spring *LRTS* publishes a critical review of the preceding year's developments in copying methods. Throughout the year appear articles and reviews by seasoned librarians and document reproduction specialists who are free to discuss their experiences with various techniques and processes employed in specific library situations.

20. *Microdoc*. Journal of the Microfilm Association of Great Britain. London, 1962 to date. Quarterly. 30/-. per year.

Contains both descriptive and promotional articles of extraordinarily wide scope, contributed by librarians and others: new items, reports of conferences, patents, equipment announcements and reviews, book reviews, abstracts, and bibliographies. Issues are accompanied by microcards of the preceding numbers.

21. *The National Micro-News*. Vernon D. Tate (ed.). Official Journal of the National Microfilm Association. Annapolis: 1958 to date. Bimonthly. $7.50 per year.

Provides current information on all aspects of the microfilm industry in the United States and abroad. Keeps up to date the *Guide to Microreproduction Equipment* and summarizes much that is new and of interest to librarianship, e.g., grants from the Council on Library Resources, information on microscopic blemishes in films, case studies, bibliographies, book reviews, standards, legislation, and new technical developments. Although some of the articles are promotional, this characteristic is amply offset by the preponderance of factual information and editorial readiness to give expression freely to critical views.

22. *Revue Internationale de la Documentation*. The Hague: International Federation for Documentation. Quarterly. 26 guilders per year.

A section on Document Reproduction was edited by the late H. R. Verry for each issue from May 1961 to February 1965. Beginning with the September 1965 issue, this section was transferred to the *FID News Bulletin*, where it appears quarterly under the editorship of T. Hampshire.

23. *FID News Bulletin*. The Hague: International Federation for Documentation. Monthly. 15 guilders per year, or free to subscribers to the *Revue Internationale de la Documentation*. See No. 22.

24. *Special Libraries*. New York: Special Libraries Association. Monthly (September to April); bimonthly (May to August). $10.00 per year.

Each year for many years Loretta J. Kiersky has contributed a comprehensive, topically arranged bibliography, usually titled "Bibliography on Reproduction of Documentary Information." It generally appears in a spring issue; the latest is in the May–June, 1966, issue, pp. 311–22.

25. *UNESCO Bulletin for Libraries*. Paris: UNESCO. Bimonthly. $3.50 per year.

PERIODICALS

(Office Copying and Systems Applications)

26. *Administrative Management*. New York: Geyer-McAllister Publications. Monthly. $5.00 per year.

27. *The Office*. Magazine of Management, Equipment, Methods. Stamford, Connecticut: Office Publications, Inc. Monthly. $5.00 per year.

28. *Reproductions Review*. New York: Wolf Business Publications, Inc. Monthly. $5.00 per year.

29. *Systems*. New York: United Business Publications. Monthly. $6.00 per year.

PERIODICALS

(Laboratory, Technical, or Scientific Applications)

30. *Abstracts of Photographic Science & Engineering Literature*. New York: Engineering Index, Inc. (for the Society of Photographic Scientists & Engineers). Monthly. $40.00 per year for libraries; $15.00 per year for personal, individual use ($10.00 to members of the Society).

31. *Graphic Science*. New York: Kinelow Publishing Co. Monthly. $16.00 per year.

32. *Industrial Photography*. New York: United Business Publications. Monthly. $6.00 per year.

*33. *Monthly Abstract Bulletin*. Rochester, New York: Eastman Kodak Company, Research Laboratories, 1915–61. 47 vols. (Succeeded by *Abstracts of Photographic Science & Engineering Literature*.)

34. *Nachrichten für Dokumentation*. Frankfurt a.M.: Deutsche Gesellschaft für Dokumentation. Quarterly. DM 24.– per year.

35. *Perspective*. A Quarterly Review of Progress in Photography, Cinematography, Sound and Image Recording. London: Focal Press. Quarterly. $15.00 per year.

36. *Photographic Science & Engineering*. Easton, Pennsylvania: Society of Photographic Scientists & Engineers. Bimonthly. $15.00 per year.

37. *PMI: Photo Methods for Industry*. New York: Gellert-Wolfman Publishing Corp. Monthly. $5.00 per year.

38. *Plan and Print*. Chicago: International Association of Blue Print and Allied Industries (IABPAI). Monthly. $4.00 per year. (Successor to *The International Blue Printer* and *Reproduction Engineer*.)

39. *RM: Reproduction Methods for Business & Industry*. New York: Gellert-Wolfman Publishing Corp. Monthly. $4.00 per year.

40. *Reprographics*. New York: United Business Publications. Bimonthly. $3.00 per year.

41. *Reprographie: Zeitschrift für die Gesamte Kopier- und Vervielfaeltigungstechnik*. Bad Homburg, Verlag Internationale Public Relations. Bimonthly. (Monthly, starting January, 1966). DM 48.– per year.

42. *Science et Industries Photographiques*. Paris: Societe de la Revue d'Optiques. Monthly. NF 45.–.

CONFERENCE PROCEEDINGS

43. National Microfilm Association. *Proceedings*. Vernon D. Tate (ed.). Annapolis: 1952 to date. Annual. Prices vary. (Volume 6 never published.)

Although most of the contributors write highly technical papers dealing with government and industry applications, a substantial number of librarians consistently contribute papers and proposals of bibliographic interest. New developments and one-of-a-kind systems built for government use are frequently described in detail, and these often point the way toward the future trends of significance to libraries. For instance, the *Proceedings* document the history of the Xerox Copyflo printer from a one-shot effort aimed at enlarging microfilms for the U.S. Navy to the reproduction of library cards and out-of-print books.

44. *Reprographie: Bericht Über den I. Internationalen Kongress für Reprographie, Köln, 14.–19. Oktober, 1963*. Hrsg. von Othmar Helwich. Darmstadt: Helwich, 1964. 397 pp. DM 156.–.

Provides a worldwide perspective of reprographic research and applications. Of the more than one hundred papers, about one-third deal with reprographic applications in libraries, archives, the social sciences, and the humanities; fortunately, many of these applications are unusual and original and are worth reading. Most of the papers dealing with foreign developments are in German or French. The high cost of this book makes its possession a luxury.

ADMINISTRATION

45. Boone, Samuel M. "Current Administrative Practices in Library Photographic Services." Chapel Hill, N.C.: University of North Carolina, 1964. 81 pp. Unpublished M.A. thesis.

Based upon forty-five responses to a questionnaire sent to libraries having extensive photoduplication facilities, this thesis establishes as fact the suspicions long feared by many, namely, that the field of library photoduplication is virtually lacking in standardization regarding policies, organization, and financing. "Local conditions govern the organization of the photographic service," Boone comments succinctly. His thesis also clearly indicates that the desire for standardization in library photocopying may be misdirected, for the wide variations merely reflect the distinct institutional differences in teaching, library holdings, school regulations, and the like. While standardization of administrative practices may elude us forever, Mr. Boone's survey is instructive; he enumerates the major varieties and one can only hope that no new species will turn up.

46. Brinkley, Cosby. *Directory of Library Photoduplication Services in the United States, Canada, and Mexico*. Chicago: University of Chicago Library Photoduplication Service, 1966.

Contains complete information on types of services available, rates, and addresses to which orders should be sent. Rules for ordering are fairly simple and are explicitly detailed in the preface, which should be thoroughly digested by anyone involved in photocopying.

47. GREEN, NEVILLE. *A Directory of British Photoreproduction Services.* 2d edition. London: Council for Microphotography and Document Reproduction. 1964. 65 pp. $3.00.

216 entries alphabetically arranged by location. Includes private and government libraries and commercial firms in Great Britain, Scotland, and Ireland. In many instances, this *Directory* details the model names and numbers of the equipment available at an installation, information which is useful to the experienced photocopyist.

48. FUSSLER, HERMAN. *Photographic Reproduction for Libraries: A Study of the Administrative Problems.* Chicago: University of Chicago Press, 1942. 208 pp. Out of print.

Although much of its technological information has been superseded, this text still offers the best treatment of administrative problems, some of which have grown even more vexing with the improvement in machines and processes, and the consequent vast increase in copying. Especially recommended is Chapter IV, "The Administrative Integration of the Service with the Institution," in which is discussed the degree of self-support in library microreproduction services. "This seemingly simple point," Fussler wrote in 1942, "is most difficult of solution." A generation later, it is still far from resolved. Chapter V, "The Place of the Photographic Service in the Library Organization," discusses a multitude of modern microreproduction headaches that are still with us: inspection of film returned from interlibrary loan, who shall make estimates, who shall handle the correspondence, the bibliographic control of films, how films shall be acquired, and quality control in the laboratory. Chapter VI, which deals with the servicing and storage of films, is still useful for those desiring to establish microtext reading rooms. Finally, Chapter X treats of problems which, after twenty-five years, remain and will probably still be here twenty-five years hence: personnel standards, and the records and statistics necessary for efficient management.

49. *Photocopies from Abroad: Directory of Photocopying and Microcopying Services.* 3d and rev. edition (F.I.D. Publications, 347). The Hague: International Federation for Documentation [1963]. 28 pp. 5 guilders.

50. SKIPPER, JAMES E. (ed.). *Photoduplication in Libraries* (Library Trends 8:3, January, 1960). Urbana: Graduate School of Library Science, University of Illinois, 1960. 148 pp. $2.00

This is a kind of handbook or guide for those who administer library photoduplication activities. Not a "how to do it" publication, it deals with the organizational and administrative aspects of photoduplication: acquisition and other technical processes, bibliographic control, copyright, micropublication, interlibrary loan, and general policy matters. Owing to rapid technical advances in photoduplication, some of the information presented is dated, but it is still profitable reading for technical service librarians. One of the best articles is Lester K. Born's "History of Microform Activity."

51. DONKER DUYVIS, FRITS. *Document Reproduction Services: Their Efficient Organization and Management.* Paris: UNESCO, 1961. 24 pp. (Also in: *UNESCO Bulletin for Libraries,* 14:241–259, November, 1960.)

Taking the position that the head of a document reproduction service manages a business enterprise whose output cannot be planned in advance, and whose work must be done on short notice, the author enumerates twenty-five management principles aimed at alleviating the inherent inefficiency of all but the largest laboratories. Included are planning work flow, promotion of cooperation with other institutions, full employment, cleanliness, preference for continuous over step processes, strict cost accounting, adherence to standards, and others.

This publication is a fine supplement to Fussler's book (see No. 48); it details many of the management problems which tend to make scholarly reproductions more costly than office copies. Highly recommended for librarians and heads of reproduction services.

52. *Photocopying of Library Materials for Students and Scholars; a Guide to Selection of Methods.* Chicago: American Library Association, 1965. 4 pp. Free.

The best description of this pamphlet, which was prepared by the Copying Methods Section of the American Library Association, is derived from direct quotation:

"This leaflet is intended to help students and scholars in selecting photocopy processes, when they have a choice, or to inform them what they can normally expect from a particular process if they have no choice. It should be understood that there is no single 'best method' for every purpose. Every method has both advantages and disadvantages when compared with the others, and the choice, when choice is possible will depend upon the balancing of these with respect to the original to be copied, size of the original and of the copy, permanence, detail cost, speed, etc."

EQUIPMENT

53. BALLOU, HUBBARD W. *Guide to Microreproduction Equipment.* 3d edition. Annapolis: National Microfilm Association, 1965. 552 pp. $12.50.

Begun in 1959 with support from the Council on Library Resources, this work quickly became the master reference work on microreproduction equipment. In the latest edition almost 300 pieces of equipment are described, illustrated, and priced insofar as information has been made available by the manufacturers. From time to time the publisher issues supplements to the *Guide* and also furnishes current information on equipment in its official journal, *National Micro-News.*

Foreign equipment is listed in the *Guide,* if it is handled by established United States dealers.

Earlier editions should be retained, or if not already held, acquired, for their information on superseded models, many of which are still in active production use in libraries throughout the world, or which might be sought on the second-hand market. Equipment listings appear classified according to function and the book is indexed by manufacturer, trade name, and model designation. If any one book can be called indispensable for planning microreproduction operations, this is it.

54. DAVIDSON, GEORGE H. *1962 Review of Equipment for Microtext.* London: Council for Microphotography and Document Reproduction, 1962. 14/−.

This British counterpart to Ballou's *Guide* lists chiefly British and continental microreproduction equipment. Although this book lacks illustrations, the text is sufficiently discursive (and very well written) to be quite informative. The operating characteristics of most of the listed equipment are analyzed in considerable detail.

55. HAWKEN, WILLIAM R. *Enlarged Prints from Library Microforms* (LTP Publication No. 6). Chicago: American Library Association [1963]. 131 pp. $4.00.

Analyzes the equipment, methods, and operating characteristics of various reader/printers commonly available to libraries for making on-the-spot "blow ups" of selected pages from microforms. Because there has been little significant advance in the design of reader/printers for library use since publication of this guide, both librarians and manufacturers will still find this text useful, the former for its caveats, the latter for its design recommendations (p. 128–131) which have, unfortunately, gone unheeded.

Current enlarging equipment is analyzed in *Library Technology Reports* (see No. 57).

56. HAWKEN, WILLIAM R. *Photocopying from Bound Volumes.* 3 supplements. Chicago: American Library Association, 1964. Nos. 1–2, $2.00 each; No. 3, $5.00.

Evaluations of book-copying equipment produced subsequent to the publication of the original volume. Included are studies of the Docustat copier, several 3M copiers, the Vico-Matic copier, and others. Reports on currently produced copiers are now incorporated into *Library Technology Reports* (see No. 57).

57. *Library Technology Reports;* A Service to Provide Information on Library Systems, Equipment, and Supplies to the Library Profession. William P. Cole (ed.). Chicago: American Library Association, Library Technology Project, 1965 to date.

Kept up to date by supplementary material issued bimonthly; $100/year. Contains sections on photocopying equipment, microforms and equipment, catalog card reproduction, and abstracts of articles.

*58. STEWART, JEAN. *Reading Devices for Micro-Images* (The State of the Library Art, Vol. 5, Pt. 2). New Brunswick: Rutgers, 1960. 205 pp. $5.00.

MICROFILMING

59. *How to Use the Recordak Micro-File Machine, Model MRD-2.* New York: Recordak Corporation, 1961. 26 pp. Free.

60. *The Recordak Micro-File Machine, Model C-1.* New York: Recordak corporation, 1949. 24 pp. Out of print.

Microfilm camera instruction booklets are much like the owners' handbooks found in the glove compartments of new cars: they provide little more than the simplest operating instructions and routine maintenance information. These booklets neither substitute for the serviceman's technical know-how in camera maintenance and repairs nor do they inform the user of the special techniques required for microfilming research materials. They can be of some use for indoctrinating new staff members in loading and unloading film and making actual exposures, but they provide virtually no guidance toward the proper physical handling of research materials under the lens of the camera, or toward the development of proper judgment in achieving correct exposures. The reader is referred to Part 4 of the present work for this information.

61. *Microfilming with Kodagraph Micro-File Equipment and Materials* (Kodak Publication P-1). Rochester: Eastman Kodak Company, 1952. 60 pp. Out of print.

A very helpful booklet for the laboratory technician who wishes to go beyond the simplified information normally found in the camera instruction booklets supplied with Recordak and/or Kodagraph cameras. Although the technical data on film characteristics are now obsolete, the fundamental information on camera technique, exposure, and permanence has not changed. As it is in this area of fundamental information where a substantial folklore and mythology have grown up concerning the capabilities of microreproduction systems, this booklet is a valuable source of factual information and an excellent introduction to the next cited work which is more detailed and more up to date.

62. NELSON, CARL E. *Microfilm Technology: Engineering and Related Fields.* New York: McGraw-Hill, 1965. 372 pp. $16.00.

As Ballou's *Guide* is fundamental for equipment selection, Nelson's *Microfilm Technology* is fundamental for laboratory management in microreproduction centers. This book is the result of over 25 years' commercial and government experience with a wide variety of materials and equipment. It is replete with excellent illustrations and explicit, exact information heretofore available only in laboratory reports or in scattered technical journals. Particularly commendable is the author's exceptional clarity of language which makes for easy comprehension of a subject that has not previously enjoyed this luxury. A 48-page bibliography of engineering applications is supplied with the book as a 4- by 6- inch microfiche. Highly recommended as the book which will become the classical text on microphotography.

63. LA HOOD, CHARLES G. "Production and Uses of Microfilm in the Library of Congress Photoduplication Service," *Special Libraries*, 51:68–71, February, 1960.

Offers an informative description of management practices, a historical outline of the changing techniques in use at the Library of Congress, and one of the earliest descriptions of the Xerox Copyflo method of card reproduction originated by LC.

64. LA HOOD, CHARLES G. "The Serial Microfilm Program at the Library of Congress," *Library Resources & Technical Services*, 10:241–248, Spring, 1966.

This paper deals with the microfilming of the world's most transient printed resource: newspapers. Probably no library faces a larger newspaper preservation task than the Library of Congress. Its backlog of papers to be filmed was estimated at 75,000,000 pages when the Library began its preservation program. One special problem inherent in existing microfilm technology is well elucidated by Mr. La Hood; this is the inability, and inadvisability, of microfilming a given newspaper title until the file is complete:

"The problem I mention here, inherent to the preparation of high quality microfilm, is that of supplying to the microfilming facility a file *ideally in perfect arrangement, and above all as complete as possible.*"

With newspaper material, the author indicates that "the cost of preparing a microfilm negative and service positive, is approximately the same as the cost of binding a three-inch-thick volume!" The author does not extend this price comparison to non-newspaper material, and wisely so, for with presently available equipment and methods, only micropublishing or cooperative enterprise can produce microfilms of ordinary serials at less cost than binding. An excellent summary of the historical and organizational aspects of preservation microfilming for newspapers; one wishes, however, for more specific information on the filming of non-newspaper materials.

65. SALMON, STEPHEN R. *Specifications for Library of Congress Microfilming*. Washington, D.C.: Library of Congress, 1964. 21 pp. $.25.

Publication of this document originated with the Library of Congress' need to furnish to its suppliers a statement of specifications to be met by films purchased for the Library's permanent master collections. Prefilming bibliographic and physical preparation of the original is described in the first chapter. Following this are instructions for bibliographic arrangement of films, the making of proper targets, selection of image placement and reduction, and information on film stock, actual filming techniques, and processing specifications. Additional brief chapters cover inspection, positive copies, and storage. As a product of one of the nation's most experienced and respected library microreproduction laboratories, these specifications deserve the closest observance. Recommended reading for camera operators as well as librarians and laboratory managers.

66. SCOTT, PETER R. *Microfilm Norms*. Library Standards for Microfilm Committee, Copying Methods Section, Resources & Technical Services Division, American Library Association. Chicago, 1966. (In preparation.)

Microfilm Norms is an attempt to develop recommended microfilm practices *de novo*, and thereby to encourage equipment manufacturers, producers, and users to evolve a rational microfilm system for library materials. Fixed reduction ratios—common in industrial and military applications—are a definite novelty in library microfilming and the most distinctive feature of this publication. *Microfilm Norms* recommends either 14X or 20X, making exception only for newspapers.

To carry out its recommendations regarding hypo tests, frame numbering, and reading resolution values, the reader will have to go to appropriate parts of the present *Manual* or to Nelson's *Microfilm Technology*, since *Microfilm Norms* provides no instructions on camera or laboratory technique. Whether library materials will be found tractable enough for the apodictic approach of the *Norms* or whether the more pragmatic Library of Congress *Specifications* will prove more popular, will be decided by their users.

67. PRITSKER, ALAN B. and SADLER, J. WILLIAM. "An Evaluation of Microfilm as a Method of Book Storage," *College & Research Libraries*, 18:290–296. July, 1957.

CLAPP, VERNER W. and JORDAN, ROBERT T. "Re-evaluation of Microfilm as a Method of Book Storage," *College & Research Libraries*, 24:5–15. January, 1963.

FORBES & WAITE, INC. *Costs and Material Handling Problems in Miniaturizing 100,000 Volumes of Bound Periodicals*. Prepared for the Council on Library Resources. Lexington, Mass., 1961. 30 pp. Processed.

Elimination of binding and minimal storage space have often been claimed as two major, cost-saving features of microfilm systems. Yet, since no large-scale, total microfilm conversions have been made, the discussion in all three of these citations is largely theoretical and inconclusive. In comparing costs, Clapp and Jordan indicate that microfilming may be cheaper than construction of storage space "if suitable conditions exist," and "in the right combination of circumstances," when one considers cost *alone*. The Forbes & Waite study indicates that, contrary to Pritsker and Sadler's views, it is not necessary to give up film inspection, to use second-rate camera equipment, or to use the negative as a service copy, *if* a cooperative project could be organized. Clapp and Jordan cite the difficulty of organizing and managing cooperative projects, and conclude by suggesting that aspects of library work other than storage may be of greater importance: acquisition, preservation, binding, and service. Though they hoped that once the storage aspect had been disposed of, these other problems could be given "their rightful attention," very little study has been given to them.

68. VERRY, H. REX. *Microcopying Methods.* London: Focal Press, 1963. 175 pp. $10.50.

*69. HAWKINS, REGINALD. *Production of Microforms* (The State of the Library Art, Vol. 5, Pt. 1.) New Brunswick: Rutgers, 1960. 208 pp. $5.00.

*70. LEWIS, CHESTER M. and OFFENHAUSER, WILLIAM H. *Microrecording: Industrial and Library Applications.* New York: Interscience, 1956. 456 pp. Out of print.

*71. LUTHER, FREDERIC. *Microfilm: A History, 1839–1900.* Annapolis: National Microfilm Association, 1959. 195 pp. $7.50.

72. Microcopy Resolution Test Chart: Standard Sample 1010. Washington, D.C.: National Bureau of Standards, 1964. $.60 each; minimum order $3.00 plus $2.00 handling.

Indispensable for maintaining quality control throughout the entire microreproduction process. Each set of charts is accompanied by full instructions for use and for evaluation of the resulting patterns. Charts issued prior to December 1, 1964, differ slightly from the latest charts, but no significant measurement differences will result when changing from the old to the new; if older charts are in good physical condition, they may still be used.

SOME USER VIEWPOINTS

73. CLAPP, VERNER W., HENSHAW, FRANCIS H., and HOLMES, DONALD C. "Are Your Microfilms Deteriorating Acceptably?" *Library Journal,* 80:589–95, March 15, 1955.

The discovery at the Library of Congress of films so irreversibly deteriorated that they were total losses stimulated the Library to investigate new, incoming films. The results portended disaster: inadequately processed purchased films ranged from 18 percent of receipts from two commercial suppliers, to 55 percent of one shipment from a noncommercial supplier. The writers correctly conclude that ". . . the most serious film defects—non-safety film base creating a fire hazard, excessive residual hypo causing eventual deterioration of the entire reel, inadequate definition resulting in poor readability, insufficient fixation resulting eventually in partial image loss—can only be detected by means of expensive tests or

after a period of time when the damage may have become irreparable."

This dictum is one which must be comprehended and firmly believed by every person concerned with the production of film. As long as we continue to produce microfilms by conventional silver processes, this article will be as significant as if written yesterday. Contains substantial technical detail and references to chemical tests and standards.

74. CUMMINGS, LAURENCE A. "Pitfalls of Photocopy Research," *Bulletin of the New York Public Library,* 65:97–101, February, 1961.

A revealing account of how the photographer's failures have inconvenienced and frustrated the scholar who consults a photocopy because he cannot gain access to the original. Mr. Cummings obviously has had much experience with blurred copies, copies of unordered material, no copies of wanted material, lack of information on film reduction, and the results of defective equipment or technique. He seems to have borne his incubus with much patience and he rightly concludes that "the camera lens cannot replace the scholar's eye." Administrators could profitably require every employee to read and know thoroughly this excellent example of feedback from a highly qualified user. Written in witty, polished prose.

75. HALE, RICHARD W. "The User Looks at Academic Microreproduction," National Microfilm Association, *Proceedings* [8]:241–49, 1959.

The author, who is the Archivist of Massachusetts and editor of the *Guide to Photocopied Historical Materials in the United States and Canada* (Ithaca: Cornell, 1961), having been the victim of much badly made microfilm, sets out specific "horrible examples" of practices to be avoided. These center mostly on the need for adequate targeting and the preference for the reproduction of complete bibliographic units over selected miscellaneous parts. A plea for building in, at the time of filming, the information necessary for the archivist or librarian to administer the film on behalf of the scholarly user, i.e., the elementary identifying information so sadly lacking on many films: author, title, place and date of filming, name of institution, owner of the material, restrictions, reduction, frame numbers, and the like. One is reminded of Vernon Tate's excellent advice: "The time to plan to use microfilm is before it has been made."

76. JACKSON, WILLIAM A. "Some Limitations of Microfilm," *The Papers of the Bibliographical Society of America,* 35:281–88, 1941.

To the librarian who doubts the future of the book, to the document reproduction expert who may be overconfident of modern technical achievements, this article is commended. Concerning films, Jackson says, "Really all I have to say is that microfilms are microfilms and not the original book or manuscript. . . ." He fulminates, quite justifiably, against the photographer who neglects to target his films: "A book lacking its title, . . . is merely an interesting problem, but a microfilm of a manuscript or a book without any mark of identification, which could have been so easily supplied, is an abomination." Admitting his own prejudices, the author shows with conviction and vigor how indispensable is consultation of the original for the solution of genuine bibliographical problems; indeed, the original is characterized by a sanctity which Jackson felt was endangered by careless photographers:

". . . the rapidity with which our microfilm equipment now can reproduce an entire book carries with it a great responsibility and even terror. . . . By cajolery, threats, exhortation, and constant vigilance the librarians of today must guard their treasures against this danger which lurks in the distant corner where, amid his livid lights and chemical smells, the photographer has his lair." The "lair" and the chemical smells may be on the way out, but the careless machine operator is still a natural hazard which every librarian and laboratory supervisor must extirpate to prevent catastrophe.

77. MCDONALD, JERRY. "The Case Against Microfilming," *American Archivist,* 20:345–56, October, 1957.

78. WEIS, MARGARET M. "The Case *for* Microfilming," *American Archivist,* 22:15–24, January, 1959.

Miss McDonald recounts painful tales of woe originating from badly planned and poorly executed microfilm projects, mostly in business and industry. Miss Weis's rejoinder assails bad human judgment, mismanagement, and inadequate supervision for most of the dissatisfactions analyzed in Miss McDonald's article. Both women were employed in records management positions at the time these articles were written, and both write with vehemence and the authority of experience. An excellent pair of readings for the laboratory supervisor, but both should be read concurrently.

79. NOLL, DANIEL F. "From the Microphotographer's Mail," *American Archivist,* 11:238–45, July 1948; 11:316–24, October, 1948; 12:36–41, January, 1949.

To the modern, sophisticated reader this series of articles may appear too naïve; certainly much of the material is dated. But to the novice, be he librarian or laboratory trainee, there can be no better kind of beginning reading. Articles are in the form of questions and answers which cover a wide range of subjects: legal status of microfilm, terminology, technical aspects of microphotography, and so forth. A measure of the series' relative naïvete may be observed by a reader's question: "Where should retakes be spliced, at the beginning or the end of the microfilm reel?" Mr. Noll gives the definitive reply which one hopes will always be observed: "The ideal location for a retake is in the same position that the original occupied in the paper file . . . To splice a retake at any other location . . . would be unthinkable." It is regrettable that only three articles could be issued in this series.

MATERIALS

80. *Recordak Films for Microfilming* (Recordak Pamphlet P-105). New York: Recordak Corporation, 1964. 16 pp. Free.

A handbook for the laboratory manager or advanced amateur. Contains full technical specifications and developing instructions for all currently available Recordak camera and print films except the new AHU film, type 5459. Includes time-temperature charts, sensitometric and spectral response curves, and spooling, packaging, and ordering information.

Note: Technical data on AHU film, type 5459, is available in a supplementary pamphlet, P-107, also available without charge.

81. *Kodak Photographic Papers* (Kodak Publication G-1). 7th ed. Rochester, New York: Eastman Kodak Company, 1960. 32 pp. $.75.

CATALOG CARD REPRODUCTION

82. *Catalog Card Reproduction* (LTP Publication No. 9). Chicago: American Library Association, 1965. 81 pp. $8.50.

This book was written to assist librarians in selecting and costing appropriate methods for card reproduction; it is not a handbook for machine or press operators. Prepared by George Fry & Associates, the text gives most of its attention to the offset method of card reproduction and will prove of greatest value to those libraries using or planning offset operations. Charts are provided to assist in the development of cost figures and excellent illustrations of representative equipment are supplied.

Current card reproduction equipment and methods are analyzed in *Library Technology Reports* (see no. 57).

83. VEANER, ALLEN B. "High Speed Reproduction of Library Cards Through Microreproduction Techniques," National Microfilm Association *Proceedings*, 13:159–163 (1964).

84. VEANER, ALLEN B. and FRASER, JOHN. "Library Card Reproduction by Xerox Copyflo," *Library Resources & Technical Services* 8:279–284, Summer, 1964.

Two articles detailing the problems and techniques of the Xerox Copyflo method for library card reproduction, now used in a number of large research libraries. The *Library Resources & Technical Services* article outlines some of the bibliographic and administrative aspects; the National Microfilm Association paper is entirely technical.

STORAGE AND PRESERVATION OF MICROFILMS

85. *Storage and Preservation of Microfilms* (Kodak Pamphlet P-108). New York: Recordak Corporation, 1965. 10 pp. Free.

This revision of an earlier pamphlet takes into account the recently discovered microfilm blemishes, and outlines recommended methods for their prevention. It starts with well-written definitions of technical terms and distinguishes carefully between commercial and archival permanence. The pamphlet goes on to detail microfilm's response to and protection from a wide variety of hazards: fire, water, high and low humidity, fungus, microfilm blemishes or spots, and atmospheric contaminants. Detailed explanations justify the need for careful processing, particularly complete fixing and thorough washing, adequate squeegeeing and drying, and the avoidance of hypo eliminators. Further details are furnished on Recordak's gold protective treatment—a method of inhibiting the formation of blemishes—lacquering, underground storage, and protection from nuclear explosions. For those who wish to seal microfilms in time capsules or cornerstones, instructions are supplied and suitable containers offered by Recordak. A final section outlines recommended handling, filing, and inspection techniques. A bibliography thoroughly documents all recommendations. This pamphlet is the best single source of information on a most important topic; it obsoletes two earlier Kodak pamphlets: *Storage of Microfilms* (1956) and Pamphlet F-11, *Storage of Microfilm, Sheet Films, and Prints*.

86. McCAMY, CALVIN S. *Inspection of Processed Photographic Record Film for Aging Blemishes* (National Bureau of Standards Miscellaneous Handbook, 96). Washington, D.C., 1964. 11 pp. $.25.

Essential to libraries creating or maintaining master microfilms. The author describes in complete detail a program for periodic film inspection to aid detection of blemishes. Inspection techniques are illustrated by photographs, and the blemishes themselves are shown as colored photomicrographs. Full details are given for constructing inspection apparatus and for reporting defects to the Bureau.

87. McCAMY, CALVIN S. *Summary of Current Research on Archival Microfilm* (National Bureau of Standards Technical Note, 261). Washington, D.C., 1965. 24 pp. $.25.

Summarizes known factors in formation of "microfilm measles" and analyzes the effects of cardboard storage cartons, atmospheric contaminants, high density, scratches (which can trigger blemishes), and splices. The report recommends extreme caution in the processing, storage and handling of archival microfilm, regular inspections, and the making of multiple positive copies to be stored in separate places. It would appear essential for all libraries to see that the recommendations of this report are stringently adhered to in the preparation of archival master films reported to the National Register of Microform Masters.

COPYING WITH HAND CAMERAS

88. *Copying* (Kodak Publication M-1) 6th ed. Rochester, New York: Eastman Kodak Company, 1958. 48 pp. $.75.

Except for setting up bound volumes for copying, almost everything the advanced amateur needs to know is in this booklet: films, lighting, exposure, the use of filters and supplementary lenses, and detailed processing instructions. A word of caution is necessary: this booklet is definitely for the advanced amateur who knows his equipment and methods and is accustomed to film processing. The tyro must first learn the fundamentals of photography if he is to benefit from its advice.

89. SIMMONS, ROBERT. *Close-up Photography and Copying.* Philadelphia: Chilton, 1961. 128 pp. $1.95.

This is the best modern guide for those scholars who are experienced amateur photographers. The author describes very explicitly the distinct materials and techniques needed for copying documents and illustrations—a necessary distinction even for the advanced amateur, who usually has little experience in copying. The text is extensively illustrated with examples of different subjects, and the recommended lighting and camera setups for each. Of special value are the specific discussions of techniques dealing with copying photolithographs, charcoal sketches, etchings, textile patterns, paintings, and line copy. Microfilming with 35 mm. hand cameras is also explained in some detail.

FOREIGN LANGUAGE REFERENCES

90. FRANK, OTTO. *Die Mikrofilmtechnik* (Handbuch der Reprographie, 2; F.I.D. Publication, 321; A.W.V. Schriftenreihe, 241). Stuttgart, Dorotheen Verlag, 1961. 336 pp. DM 32.–.

This work includes virtually no library applica-

tions and is mentioned here only as an example of one of the modern European works on the subject. Profusely illustrated; brief bibliography.

91. POINDRON, PAUL. *Manuel Pratique de Reproduction Documentaire et de Selection* (F.I.D. Publication, 353). Paris: Gauthier-Villars, 1964. 341 pp. NF 46.–.

Only the first half of this book deals with document reproduction; the second half is devoted to a variety of data processing, documentation, and information retrieval techniques. Of special value to the reader interested in reprography are chapters 7, 15–17, which handle, respectively, microfilming, electrophotography, process selection, and the reproduction unit's place in the library. The chapter on process selection contains an excellent survey of citations dealing with the bibliographic aspects of reprography, including references to publications of the International Standards Organization (ISO). Poindron's *Manuel* is the best of its kind not in English; it is worth noting that his book is specifically addressed to the librarian and documentalist rather than the photographic technician.

BIBLIOGRAPHIC CONTROL

92. SIMONTON, WESLEY. "The Bibliographical Control of Microforms," *Library Resources & Technical Services,* 6:29–40, Winter, 1962.

Prepared at the request of the Association of Research Libraries, Professor Simonton's report profoundly influenced the recording and reporting of microtexts by urging that they be treated bibliographically just as if one were working with originals. His recommendations culminated in the establishment of the National Register of Microform Masters. An article essential for those who administer microfilm preservation projects.

93. [BORN, LESTER K.]. "Planning for Scholarly Photocopying," *PMLA,* 79:77–90, September, 1964. No. 4, Pt. 2.

The intention of this article is to arouse for constructive purposes the ire and wrath of all who make and use scholarly photocopies. With little mercy, Mr. Born flays scholars, bibliographers, technicians, foundations, and publishers for their failures, errors, and follies: "Like the comic hero, photocopying has ridden madly off in all directions; if dissipation of resources is not to continue it must now be systematically ordered." Or: "Like war, photocopying is too important a matter to be left to technical experts." These examples typify the highly critical attack Mr. Born makes upon the plethora of mismanaged, wasteful, and duplicative photocopying projects which have competed for academic support. Highly recommended as the best diagnosis of the ills afflicting scholarly photocopying; concludes with remedial recommendations aimed at scholars, librarians, and the micropublication industry.

94. APPLEBAUM, EDMOND L. "Implications of the National Register of Microform Masters as Part of a National Preservation Program," *Library Resources & Technical Services*, 9:489–94, Fall, 1965.

95. BIBLIOTHEQUE NATIONALE. "Bibliographical Control of Microcopies," Paris. *UNESCO Bulletin for Libraries*, 19:139–60, 172, May–June, 1965.

This article is somewhat different from the Simonton article of practically the same name; it is based upon an international survey whose purpose was to determine how well existing, "published" microcopies were reported in national and trade bibliographies, and what works needed to be republished or micropublished for the needs of developing libraries. The authors recommend the creation of national registers of microforms in each country, and, in general, deplore the lack of planning and poor communications detailed in the Born article (see No. 93).

COPYRIGHT

96. GOSNELL, CHARLES F. "The Copying Grabbag; Observations on the New Copyright Legislation," *ALA Bulletin*, 60:46–55, January, 1966.

An excellent, short review and summary of the many-faceted copyright problem with particular emphasis on the library viewpoint. Outlines the variety of arguments used by the proponents of conflicting interests and carefully analyzes the knotty issues that have arisen with the improvement in technology since 1909. A very good introduction to the more technical works listed below. (See also Appendix C in this *Manual*, where a summary of copyright information has been prepared by Mr. Gosnell.)

97. HATTERY, LOWELL H. and BUSH, GEORGE P. (eds.). *Reprography and Copyright Law*. Washington, D.C.: American Institute of Biological Sciences, 1964. 204 pp. $4.50 (paper: $3.00).

Presents the formal papers given at a copyright symposium organized in 1963 by American University to air the views of authors, publishers, librarians, educators, the photocopy industry, scientists, documentalists, abstracting services, and copyright lawyers. Includes papers by Luther Evans, Eugene Garfield, W. R. Hawken, L. B. Heilprin, Foster Mohrhardt, and Ralph Shaw. This book plus the six parts of *Copyright Law Revision* (see No. 98) constitutes the basic reference materials on the copyright aspects of library reprography.

98. *Photocopying and the Law* [London]: The Society of Authors, The Publishers Association [1965]. 8 pp. 1/–.

Sets out guidelines for teachers and librarians (of nonprofit libraries) in Great Britain, concerning "fair use" of copyrighted material "in the absence of any legal definition of the extent to which copyright works may be used without infringement." This pamphlet provides only a rule of thumb—not a legal statement—which indicates that its sponsors would not regard as "un-fair" the copying of up to 10 percent of a copyrighted work, in accordance with an explicit formula involving the number of words and other factors. Multiple copying is expressly prohibited by the agreement.

99. *Copyright Law Revision*. Parts 1–6. Washington, D.C.: 1961–65. $6.20 the set. (For sale by the Superintendent of Documents; class no. Y4.J89/1:C79/2/Pt.1–6.)

Contains preliminary draft of the revised copyright law, reports from the Register of Copyrights, and comments, discussions, and testimony brought before the Judiciary Committee of the House of Representatives. The views of authors, lawyers, librarians, publishers, and other interested parties, are presented in more than 2200 pages of text.

BIBLIOGRAPHY

100. BIJMANS, B. P. E. M. *Bibliography on Microfiche* (Publications on the Microfiche, 4).

Delft: Microfiche Foundation [1965]. 15 pp. $.50.

Classified bibliography citing over 200 articles from 1907 to 1965. Refers to citations on processing and equipment, standardization, applications for libraries, documentation centers, archives, and individual researchers. Author index.

101. KIERKSY, LORETTA J.
See No. 24.

102. VEANER, ALLEN B. "The Literature of Document Reproduction," *The Literature of Library Technical Services,* pp. 24–35. (University of Illinois Graduate School of Library Science, Occasional Papers, 58, Revised April, 1963.) [Urbana]: 1963. 46 pp. $1.00.

Cites many works which are outside the scope of the present bibliography, including histories of photography, books of general reprographic interest (but having no library applications), guides for the procurement of commercial and industrial photographic equipment, and older books now considered obsolete or mainly of historical interest.

GLOSSARY

acetate film (acetate base). Film which has a base of cellulose acetate or triacetate rather than the highly inflammable cellulose nitrate. Commonly called "safety film." See also *cellulose acetate and cellulose triacetate*.

A.C.R.P.P. Association Pour la Conservation et la Reproduction Photographique de la Presse. A department of the Bibliotheque Nationale in Paris, France, whose principal activity is the preservation of newspapers on microfilm.

activator. In variant forms of the silver halide process, an alkaline solution used to energize the developing agent contained in the sensitized coating.

additive direct-positive process. A direct-positive process—a process not requiring the production of a negative intermediate—which acts in such a way that the longer the length of time the sensitized materials are exposed, the darker the resultant image will be.

add-on capability. With sheet microforms, the ability to add further micro-images to the sheet.

adherography. A trade name of the 3M Company for a thermographic duplicating process.

aging blemish. See *blemish*.

ambient light. Surrounding light; general room illumination or light level.

amines. Derivatives of ammonia which, when combined with diazonium salts by the action of a coupler, produce substances which are strongly colored.

ammonia process. Two-component diazotype process in which both the diazo and the coupler are on the base, and development is achieved by neutralizing the acidic stabilizers with vapors derived from evaporating aqua ammonia.

Angstrom unit. A standard of measurement in speaking of wavelengths of light, equal to one ten-millionth of a millimeter. (Abbreviated A. Symbol λ.)

aniline dye. Any dye from aniline—a colorless, poisonous, oily, liquid derivative of benzene. Aniline dyes are used in most colored inks and do not absorb sufficient heat to reproduce by thermographic processes.

aperture. In an optical system, the diameter of that part of the lens through which light passes.

aperture card. A card, usually of a size used in electric accounting machines, with a rectangular hole or holes specifically designed to hold a frame or frames of microfilm.

archival permanence. Lasting or intended to last indefinitely without change. See also *permanence*.

ASA. American Standards Association. The official United States standards organization.

autofocus. See *automatic focus*.

automatic focus. A mechanical device on certain enlargers and cameras which keeps the image in focus as the lens-to-subject or lens-to-easel distance is changed.

autopositive printing. A term applied to photographic materials which, when processed, yield a positive image when exposed to a positive and a negative image when exposed to a negative.

autopositive process. A variant form of the silver halide process which yields a positive copy from a positive intermediate.

autopositive stabilization. A term used to refer to materials which are autopositive in their behavior but can be processed by stabilization.

azo dye. Dye formed by the reaction of diazonium salts and coupler, as in the diazo process.

The term *azo* stems from the French word "azote" meaning nitrogen. See also *diazo*.

backing materials. Rigid or semi-rigid sheets (e.g., cardboard, plastic, metal) used in contact reflex copying to provide a smooth, firm surface for contact between the sensitized material and the document being copied. Rigid and semi-rigid backing materials are also referred to as *non-conformable* or *conformable*.

base exposure. The exposure setting required for a typical black-on-white document of average quality. Variations in exposure for atypical documents are expressed in percentage or time intervals greater or less than the base exposure.

base, film. A transparent plastic material, usually of cellulose acetate, on which a light-sensitive emulsion is coated or on which an image can be formed by transfer processes (e.g., gelatin-dye-transfer, diffusion-transfer-reversal, and others).

Berceau angle bookholder. A type of bookholder developed at the Bibliotheque Nationale in Paris for holding books which cannot be opened flat.

blanket roller. In offset printing, a roller covered with a sheet of rubber which receives an ink image from the master and transfers it to a sheet of copy paper.

bleaching bath. In reversal processing, a bath used to remove the primary negative image.

blemish. A microscopic spot usually reddish or yellowish in color ranging in size from 15 to 150 microns in diameter; sometimes termed aging blemish or microscopic spot. Examples have recently been discovered in apparent random incidence in a relatively small number of negative microfilm in storage for periods of from 2 to 20 years. The cause and nature of the spots are not yet completely understood and they are under active study.

blueprint. A print made by a contact process employing light-sensitive iron salts which yields copies having white lines against a blue background.

body height. In typography, the dimension of the printing surface of a piece of type from front edge to back edge.

bookholder (book cradle). In optical copying, devices of various designs used to hold the facing pages of an open bound volume in a level or near-level plane.

book position angle. The angle to which a book must be opened to be copied by the contact-reflex method on flatbed printers.

Book Printing Pillow. Trademark of the Nord Photocopy and Business Equipment Corp. for a plastic envelope partially filled with air used as a conformable backing material to aid in achieving contact. See also *backing materials*.

butt splicing. A method of splicing two lengths of film or paper together without overlap. Butt splices can be made by using a tape overlay or by fusing the materials by the application of heat. See also *splice*.

cadmium sulfide exposure meter. See *exposure meter, cadmium sulfide*.

calendered stock. Paper stock which has been made smooth and glazed by running it between rollers which apply both heat and pressure.

camera, cataloger's. Camera and auxiliary equipment used to produce enlarged copies from reduced-size entries in book-form catalogs. May also be used to record catalog cards at full size.

camera, Dexigraph. The trade name of a prism-type camera manufactured by Remington Rand, Inc.

camera, flow. A camera in which loose-sheet documents are transported on a series of belts past a lens which records the document on roll film moving synchronously with the rotating drum at a speed equal to the reduction ratio.

camera, Photostat. The trade name of a prism-type camera manufactured by the Photostat Corporation.

camera, photostat-type. Cameras similar in function to those manufactured by the Photostat Corporation and which produce a similar type of copy.

camera, planetary. A type of microfilm camera in which, during exposure, the film is held stationary in a horizontal plane parallel to the subject being copied.

camera, press. A type of hand-held view camera equipped with a range finder as well as a ground-glass screen which is widely used in photojournalism.

camera, prism. A camera equipped with a prism over the lens which reverses the image so that a right-reading instead of a reverse-reading image can be formed directly on the surface of the sensitized material used.

camera-recorder. A device used for the production of Photochromic Micro-Images (q.v.) in which high-reduction microforms are produced from a microfilm intermediate instead of from an original.

camera, Rectigraph. The trade name of a prism-type camera manufactured by the Xerox Corporation, Haloid Photo Division.

camera, rotary. A camera in which loose-sheet documents are transported on the surface of a rotary drum past a lens which records the document on roll film moving synchronously with the rotating drum at a speed equal to the reduction ratio.

camera, SLR (single-lens reflex camera). A camera equipped with a mirror and prisms with which it is possible to view the subject being copied through the lens of the camera rather than through a separate viewfinder.

camera speed materials. Sensitized materials which are high enough in speed to use for recording images through a lens.

camera, step-and-repeat. A microfilm camera used for making microfiches which records images in a series of rows either on single sheets of film or on large rolls of film on which a succession of microfiches can be made.

camera, TLR (twin-lens reflex camera). A camera equipped with two lenses, one for viewing and focusing the subject to be copied and the other for forming the image on the sensitized material.

camera, view. A type of camera equipped with a ground-glass screen equivalent in size to the film used and having one or more movements or swings for controlling the position of the lens and film plane.

carrier. In xerography, the substance in the developer which conveys the toner and gives the toner an electrical charge opposite to that of the latent image, but does not itself become a part of the image. In thermographic copying, a plastic sheet covered with a silk screen in which the original and sensitized material are placed before they are passed through the machine.

cascade development. In xerography, a method of developing an electrostatic latent image in which the toner and carrier particles are made to slide or to cascade back and forth over the surface of the selenium plate.

cataloger's camera. See *camera, cataloger's.*

cellulose acetate and cellulose triacetate. Transparent plastic materials widely used for film bases and for protective layers for films. See also *acetate film.*

cellulose nitrate. A transparent plastic which was once used almost universally as a film base. Because of its inflammability it has largely been replaced by cellulose acetate as a film base.

characteristic curve (sensitometric curve, H&D curve). A graph relating increases in exposure to increases in density in a developed photographic image.

color-blind. A term used to describe the color sensitivity of simple silver-halide emulsions which are sensitive to blue light only.

color-coded copies. Copies made on paper stocks having different tints.

color proofing. The making of a set of transparent copies, each of a different color, which can be superimposed to check color balance.

color sensitivity. The degree of response of light-sensitive materials to colored light of various wavelengths in the visible portion of the spectrum.

conformable backing materials. See *backing materials.*

contact copying. A method of copying in which a sheet of suitable sensitized material is held in firm and even contact against the surface of the document being copied.

contact copying, direct method of. A method of contact copying in which the subject being copied is placed against a sheet of sensitized material and held in contact with it while light or heat is passed through the subject to form a latent image on the sensitized material.

contact copying, reflex method of. A method of contact copying in which the subject being copied is placed against a sheet of sensitized material and held in contact with it while light or heat is passed through the sensitized material to the surface of the subject where it is reflected back to the sensitized coating.

contact paper. Sensitized paper, generally low in speed, used for making prints by contact methods.

contact print. A print made by the contact or contact-reflex method.

contact printing frame. A rectangular frame, similar in appearance to a picture frame, having a sheet of glass and a hinged, spring-loaded platen which holds the original and sensitized material in firm contact.

contact speed—darkroom materials. Photographic materials which are too sensitive to be handled under room light but which are too slow for projection printing.

contact speed—room-light materials. Photographic materials which are slow enough to be handled under conditions of ordinary room light for a reasonable period of time without effect from ambient light.

continuous printer. See *printer, continuous.*

continuous processor. A device which, by means of rollers, transports roll microfilm through tanks containing the processing solutions and through a drying cabinet.

continuous-tone copy. A copy exhibiting, in whole or part, an unbroken sequence of gradation in tone.

contrast. Differences in tonal values. Where the degree of difference is slight, contrast is said to be low. Where the degree of difference is marked, contrast is said to be high.

contrast, controllable. A condition in which the contrast of a given sensitized material can be altered by changes in exposure and processing.

contrast grades. Differences in the inherent contrast of particular silver halide coatings ranging from low to high.

contrast, inherent. A condition in which the contrast of a given sensitized material is fixed in manufacturing and generally cannot be significantly altered by changes in exposure and processing.

contrast, relative. The relationship between the tonal gradation of the subject being copied and the tonal gradation of the copy.

contrast, visual. The apparent difference between areas of different tonality (e.g., background and image areas) as seen by the eye.

convenience copies. Copies made to meet a temporary need and for which the primary requirement is utility rather than quality or permanence.

copyboard. A flat surface which may be of wood, metal, or glass on which documents are placed for reproduction by optical means.

Copy-Chrome process. Trade name of Copymation, Inc., for a process employing photochromic substances.

Copyflo. Trade mark of the Xerox Corporation for a line of xerographic printing devices and materials.

copyholder. Any device used to hold material in position for copying. Copyholders include spring-loaded metal arms, bookholders of various types, or vacuum frames.

corona discharge. A term applied to a type of high voltage electrical charge given to photoconductive materials to sensitize them to the action of light.

coupler. A chemical compound which combines unexposed diazonium salts with phenols or amines to produce a strongly colored visible dye.

coverage. In contact copying, positioning the volume being copied on the copier so that the entire text area is on the exposure surface where light can reach it.

creep. In a newly opened volume or unfolded sheet, the slight inward movement caused by the pull of the binding or the centerfold.

definition. Sharpness or clarity of an image. See *resolving power*.

densitometer. An instrument used to measure the opacity of images on transparent supports or the reflectance of images on opaque supports.

density. The light-absorbing quality or opacity of an image.

density, background. In a copy of a document, the degree of opacity or light absorption of the non-text areas.

density, line. In either an original document or a copy of a document, the degree of opacity or light absorption of the lines which make up the image or the text.

density, maximum. The highest degree of opacity or light absorption that can be produced with any given type of sensitized material. Abbreviated D-max.

depth of field. The distance between the points nearest and farthest from the camera which are acceptably sharp, at a given lens setting.

depth of focus. The allowable tolerance in lens-to-film distance within which an acceptably sharp image of the subject focused upon will still be obtained.

developer. Any of a variety of substances in dry, liquid, or gaseous form used to make visible a latent image.

development. The process whereby a latent image formed on light- or heat-sensitive materials is made visible through the action of chemical or physical agents or both.

Dexigraph camera. See *camera, Dexigraph*.

diameter. A measure of the number of times a given linear dimension of a document is reduced or enlarged when optically copied or projected.

diaphragm. A device such as a perforated plate or an iris, which is used to control the amount of light passing through a lens.

Diaversal. A variant form of DTR in which both the negative and the positive image-forming layers are coated on a single support.

diazo. (diazotype, diazotypy, whiteprinting). A generic term relating to light-sensitive reproduction systems involving diazonium salts.

diazonium compounds (diazonium salts). Light-sensitive compounds which form the basis of the diazo process.

diffused light. Light which either passes through or is reflected from a surface which causes the rays to move in many different directions.

diffusion-transfer-reversal. A term (usually abbreviated DTR) used to refer to a variant form of the silver halide process in which both a positive and a negative copy are formed simultaneously.

DIN. Deutsche Industrie-normen. The official German standards organization.

direct contact copying. See *contact copying, direct method of.*

direct optical copying. See *optical copying, direct.*

direct-positive process. Any process which produces a positive image directly from a positive original (or negative from a negative original) without the use of a negative intermediate.

disprint. In the Imagic process, the latent image formed of condensed oil on the receptor sheet.

distribution copies. Copies of the second or higher generation made from a master copy for the purpose of disseminating the information contained therein. See *generation printing.*

D-max. See *density, maximum.*

double-frame image. An image on 35 mm. perforated film measuring 1 by 1½ inches. Called "double frame" because it is twice the size of the standard motion picture frame which measures 1 by ¾ inches.

double-perforated film. See *perforated film.*

Dry Silver process. A trade name of the 3M Company for a process in which a latent image is formed on silver-sensitized material by the action of light and developed by means of heat.

DTR. Abbreviation for the diffusion-transfer-reversal process.

duplicating. In microphotography, the making of a second copy from a master negative. The making of multiple copies of a document by processes such as mimeography, spirit duplicating, or offset printing.

duplicator. Any of a number of devices used for making duplicates of documents, usually by means of a master as in mimeography, spirit duplicating, or offset duplicating.

dye-based inks. Inks in which the principal colorant is an aniline dye.

easel. A device used in projection printing for holding light-sensitive materials flat during exposure.

effective lens opening. The relationship between the diameter of the opening of the iris diaphragm and the lens-to-film distance.

Eichner process. A trade name of a German firm, Eichner Drycopy GMBH, for a thermographic process employing a heat-sensitive carbon intermediate.

Ektafax. A trade name of the Eastman Kodak Company for a thermographic copying process employing masters from which either single or multiple copies can be made.

Ektalith. A trade name of the Eastman Kodak Company for a silver halide-based copying process used principally for the making of offset plates.

Electrofax. A trade name of the Radio Corporation of America for an electro-photographic process employing zinc oxide as the photoconductor.

electrolysis. The decomposition into ions of a chemical compound in solution by the action of an electrical current passing through the solution.

electrolyte. Any substance which in solution is dissociated into ions and is thus made capable of conducting an electric current.

electrolytic process. A process developed by the 3M Company for making hard copy from microtransparencies in the company's "Filmac" line of reader-printers.

electromagnetic spectrum. The entire spectrum of electromagnetic energy, including light, heat, X-ray, gamma rays, radio waves, etc.

electronic scanning. A method of producing a stencil for mimeography from an existing original which employs a scanner which converts differences in reflectance in the original document to electrical impulses which perforate the stencil.

electrophotography. A generic term used to refer to photographic processes in which electrical energy is used to sensitize certain materials to the action of light or to form a visible image.

electroplating. The deposition of ions on a metal plate in solution by electrolytic action.

electrostatic. Pertaining to a form of electrical energy called static electricity which has the capability of attracting and holding small particles having an opposite charge. Used in connection with photoconductive substances in xerography and the Electrofax process.

electrostatic latent image. The invisible image formed on a charged photoconductive surface by the action of light.

electrostatic processes. Processes employing static electricity.

emulsion. A suspension of silver halides and other substances in gelatin (or, in some instances, collodion). Emulsions may be coated on a variety of supports, the most common of which are film and paper.

emulsion blisters. Tiny bubbles in a film coating caused by chemical action.

enlargement. A copy, usually made by projection printing from a translucent intermediate such as a film negative, which is larger than the intermediate.

enlargement ratio. A numerical expression of the number of times an enlargement is greater, linearly, than the intermediate from which it was made (e.g., 2X, 13.1X, 20X).

enlarger. An optical device used for making prints by projection which are larger than the intermediate from which they are made.

enlarger-printer. An enlarger which is equipped with a processing device for the rapid production of finished prints under room light conditions.

enlarging. Process of producing an image or a copy larger than the intermediate or original from which it is made.

exposure. (a) The act of subjecting sensitized materials to forms of radiant energy, particularly light and heat. (b) An individual image making up part of a group, such as a roll of microfilm having 600 exposures. (c) The duration of the time interval during which radiant energy acts on a sensitized surface. (d) The combination of all factors affecting the action of radiant energy on sensitized surfaces including the intensity of the energy source, the time interval and, in optical copying and projection printing, the lens opening.

exposure latitude. Allowable margin of error within which exposures somewhat shorter or longer than optimum will still yield satisfactory copies.

exposure meter. An instrument used for determining the amount of light falling on or reflected from a subject to be copied.

exposure meter, CdS. An exposure meter in which cadmium sulfide (CdS) is used as the photoconductor.

exposure surface. In flatbed contact printers, the glass or plastic sheet on which the original and sensitized material are placed and through which light is transmitted.

eye-legible copies. Copies which are either the same size as, larger than, or smaller than, the original documents from which they were made, but always legible with the unaided eye.

facsimile. A term used in reference to certain types of electronic systems used for transmitting line or continuous-tone images over long distances and at great speed.

facsimile master. In the adherography process, a photosensitive duplicating master.

facsimile transmission systems. Systems used to convey graphic data (printed matter, drawings, photographs) by means of a scanner which converts differences in reflectance in the document being reproduced into electrical impulses which can be transmitted by wire. At the receiving point, these electrical impulses are reconverted into different light intensities to form a photographically produced reproduction of the original document.

fast. With reference to sensitized materials, having a rapid response to radiant energy.

Federal Microfiche Standards. Standards promulgated by agencies of the Federal government, principally for microfiches of technical reports.

F.I.D. Federation Internationale de Documentation. The International Federation for Documentation, The Hague, Netherlands.

film plane. The plane within a camera on which film is positioned.

film positive. A translucent or transparent film having a positive image.

filter. Any of a number of transparent or translucent glass or plastic devices in the form of sheets which are interposed between the sensitized material used and the light source to prevent light rays of particular wavelengths

from reaching the surface of the sensitized material.

finder light. A light incorporated in certain types of microfilm cameras which projects a beam through the camera lens to the copyboard to show the exact area covered by the lens.

first generation copy. In contact and optical copying, the first copy made directly from an original document, as opposed to 2nd, 3rd, or higher generation copies which are copies made from copies. See *generation printing*.

fixing bath. A solution used in silver halide processing which dissolves out all unexposed and undeveloped silver halides.

flashing. Giving a brief, over-all pre-exposure to a sheet of light-sensitive material. This is sometimes useful for increasing the effective speed of the material or for reducing contrast.

flatbed printer. See *printer, flatbed*.

flow camera. See *camera, flow*.

"f" numbers, "f" stops. The number system used on lenses to indicate the diameter of the lens opening in relation to the focal length of the lens when the lens is focused at infinity.

focal length. The distance between the center of the lens and the film plane when the lens is focused at infinity.

fog. A partial or over-all gray tone on a print or film caused by accidental exposure to light, by changes in the emulsion of photographic materials which have been stored too long, or from an imbalance of chemicals in the developing solution.

font. A complete assortment of type in one size and style.

foxed (foxing, fox marks). Small yellow-brown, reddish-brown, or brown spots on paper stock caused by mildew or bacterial agents.

frame. In microphotography, that area of the

film on which light can fall during each single exposure.

frost imaging. A term applied to a variant form of xerography in which image formation is accomplished by a change in the physical characteristics of a thermoplastic layer.

gelatin-dye-transfer process. A term used to refer to the Verifax, Readyprint, and Ektalith processes developed by the Eastman Kodak Company, in which photographically produced dye images are physically transferred from a light-sensitive matrix to a receiving sheet.

generation printing. The printing of copies from copies, e.g., a positive microfilm made from a negative microfilm would be of the second generation. A duplicate negative film or hard copy made from the positive film would be of the third generation.

graded silver halide materials. Silver halide coatings on paper which can be obtained in several degrees (grades) of contrast ranging from low to high.

gray scale. A succession of squares or rectangles ranging in tone from white through gray to black in steps having uniform density increments.

gutter. The area between the inner margins of facing book pages.

half-tone illustration. A printed illustration in which tonal gradation is simulated by a pattern of small dots which vary in size. See *half-tone screen.*

half-tone screen. Screen placed in the camera between the sensitized material and the lens to produce gradation of tone in a reproduction of a continuous-tone illustration by breaking the illustration into minute dots. See *half-tone illustration.*

halide. Generic term given to salts of the halogen group (chlorine, iodine, bromine, fluorine). The principal halides used with silver in the silver halide process are silver chloride, silver bromide, and silver iodide.

H&D curve. See *characteristic curve.*

hard. With reference to photographic papers, an adjective denoting high contrast.

hard copy. Eye-legible prints enlarged from microforms.

Hectograph process. A British term used to refer to spirit duplicating processes.

helical mount. A mount, usually for a lens, having a spiral thread which provides for in and out movement of the lens for focusing when the lens is rotated.

Herschel Effect. The bleaching effect of red light upon images on silver chloride printing-out papers. The basis of the autopositive process.

hot spots. In a copy, areas of excessive density caused by uneven illumination or reflections from shiny surfaces.

hydrocarbon. Any compound containing only hydrogen and carbon such as benzene. Hydrocarbons are used in liquid development Electrofax processing.

hypo. Originally an abbreviation for sodium hyposulfate but now universally used to refer to sodium thiosulfate, which is the principal chemical agent in most fixing baths, and to the fixing bath itself.

hypo eliminating solutions (hypo clearing solutions, hypo clearing agents). Solutions used after a silver halide image has been fixed which facilitate the removal of hypo in the washing step.

image area. The area on a sheet of sensitized material on which the image appears. With some types of equipment the image area may be considerably smaller than the print size; e.g., an 8½- by 11-inch print having an image area of 7 by 9 inches.

image degradation. The progressive loss in quality which occurs when copies are recopied, especially by processes which weaken or exaggerate characteristics such as resolution or contrast.

Imagic process. A trade name of Imagic Processes, Ltd. (Great Britain), for a thermographic process in which a volatile oil is used to form a latent image which is made visible by the application of a toner powder.

impression roller. In duplicating process equipment, a roller which presses a master against a sheet of copy paper to transfer the image.

indirect method. A method of optical and contact copying for eye-legible copies which requires the formation of an intermediate image.

infrared. An invisible portion of the spectrum just beyond visible red involving heat rays which can be employed for the formation of images in thermographic processes.

intermediate master. A copy made for the purpose of producing additional copies, usually by some other process.

iris diaphragm. A mechanical device used in lenses to control the size of the opening through which light passes. So called because of its functional similarity to the iris of the human eye.

ISO. International Standards Organization. An international organization for standards composed of representatives of the national standards organizations of twenty-seven countries.

jacketed film. A clear acetate sheet containing pockets in which flat strips of either 16 or 35 mm. film can be inserted.

jig. In document copying, a device used to hold two or more uniform-size documents (e.g., catalog cards) in a precise positional relationship and to facilitate the positioning of a series of such groups.

Kalvar process. A trade name of the Kalvar Corporation for a process employing certain diazonium salts which can be exposed by ultra-violet light and developed by heat.

Kodak "Q" System. See "Q" System.

lantern slides. Film positives used in still projectors (as opposed to motion picture projectors) for presenting enlarged images on a screen for instructional purposes.

latent image. The image formed on sensitized materials by the action of light or heat which remains invisible until subjected to some form of physical or chemical development.

LDX. See *long distance xerography.*

leader. Blank film at the beginning and ending of a roll of microfilm which is used for threading a microfilm reader from the supply spool past the lens to a take-up spool.

lens board. In view- and press-type cameras and in enlargers, the wood or metal plate in which the lens is mounted.

lens hood. A cylindrical or boxlike shield placed over a lens to prevent unwanted light from striking the lens surface.

lens-to-film distance. In optical copying, the distance between the center of the lens and the film plane. This distance varies with the lens-to-subject distance. See lens-to-subject distance.

lens-to-subject distance. In optical copying, the distance from the center of the lens to the subject. This distance affects the lens-to-film distance which, in turn, affects the effective lens opening.

light fogging. See *fog.*

light-scattering effects. A term used to refer to a loss of sharpness in copies made by the contact-reflex method which is caused by the dispersion of light rays reflected from the surface of the original being copied.

litho films. Films of high contrast used in the production of lithographic plates for printing.

lithography. (A term derived from the Greek words "lithos" = stone, and "graphein" = to write.) A method of printing employing a flat stone and which is based on the repulsion of grease or oil (inks) and water. Today applied to any printing process employing the oil-water repulsion principle. Modern "lithography" usually employs metal or paper masters.

long distance xerography (LDX) A facsimile transmission system employing xerography.

magnification ratio. The size relationship, expressed linearly, between an optically enlarged image and the original or intermediate from which the enlarged image is made. Magnification ratio is expressed in diameters, such as 2X, 4.5X, 10X, and so on.

masterless duplicating. A form of direct copying in which a number of copies are produced directly from the original document without the use of an intermediate master or stencil.

master negative. In microfilming, a negative which is used solely for the production of additional positives.

matrix. In document reproduction, a physical impression in a suitable material from which copies of the impression can be made by physical transference, usually by pressure.

matte. Having a dull finish. A term applied to photographic paper surfaces.

maximum aperture. In lenses, the largest opening of the iris diaphragm.

maximum density. See *density, maximum.*

Microcard. Registered trademark of the Microcard Corporation for photographically produced micro-opaques 3 by 5 inches in size.

Microcite. A name given by the National Bureau of Standards to a microform information storage and retrieval system and to the equip-

ment used. Micro-images in the Microcite system are in the form of large sheets of film containing as many as 18,000 images.

microcopies. Copies which have been so greatly reduced in size that some optical aid in the form of a magnifier or projecting device is required to read them.

microcopying. A form of optical copying in which the copy produced is very greatly reduced in size.

microcopy test chart. See *National Bureau of Standards Microcopy Resolution Test Chart.*

microfiche. A microtransparency in sheet form having a number of rows of images.

Micro-File. A trade name of the Eastman Kodak Company for a line of equipment and materials used in the production of microfilms.

microfilm. A term applied to the raw film used for microrecording to the finished film and, as a verb, to the process of microrecording.

Micro-Folio. A registered trademark of the Atlantic Microfilm Corporation for a method and the equipment used for producing micro-transparencies in sheet form and for the sheets themselves.

microform. A generic term for all forms of micro-images, whether transparent or opaque, or in roll or sheet form.

micro-image. The image of a single microcopy.

Microlex. Registered trademark of the Lawyer's Cooperative Publishing Company for a two-sided photographically produced micro-opaque 6½ by 8½ inches in size.

micro-opaque. Any microform in which the images are on an opaque (e.g., paper, card stock) support.

microphotography. The photographic recording of documents at a substantial reduction in size.

Microprint, Readex. Registered trademark of the Readex Microprint Corporation for a photolithographically produced micro-opaque 6 by 9 inches in size.

micro-publishing. The publishing (or republishing) of materials in microform.

microrecord. A record of information in the form of micro-images.

Microstrip. A trade name originally used by the Hall and McChesney Company but now used by others as well for micro-opaques in the form of strips which are produced by contact printing on photographic paper from microtransparencies in roll form.

Microtape. A trade name of the American Microfilming Service Company for micro-opaques in strip form backed with a pressure-sensitive adhesive.

microtransparency. Any microform which is on a transparent (e.g., acetate film) support.

microxerography. A method of microrecording in which images are formed xerographically.

mimeography. Originally a trade name of the A. B. Dick Company for a duplicating process involving the use of stencils but now broadly used to refer to any stencil duplicating process.

Minicard. A trade name of the Eastman Kodak Company for a system and the equipment used in an automated microform information storage and retrieval system. In the Minicard system, small chips of film called Minicards which contain one or more documents and which are optically coded are used.

minimum aperture. In lenses, the minimun opening of the iris diaphragm.

Mini-Print. Registered trademark of Mini-Print, Inc., for low-reduction micro-opaque images in book form.

monobath. In stabilization processing, a single solution which contains both the image-forming and the stabilizing chemicals.

monochromatic. Having a single color. Documents printed in ink of a single color or on a colored paper stock.

National Bureau of Standards Microcopy Resolution Test Chart. A small chart containing a series of blocks of fine lines and spaces used for determining the optical performance of microfilm equipment and the resolution characteristics of materials used in microrecording.

NBS. The U.S. National Bureau of Standards.

negative. Strictly speaking, a copy exhibiting tone values which are the reverse of those of the original but more generally used to refer to copies which have a white image on a black background.

negative intermediate. A negative which has been produced expressly for the purpose of making additional positive copies.

negative-positive process. A process, such as gelatin-dye-transfer or diffusion-transfer-reversal, in which both a negative and a positive copy are produced.

negative-working process. A process, such as the silver halide process, in which the finished product is reversed in tonal values.

NMA. National Microfilm Association (U.S.)

non-conformable backing materials. See *backing materials*.

octavo. A book or page-size designation for books made up from printed sheets which are folded to form eight leaves and which range in size from 5 by 8 to 6 by 9 inches approximately.

office copier. Any of a large number of different types of copying devices designed principally for the copying of records up to 8½ by 14 inches in size in loose-sheet form.

offset. A condition which occurs when printed sheets are stacked before the ink is dry, causing a partial impression of the text of one page to become superimposed on that of another.

offset duplicating. A term used to denote duplicating processes in which an image is first transferred to an intermediate surface and thence to a receiving sheet.

offset masters. Metal or paper sheets on which an image has been created or transferred and which can be used for edition printing by the offset process. Paper masters are commonly called *mats,* and metal masters, *plates.*

offset mats. See *offset masters.*

offset plates. See *offset masters.*

offset printing. A printing process in which the inked impression is first made on a rubber-covered roller and then transferred to paper.

one-to-one (1:1) copying. Copying to 100 percent of the size of the original.

optical axis. In optical copying, a line passing through the center of a lens which is perpendicular to the subject plane and the film plane.

optical copying, direct. A method of copying employing a camera equipped with a prism in which a right-reading image is formed directly on a sheet of sensitized material.

optimum exposure. Theoretically, the one correct exposure of precisely the correct intensity and duration yielding a copy of optimum quality.

orthochromatic. A term used to specify the color sensitivity of light-sensitive materials. Orthochromatic materials are sensitive to blue and green light but not to red.

overexposure. Exposure to light or heat at too great an intensity or for too long a time.

Ozalid. Registered trademark of the General Aniline and Film Corporation for a line of diazo equipment and supplies.

"package" system. A term used with reference to Polaroid process materials in which all of the materials required to form a finished copy are contained within a single unit or enclosure.

panchromatic. A term used to specify the color sensitivity of light-sensitive materials. Panchromatic materials are sensitive to light of all colors.

parallax. In cameras, the difference in viewpoint, and hence of the area covered, between a viewfinder and the camera lens or, in twin-lens reflex cameras, between the viewing lens and the taking lens.

PCMI. Abbreviation for Photo-Chromic Micro-Images (q.v.).

perforated film. Film in roll form having an evenly spaced sequence of sprocket holes along one or both edges and which are used to control film advance in cameras and projectors. Film with sprocket holes along one edge is called *single-perforated.* Film with sprocket holes along both edges is called *double-perforated.*

permanence. The state or quality of (a) lasting or intended to last indefinitely without change and of (b) lasting a relatively long time.

phenols. Chemical substances which, when combined with diazonium salts by the action of a coupler, produce substances which are strongly colored.

photo cell. Shortened version of photoelectric cell (q.v.).

Photo-Chromic Micro-Images (PCMI). A trade name of the National Cash Register Company for a high-reduction microform process employing photochromic substances.

photochromic processes. Processes employing photochromic substances for image formation by the action of light.

photochromism. A phenomenon peculiar to certain substances which can exist in two states —a colorless state and a colored state, and which can be changed from one state to the other by the action of light of appropriate wavelength.

photoconductors. Materials such as selenium or zinc oxide which act as insulators but become electrically conductive when exposed to light.

photocopying. Copying by processes which employ materials which are sensitive to light.

Photo-Direct system. A trade name of the Addressograph-Multigraph Corporation for a system used to produce direct-positive offset masters.

photoelectric cell. A cell which converts energy in the form of light into electrical energy. In photoelectric exposure meters, the electrical energy actuates a pointer on a dial scaled to indicate exposure times or light intensities.

photolithography. Process by which lithographic printing plates are prepared photographically.

photo offset. A method of offset printing in which images are photographically transferred to metal plates or paper mats from which inked impressions are made on a rubber roller, and thence to paper.

photopolymer. Polymerization is the process of joining two or more like molecules to form a more complex molecule having different properties. Photopolymers are substances in which this process is induced by the action of light.

photoreproduction. See *photocopying*.

photosensitivity. Sensitive to, or reacting to, the action of light.

photostat. A term derived from the original trademark of the Photostat Corporation which has come to be used generically to refer to right-reading negative photocopies on paper produced optically by means of cameras equipped with prisms.

Photostat camera. See *camera, Photostat*.

photostat-type camera. See *camera, photostat-type*.

plane of focus. The plane within a camera on which light rays from the lens are brought into focus.

planetary camera. See *camera, planetary*.

platen. A plate. In planetary microfilm cameras, a metal plate which holds the film flat during exposure. In bookholders, a metal or wooden plate which holds the material being copied against the undersurface of the glass top. In contact printing frames, the hinged plate which holds the original and sensitized material in contact against the glass exposing surface. In Dual Spectrum copiers, a heated metal plate or drum used to make visible the latent image.

plate out. The deposition of metal ions in the formation of an electrolytically produced image.

PMI. Abbreviation for photographic micro-image—an intermediate used for printing dissemination copies of microforms in the PCMI process (q.v.).

point. A unit of measure in typography. A point is approximately equal to $1/72$ of an inch.

polarized light filters. Filters which are placed over a camera lens, over a light source, or both and which are used to reduce or eliminate specular reflections from shiny, non-metallic surfaces.

Polaroid process. A trade name of the Polaroid Corporation for a process in which prints are produced in a camera by a variant form of the diffusion-transfer-reversal process.

polymeric. Polymeric substances are the result of polymerization—a process in which two or more like molecules are joined to form a more complex molecule having different physical properties.

positive. Strictly speaking, a copy exhibiting tone values which are in the same relationship as those of the original, but more generally used to refer to copies which have a black image on a white background.

press camera. See *camera, press.*

printer, continuous. A device with which images in roll form (e.g., microfilm) can be duplicated to film or paper stocks, also in roll form, by advancing them synchronously past a light source.

printer, flatbed. A device for printing by contact methods, which consists of a box containing a light source, a glass plate used as an exposure surface, and a cover plate. Flatbed printers can be used to copy either loose-sheet or bound materials.

printer, rotary. A printing device which contains a light source and a set of belts and rollers which transport the original to be copied in contact with a sheet of sensitized material past the light source.

printing frame. See *contact printing frame.*

printing-out paper. A paper which is capable of forming a visible image through the action of light alone.

prism camera. See *camera, prism.*

process film. A type of silver-sensitized film used in the graphic arts which is very high in contrast.

processing. A general term used to refer to the physical or chemical treatment given to exposed sensitized materials to make visible a latent image and, where required, to fix the image.

Project-A-Lith system. A trade name of the Itek Business Products firm for equipment and materials used for the production of direct-positive offset masters.

projection. The formation of an image on a surface through an optical system.

projection printing. A method of photographic printing in which an image is projected via a light source through a lens to a sheet of photo-sensitive paper.

projection speed materials. Photo-sensitive materials which are high enough in speed to be used for projection printing at relatively short exposures.

push-button reader-printer. A reader-printer in which the print cycle is actuated by a push-button. By implication, any reader-printer in which the making of the print is completely automated.

quarto. A book or page size designation for books made up from printed sheets which are folded to form four leaves approximately 9 by 12 inches in size.

"Q" System. A trade name of the Eastman Kodak Company given to the materials, equipment and method of reproducing documents by means of autopositive materials processed by stabilization.

radiant energy. Energy in the form of waves of varying wavelength which make up the electromagnetic spectrum, including visible light, invisible light (ultraviolet and infrared) heat, X-rays and others.

rangefinder. An optical device used on cameras to determine the lens-to-subject distance and hence the correct distance setting for focusing. With most rangefinder-type cameras, the rangefinder is coupled to the focusing mechanism.

reduction ratio. A numerical expression of the number of times a copy is smaller in size, linearly, than the original from which it is made. Expressed either as a ratio (e.g., 1:5, 1:14.5, 1:20) or in diameters (e.g., 5X, 14.5X, 20X).

reflectance. A term generally used to indicate the relative ability of different surfaces to reflect light.

reflected light. That portion of light rays which, on striking a surface, are not absorbed but redirected away from the surface.

reflection density. The density of any given tone value as measured by the amount of light it absorbs.

reflex copying. See *contact copying, reflex method of*.

reflex negative. A negative, usually reverse-reading, produced by contact-reflex copying.

reader-printer. A type of microfilm reader equipped with both a screen for reading micro-images and an exposing and processing unit for the immediate production of hard copy of the image displayed on the screen.

Readyprint. A trade name of the Eastman Kodak Company for a variant form of the gelatin-dye-transfer process.

receiving sheet. See *receptor sheet*.

receptor sheet. A sheet to which an image is chemically or physically transferred from an intermediate or a matrix.

Rectigraph camera. See *camera, Rectigraph*.

recto. The front side of a leaf of a bound volume; any right-hand page of a bound volume.

reduction. In camera copying or projection printing, the production of a copy which is smaller in size than the original.

reduction printing. The making of a print by projection printing which is smaller than the intermediate from which it is made.

reflex optical system. An optical system employing a mirror which inverts the image so that it appears in a right-side-up position.

reprography. A term used to refer to the corpus of processes and methods used for both copying and duplicating documents.

residual hypo. Ammonium or sodium thiosulfate remaining in the film or print after washing. See also *hypo*.

resolving power (resolution). Terms, generally expressed in lines per millimeter or lines per inch, referring to the ability of different types of sensitized material to separate fine lines and spaces. Also used to describe the optical performance of lenses.

reversal. In processing, the conversion of a developed, negative, silver halide image to a positive image and vice versa by chemical means.

reversal processing. A method of processing certain types of silver halide materials in which a developed negative image (which is later removed by bleaching) is used to form a positive image by re-exposure.

reverse-reading. An image in which lines of text normally reading from left to right are inverted, as in a mirror, to read from right to left.

rheostat. A device used to regulate input of electrical energy. In particular, to regulate light intensity as an exposure control measure.

right-reading. Term used to describe an image which is directly readable, as opposed to a mirror image.

river. A narrow blank area on a page which occurs when a creased sheet of paper is fed through a printing press.

rotary camera. See *camera, rotary*.

rotary printer. See *printer, rotary*.

running title. In books, a title appearing at the top of each page or leaf. In microfilm, a title appearing at the top of each frame.

safelight. A light or light source of a particular color which filters out light rays in the area of spectral sensitivity of the sensitized materials used.

safety film. See *acetate film.*

scanner. (a) In microfilm readers, a mechanism which permits the screen image to be shifted from side to side or up and down when the entire image is too large to appear on the screen. (b) In facsimile systems, a device which traverses the surface of an original in a succession of lines and which photoelectrically converts differences in reflectance between background and text into electrical impulses which can be transmitted to a receiving unit.

second generation copy. See *generation printing.*

selenium. A chemical substance widely used as a photoconductor in exposure meters and in xerography.

sensitizing dyes. Dyes which are added to certain light-sensitive coatings to increase their speed and/or color sensitivity.

sensitometric curve. (H&D curve). See *characteristic curve.*

sensitometry. A photographic science used to determine and define characteristics such as speed, contrast, etc., of sensitized materials.

shelf life. The period of time during which sensitized material may be kept before exposure without loss of speed, contrast, or quality.

showthrough. A condition which occurs when text is printed on both sides of a sheet of paper of insufficient opacity.

shutter. Any mechanical device which regulates the time that light is permitted to act upon sensitized film or paper.

signature. A large sheet upon which are printed four, or some multiple of four, pages and which when folded and bound, forms one section of a book or pamphlet.

silver halide. See *halide.*

silver thiosulfate. A chemical compound produced by the reaction between sodium thiosulfate and silver halides during fixation.

single perforated film. See *perforated film.*

sliding subject holder. A device used to transport large materials in book-page form back and forth for the successive recording of right- and left-hand pages.

SLR camera (single-lens reflex camera). See *camera, SLR.*

soft. With reference to photographic papers, an adjective denoting low contrast.

spectral. Pertaining to the electromagnetic spectrum. Used in connection with sensitized materials to refer to that portion of the electromagnetic spectrum to which such materials are sensitive.

spectral sensitivity (response). Response to radiant energy emanating from various portions of the electromagnetic spectrum.

specular. See *specular reflection.*

specular reflection. A reflection from a shiny surface which does not diffuse the reflected light rays.

spirit duplicating. A method of duplicating in which a solvent (spirit) is used to soften a dye image so that a layer of dye can be transferred to a receiving sheet.

splice. A joint made by cementing or welding (heat splice) two pieces of film or paper together so they will function as a single piece when passing through a camera, processing machine, projector, or other apparatus. See also *butt splice.*

stabilization process. A variant form of silver halide processing in which unexposed and undeveloped silver halides are allowed to remain *in situ* but are chemically converted to forms which are relatively insensitive to the subsequent action of light, heat, or atmospheric gases.

stabilized.   Chemically converted into substances which are relatively inert and which are not readily affected by subsequent action of light, heat, or atmospheric conditions.

stable.   With reference to images produced photographically or thermographically, resistant to change from the action of light, heat, or atmospheric gases.

static electricity.   See *electrostatic.*

stencil.   A sheet of material in which an image is cut by perforating or other means and through which ink can be forced to create an image on a receiving sheet.

step-and-repeat camera.   See *camera, step-and-repeat.*

step-type bookholder.   A bookholder equipped with a series of planes or steps used to control the height of a glass overlay sheet in relation to the thickness of the bound volume being copied.

stop bath.   A dilute acid solution used to arrest development in photographic material.

strip-up method.   A method used for the production of microfiche in which short lengths of roll film are attached in rows to a transparent support which is then used as a printing master.

subsurface illuminator.   A device in the form of a light box used in optical copying to eliminate shadows caused by incident illumination at the edges of a subject.

subtractive direct-positive process.   Any process, such as Dual Spectrum and diazo, in which the sensitized material develops completely without exposure to light since light destroys its ability to develop.

swings.   Devices on some cameras which allow for adjustments in the horizontal and vertical position and also the angle of the lens and film plane.

taking lens.   On twin-lens reflex cameras, the lens which forms the image on the sensitized material.

tanning.   The hardening of a soft gelatin emulsion during development. Used in copying processes such as Verifax and Ektalith and in the Project-A-Lith and Photo-Direct systems.

target.   Any sign or note used in microfilming to provide the user with information concerning the material filmed.

test chart.   See *National Bureau of Standards Microcopy Resolution Test Chart.*

thermal diazo.   A variant form of the diazo process in which heat alone is used to render a latent image visible.

thermal sensitivity.   Response, or the degree of response, to the action of heat.

thermocarbon.   A thin sheet of material containing a heat-sensitive dye used in the Eichner process (q.v.).

thermocopying.   Copying by means of heat as opposed to copying by means of light (photocopying).

Thermo-Fax process.   A trade name of the 3M Company for a thermographic copying process.

thermographic.   A generic term used to refer to any form of copying in which image formation is accomplished by means of heat.

Thermoplastic recording.   A term used to refer to a process under development by the General Electric Company in which an image is formed by altering the surface characteristics of a heat-sensitive plastic layer.

thermoplastic substances.   Substances which can be melted by heat to cause them to adhere to a support.

thermoreproduction.   Processes employing radiant energy in the form of heat as the means for reproducing documents. Also, the copies produced by such processes.

tipped-in plates. Plates which are printed separately from the body of the text and which are affixed to book pages by means of adhesives.

TLR camera (twin-lens reflex camera). See *camera, TLR.*

tonal gradation (tonality). In black-and-white copying, variations in shades of gray from white to black.

tonal range (tone scale). (a) The difference between the lightest and darkest tones in an original or a copy. (b) The degree or subtlety of gradations of tone.

toner. In electrostatic processes and in certain heat processes (adherography, Imagic), a finely divided black or colored thermoplastic powder used to make visible a latent image and which is fused by heat to render the image permanent.

trailer. That portion of a film beyond the last images recorded which is used to span the distance from the lens to the supply reel of a microfilm reading or printing device.

transmitted light. Light traveling from a primary light source (as opposed to reflected light in which the reflecting surface acts as a secondary light source).

transparency. Any form of a copy on a transparent base for viewing or projection by transmitted light.

two-bath stabilization process. A process employing two solutions—a developer (or activator) and a stabilizer.

type face. A term used to refer to the design characteristics of fonts of type.

ultraviolet. Pertaining to invisible light immediately beyond the blue end of the visible spectrum.

underdeveloped. Pertaining to images on film or paper which have insufficient density or contrast caused by failure to carry on the developing process for a long enough time interval, from carrying on development at too low a temperature, or from the use of solutions which have become weakened by previous use.

underexposure. Insufficient exposure of sensitized material to radiant energy due to insufficient light or heat, too short an exposure interval, or, in optical copying or projection printing, the use of too small a lens aperture.

upside-down copier. Copiers with which the subject to be copied must be placed on the exposure surface in an upside-down position.

use copies. See *convenience copies.*

vapor diazo. A form of the diazo process in which a latent image is made visible by exposure to ammonia vapor.

vellum. A translucent stock having a matte surface.

Verifax process. A trade name of the Eastman Kodak Company for a form of the gelatin-dye-transfer process.

verso. The left-hand page of a bound volume or the back of a leaf.

view camera. See *camera, view.*

viewfinder. In cameras, a separate optical device or simple metal frame used to show the approximate area which can be recorded by the lens.

viewing lens. On twin-lens reflex cameras, the lens used to view the subject.

wash-off method. A method of processing certain types of autopositive materials which does not require a fixation step.

web. A continuous roll of material, usually paper.

whiteprint (diazoprint). A term occasionally

applied to diazo copies to distinguish them from blueprints.

xerography.   A coined word (xeros = dry, graphein = to write) of the Xerox Corporation for an electrostatic copying process employing selenium as the photo conductor.

x-height.   In typography, the height of a lower case "x" in any particular font.

zinc oxide coating.   A coating used in electrofax-type processes because of its photoconductive properties.

INDEX

Note: The term *"illus."* shown at the end of an entry indicates that one or more illustrations appear with the pages cited.

DATE DUE